Airplane, Missile, and Spacecraft Structures,
edited by Nicholas J. Hoff, Volume 1

Methods of
Mathematical Analysis
and Computation

Methods of Mathematical Analysis and Computation

by John G. Herriot

Professor of Mathematics
and Computer Science
Stanford University

John Wiley & Sons, Inc., New York · London

Foreword

The plan for a series of monographs on airplane and missile structures originated in the Structures Subcommittee of the National Advisory Committee for Aeronautics. Industry members of the Committee saw a need for comprehensive volumes covering specialized fields in which new information was becoming available in articles appearing in a large number of technical and scientific journals, in research technical notes of the NACA, and in company reports. Details of the plan were worked out after John Wiley and Sons and the editor reached an agreement on the size of the volumes and the selection of the topics and authors. Part of the research that was needed to produce the volumes was supported financially by the Office of Naval Research of the U.S. Navy.

The book series addresses itself primarily to practicing engineers and beginning research men who wish to acquire competence in a specialized field of structural analysis. It is hoped that the volumes will also prove useful as textbooks in college courses.

NICHOLAS J. HOFF
EDITOR

Editor's Preface

The first volume in the series on Airplane, Missile, and Spacecraft Structures presents the mathematical methods that are most useful to engineers engaged in structural analysis. The selection of the topics recognizes the modern trend in stress analysis toward an increased use of the electronic digital computer. Particular attention is paid therefore to the development of numerical methods in every chapter whether it treats interpolation, integration, matrices, Fourier series, or differential equations.

The author, Professor John G. Herriot of Stanford University, is Associate Director of Stanford's Computation Center. In this capacity, in teaching students of engineering, and in his earlier experience in carrying on research in the Ames Aeronautical Laboratory of the National Advisory Committee for Aeronautics, he has had many opportunities to develop an appreciation of the engineer's point of view. Many numerical examples contribute to his lucid presentation of the subject.

N. J. H.

Stanford, California
June 27, 1962

Preface

This book is intended to provide the aircraft engineer with an introduction to some subjects of mathematics which are frequently not included in the traditional courses of calculus and engineering mathematics. There may be some overlap, but it is hoped that much of the material will be outside these courses. In keeping with the rapid development of high-speed automatic computers and their widespread use, there is considerable emphasis on numerical methods, although this is not, strictly speaking, a book on numerical analysis. There is also a considerable body of material not numerical in nature. The ultimate responsibility for the choice of material lies with the author, but acknowledgment is due Professor N. J. Hoff, the editor of the series, for his helpful advice in the selection of the topics included.

Chapter 1 covers the subject of interpolation and the finite difference calculus. Although difference methods are not as widely used with modern high-speed computers as they were when most calculations were done by hand or with a desk calculator, the material of Chapter 1 is important because it provides the tools for deriving in Chapter 2 the formulas of numerical integration and differentiation. These formulas are useful in themselves and are also used extensively in the later chapters as a basis for various numerical methods of solution of differential equations.

Because the engineer frequently encounters the problem of solving equations of various types, Chapter 3 describes some of the more useful methods for solving equations.

Many problems in engineering lead to systems of simultaneous linear equations, and so the engineer needs an acquaintance with matrix theory in order to deal with such problems. Chapter 4 provides an introduction to matrix theory and describes several useful methods of solving systems of simultaneous linear equations, inverting matrices, and finding characteristic values and vectors. In all cases the emphasis is on methods suitable for high-speed automatic computers.

Chapter 5 begins with some commonly used analytical methods of solving ordinary differential equations and concludes with a number of useful numerical methods for obtaining such solutions. Chapter 6 gives a brief treatment of Fourier series with applications to the solution of a variety of problems. Chapter 7 gives an introduction to the use of finite-difference methods that are widely used in the solution of partial differential equations.

I wish to thank Professor Max Anliker, who read Chapters 3 and 4 and made several useful suggestions.

JOHN G. HERRIOT

Stanford, California
January, 1963

Contents

ESCAPE

chapter 1 Interpolation

1.1 INTRODUCTION

In most scientific work, functions are encountered which are conveniently expressed in the form of tables. Such tables usually list values of the function (ordinates) corresponding to certain abscissas, the abscissas belonging to some range. In some cases the function can also be expressed by means of a formula, a differential equation, or in some other manner, whereas in other cases the values of the tabulated function may be obtained empirically. Clearly a table can contain values corresponding to only a finite number of abscissas. Interpolation may be defined as a process for finding values of the function for abscissas which do not appear in the table by making use of the tabulated values of the function. Any further available information about the function is reserved for estimating the error involved in the process. Strictly speaking, the term interpolation should be used only when the abscissas lie within the range of the tabulated abscissas. Otherwise, the usual term is extrapolation.

Let us denote the function under consideration by $f(x)$. Then $f(x)$ is tabulated for certain values of x. We seek to construct an interpolating function $I(x)$ which agrees with certain of the tabulated values of $f(x)$ and to use this function $I(x)$ to calculate an approximate value of $f(x)$ for other values of x. Thus, if (x_0, f_0), (x_1, f_1), $\cdots$, (x_n, f_n) are corresponding pairs of values of x and $f(x)$, we should have $I(x_0) = f_0$, $I(x_1) = f_1$, $\cdots$, $I(x_n) = f_n$. Because of their simplicity, polynomials are widely used for this purpose. For many reasonably smooth functions, this procedure is very satisfactory.

We begin by considering the case in which the tabular values are given for equally spaced values of x. For this case the method of finite differences provides a very convenient means for determining the interpolating polynomial.

1

1.2 DIFFERENCE NOTATION

Let $f(x)$ be tabulated for uniformly spaced abscissas, with spacing h. We define the first forward difference $\Delta f(x)$ by the equation

$$\Delta f(x) = f(x + h) - f(x) \tag{1.2.1}$$

the spacing h being implied in Δ. If we want to indicate the spacing specifically, Δ_h may be used in place of Δ.

Suppose that $f(x)$ is tabulated at $x_s = x_0 + sh$, where s takes on integral values. Let $f(x_s) = f_s$. Then we have

$$\Delta f(x_s) = f(x_s + h) - f(x_s)$$

or

$$\Delta f_s = f_{s+1} - f_s. \tag{1.2.2}$$

We define also the second forward difference as

$$\Delta^2 f(x) = \Delta f(x + h) - \Delta f(x); \tag{1.2.3}$$

in general we define the rth forward difference as

$$\Delta^r f(x) = \Delta^{r-1} f(x + h) - \Delta^{r-1} f(x). \tag{1.2.4}$$

For example we have

$$\Delta^2 f_s = \Delta f_{s+1} - \Delta f_s,$$
$$\Delta^3 f_s = \Delta^2 f_{s+1} - \Delta^2 f_s.$$
$$\tag{1.2.5}$$
$$\cdots\cdots\cdots\cdots\cdots$$
$$\Delta^r f_s = \Delta^{r-1} f_{s+1} - \Delta^{r-1} f_s, \text{ etc.}$$

TABLE 1.1

x_0 f_0				
	Δf_0			
x_1 f_1		$\Delta^2 f_0$		
	Δf_1		$\Delta^3 f_0$	
x_2 f_2		$\Delta^2 f_1$		$\Delta^4 f_0$
	Δf_2		$\Delta^3 f_1$	$\cdot$
x_3 f_3		$\Delta^2 f_2$	$\cdot$	$\cdot$
	Δf_3	$\cdot$	$\cdot$	$\cdot$
x_4 f_4	$\cdot$	$\cdot$	$\cdot$	
$\cdot$	$\cdot$	$\cdot$		
$\cdot$	$\cdot$	$\cdot$		
$\cdot$	$\cdot$			

$$\tag{1.2.6}$$

Thus, given a table of values, we can form a difference table such as that shown in Table 1.1. Each entry in the difference table is the difference of the adjacent entries in the column to the left.

Example 1. Form a difference table for $f(x) = \sin x$ with the entries for $x = 0.2, 0.3, 0.4, 0.5, 0.6, 0.7, 0.8$:

x	$f(x)$	Δf	$\Delta^2 f$	$\Delta^3 f$	$\Delta^4 f$	
0.2	0.19867					
		9685				
0.3	0.29552		−295			
		9390		−94		
0.4	0.38942		−389		3	
		9001		−91		
0.5	0.47943		−480		8	(1.2.7)
		8521		−83		
0.6	0.56464		−563		2	
		7958		−81		
0.7	0.64422		−644			
		7314				
0.8	0.71736					

Note that in writing the columns of differences it is convenient to omit the decimal point as no confusion can arise. It is not desirable to carry the formation of higher differences beyond the point where they become irregular. Thus in this example, differences beyond the fourth would not normally be used.

By successive substitutions using equations (1.2.2) and (1.2.5) we easily find that

$$\Delta^2 f_0 = f_2 - 2f_1 + f_0,$$
$$\Delta^3 f_0 = f_3 - 3f_2 + 3f_1 - f_0,$$

and we deduce that in general

$$\Delta^r f_0 = f_r - \binom{r}{1} f_{r-1} + \binom{r}{2} f_{r-2} - \cdots + (-1)^k \binom{r}{k} f_{r-k} + \cdots + (-1)^r f_0$$

$$= \sum_{k=0}^{r} (-1)^k \binom{r}{k} f_{r-k}. \tag{1.2.8}$$

Here we have used the binomial coefficients

$$\binom{r}{k} = \frac{r(r-1)\cdots(r-k+1)}{r!}. \tag{1.2.9}$$

This formula can easily be established by mathematical induction.

In a similar manner, using (1.2.2) and (1.2.5) repeatedly, we obtain

$$f_1 = f_0 + \Delta f_0,$$
$$f_2 = f_0 + 2\Delta f_0 + \Delta^2 f_0,$$
$$f_3 = f_0 + 3\Delta f_0 + 3\Delta^2 f_0 + \Delta^3 f_0,$$

and we deduce that in general

$$f_r = f_0 + \binom{r}{1} \Delta f_0 + \binom{r}{2} \Delta^2 f_0 + \cdots + \binom{r}{k} \Delta^k f_0 + \cdots + \Delta^r f_0$$

$$= \sum_{k=0}^{r} \binom{r}{k} \Delta^k f_0. \tag{1.2.10}$$

Regarding Δ as a symbolic operator defined by equation (1.2.1), we can write (1.2.10) in the symbolic form

$$f_r = (1 + \Delta)^r f_0. \tag{1.2.11}$$

If we introduce the operator E defined by

$$E f(x) = f(x + h), \tag{1.2.12}$$

we see from (1.2.1) that $\Delta = E - 1$ or $E = 1 + \Delta$, and we can write (1.2.8) in the symbolic form

$$\Delta^r f_0 = (E - 1)^r f_0. \tag{1.2.13}$$

Next we note that

$$\Delta x^n = (x + h)^n - x^n$$

$$= \binom{n}{1} h x^{n-1} + \binom{n}{2} h^2 x^{n-2} + \cdots + h^n, \tag{1.2.14}$$

which is a polynomial of degree $n - 1$. Since the result of operating with Δ on the sum of any finite number of terms is the same as the sum of the results obtained by operating with Δ on each of the terms, we see that if $P(x)$ is a polynomial of degree n, then $\Delta P(x)$ is a polynomial of degree $n - 1$. Repeated application of this result shows that $\Delta^n P(x)$ is a polynomial of degree 0 and hence constant, and that $\Delta^r P(x) = 0$ for $r > n$.

1.3   NEWTON'S FORWARD-DIFFERENCE FORMULA

Suppose that the function $f(x)$ has values f_i at the tabular points $x_i = x_0 + ih$, $i = 0, 1, \cdots, n$. It is known that there is precisely one polynomial of degree n which takes on the values f_i at x_i, $i = 0, 1, \cdots, n$. We wish to find this interpolating polynomial. It is convenient to make the transformation

$$s = \frac{x - x_0}{h}, \qquad x = x_0 + hs. \tag{1.3.1}$$

Then $s = 0, 1, \cdots, n$ at the tabular points. We seek a polynomial $I(s)$ of degree n such that $I(s) = f_s$, $s = 0, 1, \cdots, n$. An obvious way to proceed would be to let

$$I(s) = c_0 + c_1 s + c_2 s^2 + \cdots + c_n s^n. \tag{1.3.2}$$

We could then set $s = 0, 1, \cdots, n$ in turn and obtain $n + 1$ equations in the $n + 1$ unknowns c_i. These equations could be solved for the c_i, but the work would be tedious. We note that we desire to express the polynomial $I(s)$ in terms of the differences Δf_i. Now if we attempt to form differences of $I(s)$ using (1.3.2), we see by equation (1.2.14) that these differences do not assume a simple form.

However, if we introduce the factorial polynomials defined by the equation

$$s^{(n)} = s(s - 1)(s - 2) \cdots (s - n + 1), \qquad n = 1, 2, 3, \cdots$$

$$= 1, \qquad\qquad\qquad\qquad\qquad n = 0 \qquad (1.3.3)$$

we easily see that

$$\Delta s^{(n)} = (s + 1)^{(n)} - s^{(n)}$$

$$= (s + 1)s(s - 1) \cdots (s - n + 2) - s(s - 1) \cdots (s - n + 1)$$

$$= s(s - 1) \cdots (s - n + 2)[s + 1 - (s - n + 1)]$$

$$= ns^{(n-1)}, \qquad (1.3.4)$$

where we have chosen h, the interval of differencing, to be 1. We note that the rule for differencing $s^{(n)}$ is completely analogous to the rule for differentiating s^n with respect to s. We also note that the binomial coefficients are closely related to the factorial polynomials for we have

$$\binom{s}{n} = \frac{s^{(n)}}{n!}. \qquad (1.3.5)$$

In addition,

$$\Delta \binom{s}{n} = \frac{ns^{(n-1)}}{n!} = \binom{s}{n-1}. \qquad (1.3.6)$$

Now since $s^{(n)}$ is a polynomial of degree n in s, it is easily seen that any polynomial of degree n in s can be expressed as a linear combination of factorial polynomials or indeed binomial coefficients. Hence instead of using (1.3.2) we shall write

$$I(s) = a_0 + a_1 \binom{s}{1} + a_2 \binom{s}{2} + \cdots + a_k \binom{s}{k} + \cdots + a_n \binom{s}{n}. \qquad (1.3.7)$$

We have only to determine convenient expressions for the a_k. If $s = 0$, $I(0) = a_0$. But $I(0) = f_0$ and so $a_0 = f_0$. We have, on using equation (1.3.6)

$$\Delta I(s) = a_1 + a_2 \binom{s}{1} + a_3 \binom{s}{2} + \cdots + a_k \binom{s}{k-1} + \cdots + a_n \binom{s}{n-1}.$$

On setting $s = 0$ we see that

$$\Delta I(0) = a_1.$$

But since $I(0) = f_0$, $I(1) = f_1$, we see that $\Delta I(0) = \Delta f_0$, and so $a_1 = \Delta f_0$. Again using (1.3.6) we have

$$\Delta^2 I(s) = a_2 + a_3 \binom{s}{1} + \cdots + a_k \binom{s}{k-2} + \cdots + a_n \binom{s}{n-2},$$

and hence $a_2 = \Delta^2 I(0) = \Delta^2 f_0$.

Continuing this procedure we see that

$$\Delta^k I(s) = a_k + a_{k+1} \binom{s}{1} + \cdots + a_n \binom{s}{n-k},$$

and hence

$$a_k = \Delta^k I(0) = \Delta^k f_0.$$

Substitution of these results into (1.3.7) gives

$$I(s) = f_0 + \binom{s}{1} \Delta f_0 + \binom{s}{2} \Delta^2 f_0 + \cdots + \binom{s}{k} \Delta^k f_0 + \cdots + \binom{s}{n} \Delta^n f_0.$$

This is the interpolating polynomial desired and it can be expressed in terms of x by making use of (1.3.1). We use this polynomial as an approximation to f_s for nonintegral s. We then write approximately

$$f_s \approx f_0 + \binom{s}{1} \Delta f_0 + \binom{s}{2} \Delta^2 f_0 + \cdots + \binom{s}{k} \Delta^k f_0 + \cdots + \binom{s}{n} \Delta^n f_0.$$

$$(1.3.8)$$

This is Newton's forward-difference formula. We note that if s is a non-negative integer r, (1.3.8) is the same as (1.2.10) because $\binom{r}{k} = 0$ if $k > r$. Here and in the sequel we use the symbol $\approx$ to indicate that two members are approximately equal. The error committed in using (1.3.8) as an approximation to the true value $f(x_0 + sh)$ will be discussed in Section 1.8. The symbol $\approx$ signifies the omission of the error term.

We note that (1.3.8) makes use of the top line of the difference table (1.2.6). We also note that the coefficient of Δf_0 involves $s - 0$ and that 0 is the first tabular value of s. The coefficient of $\Delta^2 f_0$ involves $(s - 0)(s - 1)$; 0 and 1 are the first two tabular values of s, which are also just the ones corresponding to the ordinates involved in the previous difference Δf_0. Each successive difference involves one additional ordinate, and each coefficient involves the values of s corresponding to the ordinates involved in the previous difference.

Since it involves differences at the beginning of a table, Newton's forward formula is appropriate for interpolation in this region.

The coefficients of Newton's forward formula have been extensively tabulated in the literature, for example by Davis [4]. Other tabulations are listed in the Index of Mathematical Tables [6].

1.4 NEWTON'S BACKWARD-DIFFERENCE FORMULA

For interpolation near the end of a table, care must be taken to ensure that the differences called for in the interpolation formula can be obtained from the table. These differences will involve the ordinates at the end of the table. It will be convenient to denote the last abscissa by x_0 and the previous abscissas by $x_{-1}, x_{-2}, \cdots$. The corresponding values of $f(x)$ are $f_0, f_{-1}, f_{-2}, \cdots$. Again making the transformation $x = x_0 + sh$, we note that s is negative for the points under consideration. It is then appropriate to seek the interpolating polynomial in the form

$$I(s) = a_0 + a_1 \binom{s}{1} + a_2 \binom{s+1}{2} + a_3 \binom{s+2}{3} + \cdots$$

$$+ a_k \binom{s+k-1}{k} + \cdots + a_n \binom{s+n-1}{n}. \quad (1.4.1)$$

By setting $s = 0$, $I(0) = a_0$. But $I(0) = f_0$ and hence $a_0 = f_0$. Because of (1.3.6) we have

$$\Delta I(s) = a_1 + a_2 \binom{s+1}{1} + a_3 \binom{s+2}{2} + \cdots$$

$$+ a_k \binom{s+k-1}{k-1} + \cdots + a_n \binom{s+n-1}{n-1}.$$

On setting $s = -1$ we have
$$\Delta I(-1) = a_1,$$

since for this s,

$$\binom{s+k-1}{k-1} = 0, \qquad k = 2, 3, \cdots, n.$$

But $\Delta I(-1) = f_0 - f_{-1} = \Delta f_{-1}$, and so $a_1 = \Delta f_{-1}$. Again using (1.3.6) we have

$$\Delta^2 I(s) = a_2 + a_3 \binom{s+2}{1} + \cdots + a_k \binom{s+k-1}{k-2} + \cdots + a_n \binom{s+n-1}{n-2}.$$

We find that
$$a_2 = \Delta^2 I(-2) = \Delta^2 f_{-2}.$$

Continuing this procedure we see that
$$\Delta^k I(s) = a_k + a_{k+1}\binom{s+k}{1} + \cdots + a_n\binom{s+n-1}{n-k},$$
and hence
$$a_k = \Delta^k I(-k) = \Delta^k f_{-k}.$$

Substituting these results into (1.4.1) we obtain
$$I(s) = f_0 + \binom{s}{1}\Delta f_{-1} + \binom{s+1}{2}\Delta^2 f_{-2} + \cdots$$
$$+ \binom{s+k-1}{k}\Delta^k f_{-k} + \cdots + \binom{s+n-1}{n}\Delta^n f_{-n}. \quad (1.4.2)$$

We use this as an approximation to f_s. This is one form of Newton's backward-difference formula. We note that the differences involved are those along the bottom line of the difference table:

$$
\begin{array}{llllll}
x_{-4} & f_{-4} & & & & \\
 & & \Delta f_{-4} & & & \\
x_{-3} & f_{-3} & & \Delta^2 f_{-4} & & \\
 & & \Delta f_{-3} & & \Delta^3 f_{-4} & \\
x_{-2} & f_{-2} & & \Delta^2 f_{-3} & & \Delta^4 f_{-4} \quad (1.4.3)\\
 & & \Delta f_{-2} & & \Delta^3 f_{-3} & \\
x_{-1} & f_{-1} & & \Delta^2 f_{-2} & & \\
 & & \Delta f_{-1} & & & \\
x_0 & f_0 & & & &
\end{array}
$$

Equation (1.4.2) can be written in a more convenient form by introducing a new notation of backward differences. Here we write
$$\nabla f(x) = f(x) - f(x - h),$$
$$\nabla^r f(x) = \nabla^{r-1} f(x) - \nabla^{r-1} f(x - h). \quad (1.4.4)$$

We find at once that
$$\nabla f_s = f(x_s) - f(x_s - h) = f_s - f_{s-1} = \Delta f_{s-1},$$
$$\nabla^2 f_s = \nabla f_s - \nabla f_{s-1} = \Delta f_{s-1} - \Delta f_{s-2} = \Delta^2 f_{s-2},$$
$$\cdots \cdots \cdots \cdots \cdots \cdots \cdots \cdots \cdots \cdots \cdots$$
$$\nabla^r f_s = \nabla^{r-1} f_s - \nabla^{r-1} f_{s-1} = \Delta^{r-1} f_{s-r+1} - \Delta^{r-1} f_{s-r} = \Delta^r f_{s-r}.$$

The difference table (1.4.3) may therefore be written in the form

$$
\begin{array}{cccccc}
x_{-4} & f_{-4} \\
 & & \nabla f_{-3} \\
x_{-3} & f_{-3} & & \nabla^2 f_{-2} \\
 & & \nabla f_{-2} & & \nabla^3 f_{-1} \\
x_{-2} & f_{-2} & & \nabla^2 f_{-1} & & \nabla^4 f_0 \qquad (1.4.5) \\
 & & \nabla f_{-1} & & \nabla^3 f_0 \\
x_{-1} & f_{-1} & & \nabla^2 f_0 \\
 & & \nabla f_0 \\
x_0 & f_0
\end{array}
$$

Note that the difference table is not changed—it is merely a different notation.

Making use of the backward-difference notation, instead of (1.4.2) we can write

$$
f_s \approx f_0 + \binom{s}{1}\nabla f_0 + \binom{s+1}{2}\nabla^2 f_0 + \cdots
$$

$$
+ \binom{s+k-1}{k}\nabla^k f_0 + \cdots + \binom{s+n-1}{n}\nabla^n f_0. \quad (1.4.6)
$$

The coefficient of $\nabla^k f_0$ in this formula is seen to be

$$
\binom{s+k-1}{k} = \frac{s(s+1)\cdots(s+k-1)}{k!}
$$

$$
= (-1)^k \frac{(-s)(-s-1)\cdots(-s-k+1)}{k!}
$$

$$
= (-1)^k \binom{-s}{k}.
$$

If we set $t = -s$, we can write Newton's backward-difference formula in the form

$$
f_{-t} \approx f_0 - \binom{t}{1}\nabla f_0 + \binom{t}{2}\nabla^2 f_0 - \cdots
$$

$$
+ (-1)^k \binom{t}{k}\nabla^k f_0 + \cdots + (-1)^n \binom{t}{n}\nabla^n f_0. \quad (1.4.7)
$$

Example 2. Using the difference table of example 1, calculate $\sin 0.27$ and $\sin 0.74$.

Since 0.27 lies near the beginning of the table, Newton's forward-difference formula is appropriate. We choose $x_0 = 0.2$, $h = 0.1$, and $s = 0.7$. Then we have approximately

$$\sin 0.27 \approx 0.19867 + 0.7(0.09685) + \frac{(0.7)(-0.3)}{2}(-0.00295)$$

$$+ \frac{(0.7)(-0.3)(-1.3)}{6}(-0.00094)$$

$$+ \frac{(0.7)(-0.3)(-1.3)(-2.3)}{24}(0.00003)$$

$$\doteq 0.19867 + 0.067795 + 0.000310 - 0.000043 - 0.000001$$

$$= 0.266731 \doteq 0.26673$$

which is correct to five places.

Since 0.74 lies near the end of the table, we use Newton's backward-difference formula. We choose $x_0 = 0.8$, $h = 0.1$, and $t = 0.6$. We have

$$\sin 0.74 \approx 0.71736 - (0.6)(0.07314) + \frac{(0.6)(-0.4)}{2}(-0.00644)$$

$$- \frac{(0.6)(-0.4)(-1.4)}{6}(-0.00081)$$

$$+ \frac{(0.6)(-0.4)(-1.4)(-2.4)}{24}(0.00002)$$

$$\doteq 0.71736 - 0.043884 + 0.000773 + 0.000045 - 0.000001$$

$$= 0.674293 \doteq 0.67429$$

which is correct to five places.

1.5 CENTRAL-DIFFERENCE FORMULAS

For interpolation at a point x, it is desirable to have available a formula in which the successively introduced ordinates correspond to abscissas which are as near as possible to x. If x is near the beginning of the table, Newton's forward-difference formula serves this purpose as well as possible. If x is near the end of the table, Newton's backward-difference is appropriate. Otherwise, it is convenient to start with the abscissa x_0 nearest to x, then to introduce x_1 and x_{-1}, then x_2 and x_{-2}, and so forth.

We again make the transformation $x = x_0 + hs$. To introduce the values of $f(x)$ corresponding to $s = 0, 1, -1, 2, -2, \cdots$, we shall write the interpolating polynomial in the form

$$I(s) = a_0 + a_1 \binom{s}{1} + a_2 \binom{s}{2} + a_3 \binom{s+1}{3} + a_4 \binom{s+1}{4} + \cdots$$
$$+ a_{2k} \binom{s+k-1}{2k} + a_{2k+1} \binom{s+k}{2k+1} + \cdots . \quad (1.5.1)$$

We proceed to determine convenient expressions for the a_k. On using (1.3.6) repeatedly we find that

$$\Delta I(s) = a_1 + a_2 \binom{s}{1} + a_3 \binom{s+1}{2} + a_4 \binom{s+1}{3} + \cdots$$
$$+ a_{2k} \binom{s+k-1}{2k-1} + a_{2k+1} \binom{s+k}{2k} + \cdots ,$$

$$\Delta^2 I(s) = a_2 + a_3 \binom{s+1}{2} + a_4 \binom{s+1}{2} + \cdots$$
$$+ a_{2k} \binom{s+k-1}{2k-2} + a_{2k+1} \binom{s+k}{2k-1} + \cdots , \quad (1.5.2)$$

$$\cdot \quad \cdot \quad \cdot \quad \cdot \quad \cdot \quad \cdot \quad \cdot \quad \cdot \quad \cdot \quad \cdot \quad \cdot \quad \cdot \quad \cdot$$

$$\Delta^{2k} I(s) = a_{2k} + a_{2k+1} \binom{s+k}{1} + \cdots ,$$

$$\Delta^{2k+1} I(s) = a_{2k+1} + a_{2k+2} \binom{s+k}{1} + \cdots .$$

If in equation (1.5.1) we set $s = 0$ and in equations (1.5.2) we set respectively $s = 0, -1, \cdots, -k, -k, \cdots$, we obtain

$$a_0 = I(0) = f_0,$$
$$a_1 = \Delta I(0) = \Delta f_0,$$
$$a_2 = \Delta^2 I(-1) = \Delta^2 f_{-1},$$

$$\cdot \quad \cdot \quad \cdot \quad \cdot \quad \cdot \quad \cdot \quad \cdot \quad \cdot \quad \cdot \quad \cdot$$

$$a_{2k} = \Delta^{2k} I(-k) = \Delta^{2k} f_{-k},$$
$$a_{2k+1} = \Delta^{2k+1} I(-k) = \Delta^{2k+1} f_{-k},$$

$$\cdot \quad \cdot \quad \cdot \quad \cdot \quad \cdot \quad \cdot \quad \cdot \quad \cdot \quad \cdot \quad \cdot \quad \cdot \quad \cdot$$

Substituting these values into (1.5.1) we obtain Gauss's forward formula

$$f_s \approx f_0 + \binom{s}{1} \Delta f_0 + \binom{s}{2} \Delta^2 f_{-1} + \binom{s+1}{3} \Delta^3 f_{-1} + \cdots$$
$$+ \binom{s+k-1}{2k} \Delta^{2k} f_{-k} + \binom{s+k}{2k+1} \Delta^{2k+1} f_{-k} + \cdots . \quad (1.5.3)$$

In order to write this formula in a more convenient form we introduce the notation of central differences. We write

$$\delta f(x) = f(x + \tfrac{1}{2}h) - f(x - \tfrac{1}{2}h),$$
$$\delta^r f(x) = \delta^{r-1}f(x + \tfrac{1}{2}h) - \delta^{r-1}f(x - \tfrac{1}{2}h). \tag{1.5.4}$$

We note that $\delta f_k = \delta f(x_k)$ generally does not involve tabulated ordinates. However the second central difference

$$\delta^2 f_k = \delta f(x_k + \tfrac{1}{2}h) - \delta f(x_k - \tfrac{1}{2}h)$$
$$= [f(x_k + h) - f(x_k)] - [f(x_k) - f(x_k - h)]$$
$$= f_{k+1} - 2f_k + f_{k-1} = \Delta^2 f_{k-1}$$

does involve tabular entries and the same is true of all central differences $\delta^{2m}f_k$ of even order. We also note that

$$\delta f_{k+\frac{1}{2}} = f_{k+1} - f_k = \Delta f_k,$$

and more generally $\delta^{2m+1}f_{k+\frac{1}{2}}$ involves only tabulated ordinates. We also note that

$$\delta f_{\frac{1}{2}} = f_1 - f_0 = \Delta f_0, \quad \delta f_{-\frac{1}{2}} = f_0 - f_{-1} = \Delta f_{-1},$$
$$\delta^2 f_0 = f_1 - 2f_0 + f_{-1} = \Delta^2 f_{-1},$$

and in general

$$\delta^{2k+1}f_{\frac{1}{2}} = \Delta^{2k+1}f_{-k},$$
$$\delta^{2k}f_0 = \Delta^{2k}f_{-k}.$$

We then write Gauss's forward formula (1.5.3) in the form

$$f_s \approx f_0 + \binom{s}{1}\delta f_{\frac{1}{2}} + \binom{s}{2}\delta^2 f_0 + \binom{s+1}{3}\delta^3 f_{\frac{1}{2}} + \cdots$$
$$+ \binom{s+k-1}{2k}\delta^{2k}f_0 + \binom{s+k}{2k+1}\delta^{2k+1}f_{\frac{1}{2}} + \cdots. \tag{1.5.5}$$

This formula utilizes the differences lying on the forward zigzag path indicated in the following difference table.

$$
\begin{array}{cccccc}
x_{-2} & f_{-2} & & & & \\
 & & \delta f_{-\frac{3}{2}} & & & \\
x_{-1} & f_{-1} & & \delta^2 f_{-1} & & \\
 & & \nearrow \delta f_{-\frac{1}{2}} \searrow & & \nearrow \delta^3 f_{-\frac{1}{2}} \searrow & \\
x_0 & f_0 & & \delta^2 f_0 & & \delta^4 f_0 \\
 & & \searrow \delta f_{\frac{1}{2}} \nearrow & & \searrow \delta^3 f_{\frac{1}{2}} \nearrow & \\
x_1 & f_1 & & \delta^2 f_1 & & \\
 & & \delta f_{\frac{3}{2}} & & & \\
x_2 & f_2 & & & & \\
\cdot & \cdot & & & & \\
\cdot & \cdot & & & & \\
\cdot & \cdot & & & & \\
\end{array}
\tag{1.5.6}
$$

In a completely similar way, introducing the ordinates corresponding to $s = 0, -1, 1, -2, 2, \cdots$, we obtain Gauss's backward formula

$$f_s \approx f_0 + \binom{s}{1} \delta f_{-\frac{1}{2}} + \binom{s+1}{2} \delta^2 f_0 + \binom{s+1}{3} \delta^3 f_{-\frac{1}{2}} + \cdots$$

$$+ \binom{s+k}{2k} \delta^{2k} f_0 + \binom{s+k}{2k+1} \delta^{2k+1} f_{-\frac{1}{2}} + \cdots. \quad (1.5.7)$$

This formula utilizes the differences lying on the backward zigzag path indicated in the previous difference table (1.5.6).

Neither of Gauss's formulas is used often in practice, but if we form their average we obtain a very useful formula known as Stirling's formula. Since this formula clearly involves the means of the odd differences, it is convenient to introduce the notation

$$\mu f(x) = \frac{1}{2}\left[f\left(x + \frac{h}{2}\right) + f\left(x - \frac{h}{2}\right)\right]$$

so that, for example,

$$\mu \delta f_0 = \tfrac{1}{2}(\delta f_{\frac{1}{2}} + \delta f_{-\frac{1}{2}}) = \tfrac{1}{2}(f_1 - f_{-1}), \quad (1.5.8)$$

$$\mu \delta^3 f_0 = \tfrac{1}{2}(\delta^3 f_{\frac{1}{2}} + \delta^3 f_{-\frac{1}{2}})$$

$$= \tfrac{1}{2}(f_2 - f_{-2}) - (f_1 - f_{-1}). \quad (1.5.9)$$

With this notation Stirling's formula may be written

$$f_s \approx f_0 + \binom{s}{1}\mu \delta f_0 + \frac{s}{2}\binom{s}{1} \delta^2 f_0 + \binom{s+1}{3}\mu\, \delta^3 f_0 + \cdots$$

$$+ \frac{s}{2k}\binom{s+k-1}{2k-1}\delta^{2k} f_0 + \binom{s+k}{2k+1}\mu\, \delta^{2k+1} f_0 + \cdots \quad (1.5.10)$$

or

$$f_s \approx f_0 + s\mu\, \delta f_0 + \frac{s^2}{2!} \delta^2 f_0 + \frac{s(s^2 - 1^2)}{3!}\mu\, \delta^3 f_0 + \frac{s^2(s^2 - 1^2)}{4!} \delta^4 f_0 + \cdots$$

$$+ \frac{s^2(s^2 - 1^2) \cdots [s^2 - (k-1)^2]}{(2k)!} \delta^{2k} f_0$$

$$+ \frac{s(s^2 - 1^2) \cdots (s^2 - k^2)}{(2k+1)!}\mu\, \delta^{2k+1} f_0 + \cdots. \quad (1.5.10')$$

The coefficients in this formula have been tabulated in the literature. See, for example, Davis [4]. For other tabulations the Index of Mathematical Tables [6] should be consulted.

Example 3. Using the difference table of example 1, calculate sin 0.43.

Since 0.43 lies near the middle of the table, Stirling's formula is appropriate. We choose $x_0 = 0.4$, $h = 0.1$, and $s = 0.3$. Then we have approximately

$$\sin 0.43 \approx 0.38942 + 0.3 \left(\frac{0.09390 + 0.09001}{2} \right) + \frac{(0.3)^2}{2} (-0.00389)$$

$$+ \frac{(0.3)(0.09 - 1)}{6} \left(\frac{-0.00094 - 0.00091}{2} \right) + \frac{(0.3)^2(0.09 - 1)}{24} (0.00003)$$

$$\doteq 0.38942 + 0.027587 - 0.000175 + 0.000042 - 0$$

$$= 0.416874 \doteq 0.41687.$$

Many tables provide central differences of even orders (usually δ^2 and δ^4) in addition to the tabulated functional values. In order to interpolate in such tables it is convenient to use Everett's formula which may be written in the following form:

$$f_s \approx (1 - s)f_0 + \binom{(1-s)+1}{3} \delta^2 f_0 + \binom{(1-s)+2}{5} \delta^4 f_0 + \cdots$$

$$+ sf_1 + \binom{s+1}{3} \delta^2 f_1 + \binom{s+2}{5} \delta^4 f_1 + \cdots . \quad (1.5.11)$$

We note that the values and differences from two consecutive lines of the table are involved, and that the coefficients of one line are obtained by replacing s by $1 - s$ in those of the other line. We omit the proof of Everett's formula, merely remarking that it may be deduced from Gauss's forward formula (1.5.5) by replacing the odd differences in terms of even differences of lower order. Davis [4] has also tabulated coefficients for Everett's formula.

There are a number of other interpolation formulas involving differences which are useful in special circumstances These may be found in books on numerical analysis such as Hildebrand [12].

1.6 LAGRANGIAN INTERPOLATION

For many purposes, it is desirable to express the interpolating polynomial explicitly in terms of the ordinates involved rather than in terms of their differences. In the derivation of such formulas we need not assume that the abscissas are equally spaced.

We seek a polynomial $I(x)$ of degree n, which assumes the values

$f_0, f_1, \cdots, f_n$ for the $n + 1$ distinct abscissas $x_0, x_1, \cdots, x_n$. We write it in the form

$$I(x) = f_0 l_0(x) + f_1 l_1(x) + \cdots + f_n l_n(x) = \sum_{i=0}^{n} f_i l_i(x) \qquad (1.6.1)$$

where $l_0(x), \cdots, l_n(x)$ are polynomials of degree n or less which are to be determined. It is easily seen that $I(x)$ will indeed take on the value f_i when $x = x_i$ if $l_i(x_i) = 1$ and $l_i(x_j) = 0$ when $j \neq i$. It is convenient to introduce the so-called Kronecker delta

$$\delta_{ij} = \begin{cases} 0, & \text{if } i \neq j \\ 1, & \text{if } i = j. \end{cases}$$

We may then express the desired properties of $l_i(x)$ in the form

$$l_i(x_j) = \delta_{ij} \quad (i = 0, 1, \cdots, n; \ j = 0, 1, \cdots, n). \qquad (1.6.2)$$

Since $l_i(x)$ is a polynomial of degree n which vanishes for $x = x_0, x_1, \cdots,$ $x_{i-1}, x_{i+1}, \cdots, x_n$, it must take the form

$$l_i(x) = C_i(x - x_0) \cdots (x - x_{i-1})(x - x_{i+1}) \cdots (x - x_n).$$

Making use of the requirement that $l_i(x_i) = 1$, we easily find C_i, and so we may write the desired Lagrangian coefficient function in the form

$$l_i(x) = \frac{(x - x_0) \cdots (x - x_{i-1})(x - x_{i+1}) \cdots (x - x_n)}{(x_i - x_0) \cdots (x_i - x_{i-1})(x_i - x_{i+1}) \cdots (x_i - x_n)}. \qquad (1.6.3)$$

If the values of $l_i(x)$ given by (1.6.3) are substituted in (1.6.1), Lagrange's interpolation formula is obtained.

Example 4. Write down the interpolation polynomial of degree 2 relevant to the data

x	0	1	3
$f(x)$	2	-1	1

Also find the approximate value of $f(x)$ at $x = 2$.

We have at once

$$I(x) = 2 \cdot \frac{(x - 1)(x - 3)}{(0 - 1)(0 - 3)} + (-1) \cdot \frac{(x - 0)(x - 3)}{(1 - 0)(1 - 3)} + 1 \cdot \frac{(x - 0)(x - 1)}{(3 - 0)(3 - 1)}$$

$$= \tfrac{2}{3}(x - 1)(x - 3) + \tfrac{1}{2}x(x - 3) + \tfrac{1}{6}x(x - 1)$$

$$= \tfrac{4}{3}x^2 - \tfrac{13}{3}x + 2.$$

Reduction to this final form would not be necessary for actual numerical interpolation. In order to find $I(2)$, which furnishes an approximation to $f(2)$, either the first or second form may be used. Thus

$$I(2) = \tfrac{2}{3}(2-1)(2-3) + \tfrac{1}{2}(2)(2-3) + \tfrac{1}{6}(2)(2-1)$$

$$= -\tfrac{2}{3} - 1 + \tfrac{1}{3} = -\tfrac{4}{3}.$$

If in equation (1.6.3) we make a linear transformation of the variable

$$x = a + hs, \quad x_i = a + hs_i,$$

where a and h are constants we obtain

$$l_i(x) = \frac{(s-s_0)\cdots(s-s_{i-1})(s-s_{i+1})\cdots(s-s_n)}{(s_i-s_0)\cdots(s_i-s_{i-1})(s_i-s_{i+1})\cdots(s_i-s_n)}. \quad (1.6.4)$$

Thus the form of $l_i(x)$ is invariant under such a transformation.

It is often convenient to choose a and h in such a way that the dimensionless variable s, which measures distance from a in units of h, takes on convenient values at the tabular points being used in a particular interpolation.

Example 5. Calculate an approximate value of sin 0.34 using the following data

x	0	0.30	0.40
$\sin x$	0	0.29552	0.38942

We let $x = 0.30 + 0.1s$, so that at the tabular points s takes on the values -3, 0, 1, and at the desired value $s = 0.4$. Then

$$\sin(0.30 + 0.1s) \approx \frac{(s-0)(s-1)}{(-3)(-4)}(0) + \frac{(s+3)(s-1)}{(3)(-1)}(0.29552)$$

$$+ \frac{(s+3)(s-0)}{(4)(1)}(0.38942)$$

and
$$= \tfrac{1}{12}[-1.18208(s+3)(s-1) + 1.16826(s+3)s]$$

$$\sin 0.34 \approx \tfrac{1}{12}[-1.18208(3.4)(-0.6) + 1.16826(3.4)(0.4)]$$

$$= 0.33336.$$

The true value of sin 0.34 is 0.33349.

In the case where the abscissas are uniformly spaced, the Lagrangian coefficients assume a simpler form and have been extensively tabulated.

Formulas involving an odd number of ordinates are the most often used and it is convenient to denote the abscissas by $x_{-m}, \cdots, x_{-1}, x_0, x_1, \cdots, x_m$. If the uniform spacing between abscissas is h, we may write

$$x = x_0 + hs, \qquad x_i = x_0 + hs_i,$$

so that s takes on the values $-m, \cdots, -1, 0, 1, \cdots, m$ at the tabular points. Then (1.6.4) reduces to

$$l_i(x) =$$

$$\frac{(s + m)(s + m - 1) \cdots (s - i + 1)(s - i - 1) \cdots (s - m + 1)(s - m)}{(i + m)(i + m - 1) \cdots 2 \cdot 1 \cdot (-1)(-2) \cdots (i - m + 1)(i - m)}$$

$$= L_i(s). \quad (1.6.5)$$

As an example, we take the case of 3 points. Then $m = 1$ and we obtain

$$L_{-1}(s) = \frac{s(s - 1)}{(-1)(-2)} = \tfrac{1}{2}s(s - 1),$$

$$L_0(s) = \frac{(s + 1)(s - 1)}{(1)(-1)} = -(s^2 - 1), \qquad (1.6.6)$$

$$L_1(s) = \frac{(s + 1)(s)}{(2)(1)} = \tfrac{1}{2}s(s + 1).$$

To illustrate the use of a table of Lagrangian coefficients for interpolation we give Table 1.2 which is computed directly from (1.6.6).

TABLE 1.2

Lagrange Three-Point Interpolation

s	$L_{-1}(s)$	$L_0(s)$	$L_1(s)$	
0.0	0.00	1.00	0.00	0.0
0.1	−0.045	0.99	0.055	−0.1
0.2	−0.08	0.96	0.12	−0.2
0.3	−0.105	0.91	0.195	−0.3
0.4	−0.12	0.84	0.28	−0.4
0.5	−0.125	0.75	0.375	−0.5
0.6	−0.12	0.64	0.48	−0.6
0.7	−0.105	0.51	0.595	−0.7
0.8	−0.08	0.36	0.72	−0.8
0.9	−0.045	0.19	0.855	−0.9
1.0	0.00	0.00	1.00	−1.0
	$L_1(s)$	$L_0(s)$	$L_{-1}(s)$	s

From (1.6.6) we see at once that $L_1(-s) = L_{-1}(s)$, $L_0(-s) = L_0(s)$. Thus for negative values of s, which are to be read from the right-hand column, the column labels at the foot of the table are to be used.

Example 6. Calculate approximate values of sin 0.44 and sin 0.34 using a three-point Lagrangian interpolation formula and the following data:

x	0.30	0.40	0.50
$\sin x$	0.29552	0.38942	0.47943

In both cases the central tabular point is $x = 0.40$. For $x = 0.44$, we have $s = 0.4$ and hence

$$\sin 0.44 \approx (-0.12)(0.29552) + (0.84)(0.38942) + (0.28)(0.47943)$$
$$= 0.42589.$$

For $x = 0.34$, we have $s = -0.6$ and hence

$$\sin 0.34 \approx (0.48)(0.29552) + (0.64)(0.38942) + (-0.12)(0.47943)$$
$$= 0.33355.$$

The true values are sin 0.44 = 0.42594 and sin 0.34 = 0.33349.

By choosing $m = 2$ or 3 in (1.6.5), we obtain the 5-point or 7-point Lagrangian interpolation coefficients. These, among others, have been tabulated under the sponsorship of the National Bureau of Standards [23].

We see that Lagrange's formula of interpolation has the advantage over difference formulas in that we may interpolate without first constructing a difference table. The work is relatively simple when the abscissas are uniformly spaced, especially if the tabulated coefficients are used. It has the disadvantage of requiring us to decide in advance the degree of the polynomial needed to obtain the desired accuracy. For difference formulas, the degree of the interpolating polynomial increases as each additional term in the series is added, and we can stop when it is clear that additional terms will be sufficiently small that they will not affect the result to the accuracy desired. Another advantage of Lagrange's formula is that it can be used when the abscissas are not uniformly spaced, whereas the difference formulas of this chapter are applicable only when the abscissas are uniformly spaced. The case of nonuniformly spaced abscissas can also be studied by generalizing the concept of a difference and introducing divided differences. This is done, for example, by Hildebrand [12], but will not be discussed in this book.

1.7 INVERSE INTERPOLATION

So far we have been concerned with the problem of direct interpolation, which consists in finding a value of $y = f(x)$ for some x other than the values of x for which $f(x)$ is tabulated. The problem of inverse interpolation consists in finding a value of x corresponding to a specified value of y other than the tabulated values. Now if $y = f(x)$, then in any interval in which $f'(x)$ exists and does not vanish, a unique inverse function $x = f^{-1}(y)$ exists. Hence inverse interpolation is direct interpolation of the inverse function. In other words we need only interchange the roles of x and y in our previous discussion. Even if the abscissas are uniformly spaced, however, the values of y will not in general be equally spaced, so that the difference methods of this chapter are not applicable. On the other hand, Lagrange's formula is available and may be used conveniently.

The use of Lagrange's formula assumes that the inverse function $f^{-1}(y)$ can be satisfactorily approximated by a polynomial in y. If $f'(x)$ vanishes near the point where the inverse interpolation is to be carried out, the derivative of the inverse function becomes infinite near this point, and so the inverse function cannot be accurately represented by a polynomial. In this case the following procedure may be used.

Suppose that the value $\bar{y}$ of y for which the corresponding value of $\bar{x}$ of x is desired lies between two consecutive tabulated values $y_0 = f(x_0)$ and $y_1 = f(x_1)$. If y_0 and x_1 are sufficiently close together and if $f'(x) \neq 0$ for the interval between x_0 and x_1, linear inverse interpolation may be used to obtain a first approximation $x^{(1)}$ to $\bar{x}$. One possible formula for this calculation is

$$x^{(1)} = \frac{1}{y_1 - y_0} \begin{vmatrix} x_0 & y_0 - \bar{y} \\ x_1 & y_1 - \bar{y} \end{vmatrix}.$$

We may then use any method of direct interpolation based on y_0, y_1, and a suitable number of additional known ordinates to compute an approximate value of $f(x^{(1)}) = y^{(1)}$. Then $\bar{y}$ will lie between $y^{(1)}$ and y_0 or between $y^{(1)}$ and y_1. A linear inverse interpolation based on whichever of these pairs of values is separated by $\bar{y}$ produces a second approximation $x^{(2)}$ to $\bar{x}$. Again direct interpolation is used to calculate an approximate value of $f(x^{(2)}) = y^{(2)}$. A third linear inverse interpolation based on $y^{(1)}$ and $y^{(2)}$ or on the closest pair of available values of y which are separated by $\bar{y}$ yields a third approximation $x^{(3)}$ to $\bar{x}$. The process is continued until an x is reached which by direct interpolation gives $\bar{y}$.

1.8 THE ERROR IN POLYNOMIAL APPROXIMATION

In Lagrange's formula of interpolation and in the various interpolation formulas involving differences, the function under consideration was approximated by a polynomial of specified degree. It is desirable to obtain some information concerning the error which is introduced by the use of such an approximation. If a function which is known at $n + 1$ points is approximated by a polynomial of degree n, no estimate of the error is possible unless some additional properties of the function are known. These additional properties may take various forms. Values at additional points might be known, or estimates of certain derivatives might be known, or it might only be known that the function was sufficiently smooth so that the polynomial approximation gives a good picture of the function. If values at additional points are known and if the abscissas of all the known points are uniformly spaced, higher differences can be calculated, and these may be used to obtain an estimate of the error. If the behavior of certain derivatives is known, we can give more precise estimates of the error involved.

We suppose that $f(x)$ possesses continuous derivatives up to order $n + 1$ and let $I_n(x)$ denote the interpolating polynomial whose values at x_0, $x_1, \cdots, x_n$ agree with the values of $f(x)$ at these points. Then the error in approximating $f(x)$ by $I_n(x)$ is

$$E(x) = f(x) - I_n(x). \tag{1.8.1}$$

If we let

$$\pi(x) = (x - x_0)(x - x_1) \cdots (x - x_n) \tag{1.8.2}$$

then, since both $E(x)$ and $\pi(x)$ vanish for $x = x_0, x_1, \cdots, x_n$, and $\pi(x)$ vanishes for no other value of x, we can find a function $K(x)$ such that

$$E(x) = K(x)\pi(x). \tag{1.8.3}$$

In the following discussion we consider x to be arbitrary but fixed, and $x \neq x_i$. Consider the function

$$F(t) = E(t) - K(x)\pi(t) = f(t) - I_n(t) - K(x)\pi(t). \tag{1.8.4}$$

Let I denote the closed interval determined by the greatest and least of $x_0, x_1, \cdots, x_n, x$. Then $F(t)$ vanishes for $n + 2$ distinct points, $x_0, x_1, \cdots, x_n, x$. By Rolle's well-known theorem (which may be found in any good standard calculus text) $F'(t)$ vanishes at least $n + 1$ times inside I, $F''(t)$ at least n times, $\cdots$, and hence, finally, $F^{(n+1)}(t)$ vanishes at least once inside I. Let one such point be denoted by ξ. Then from (1.8.4) we obtain

$$0 = f^{(n+1)}(\xi) - I_n^{(n+1)}(\xi) - K(x)\pi^{(n+1)}(\xi). \tag{1.8.5}$$

But since $I_n(t)$ is a polynomial of maximum degree n, its $(n+1)$th derivative is identically zero. Also, when multiplied out, $\pi(t)$ starts with the term t^{n+1} followed by terms of lower degree, and so $\pi^{(n+1)}(t) = (n+1)!$ Substitution of these values in (1.8.5) yields the result

$$K(x) = \frac{1}{(n+1)!} f^{(n+1)}(\xi).$$

If we substitute this result back into (1.8.3) we obtain

$$E(x) = \frac{1}{(n+1)!} f^{(n+1)}(\xi)\pi(x) \tag{1.8.6}$$

for some ξ in the interval I where I is determined by the largest and smallest of the numbers $x_0, x_1, \cdots, x_n, x$. In the foregoing proof it was assumed that x was different from $x_0, x_1, \cdots, x_n$ but otherwise arbitrary. It is clear, however, that (1.8.6) is valid also if $x = x_0, x_1, \cdots, x_n$, because both sides of the equation vanish.

Example 7. Find a bound for the error in the calculation of sin 0.34 in example 5.

In example 5, quadratic interpolation based on three points was used. Hence $n = 2$. Here $f(x) = \sin x$, and $f'''(x) = -\cos x$, so that $f'''(\xi)$ does not exceed 1 in magnitude. Thus

$$|E(x)| \leq \left| \frac{(0.34)(0.04)(-0.06)}{3!} \right| = 0.000136 \leq 0.00014.$$

Note that the actual error in the calculation in example 5 was 0.00013, so that this bound is a good one.

chapter 2 Numerical differentiation and integration

2.1 INTRODUCTION

In this chapter we consider the problem of finding the derivative or integral of a function $f(x)$ which is not given in explicit mathematical form but for which pairs of values (x_0, f_0), (x_1, f_1), $\cdots$, (x_n, f_n) are known. Even if the function is given in explicit form, it may be difficult or impossible to integrate. An obvious procedure is first to calculate the interpolating polynomial and then to differentiate or integrate it in place of $f(x)$. It may be hoped that this procedure will provide a reasonable approximation to the desired derivative or integral. Since the curve of the approximating function will oscillate about the curve of $f(x)$, it is evident that, even though the curves may remain close together, the slopes of the two curves may be appreciably different. It should also be observed that if the ordinates, used in the calculation of the derivatives, are quite close together, the round-off errors or errors in observation of alternating sign could have a marked effect on the calculation of the derivatives since differences of such ordinates will enter into the calculation. On the other hand, since integration is essentially an averaging or smoothing process, it may be expected that the error in integration will be small even when the interpolating polynomial provides only a fairly good approximation to $f(x)$.

2.2 NUMERICAL DIFFERENTIATION

Any of the forms of the interpolating polynomials obtained in Chapter 1 may be differentiated to obtain formulas for numerical differentiation.

If the derivative is desired at a point $\bar{x}$, it seems reasonable to suppose that the polynomials passing through an equal number of points above and below $\bar{x}$ will give the most accurate approximation to the derivative. For this reason, differentiation of the central-difference formulas may be expected to give the best results. If we recall that $x = x_0 + hs$, so that $dx = h\,ds$, and if we differentiate Stirling's formula (1.5.10'), we obtain

$$f'(x) \approx \frac{1}{h}\left[\mu\delta f_0 + s\delta^2 f_0 + \frac{3s^2 - 1}{3!}\mu\delta^3 f_0 + \frac{4s^3 - 2s}{4!}\delta^4 f_0\right.$$

$$\left. + \frac{5s^4 - 15s^2 + 4}{5!}\mu\delta^5 f_0 + \cdots\right]. \quad (2.2.1)$$

No attempt is made to give an expression for the error involved in this formula. We most often desire to obtain the derivative at one of the tabulated points, and unless the desired point is near the beginning or end of the table, it may be denoted by x_0 corresponding to $s = 0$. If we set $s = 0$ in (2.2.1) we obtain

$$f'(x_0) \approx \frac{1}{h}\left[\mu\delta f_0 - \frac{1}{6}\mu\delta^3 f_0 + \frac{1}{30}\mu\delta^5 f_0 - \cdots\right]. \quad (2.2.2)$$

It is frequently desirable to express this formula in terms of the tabular values f_i on either side of f_0. If we use a quadratic approximation to $f(x)$, we omit all terms involving differences of third and higher order. The approximation then becomes

$$f'(x_0) \approx \frac{1}{h}\mu\delta f_0 = \frac{1}{2h}(f_1 - f_{-1}) \quad (2.2.3)$$

on using (1.5.8). A more accurate formula is obtained by retaining third-order differences, but neglecting differences of fifth and higher order. If we make use of (1.5.8) and (1.5.9) to express $\mu\delta f_0$ and $\mu\delta^3 f_0$ in terms of ordinates, we easily find that

$$f'(x_0) \approx \frac{1}{12h}[-f_2 + 8f_1 - 8f_{-1} + f_{-2}]. \quad (2.2.4)$$

In a similar manner formulas involving more ordinates may be obtained by retaining more differences in (2.2.2).

Under certain circumstances, one in particular being if the derivative is desired at a tabular point near the beginning or end of the table, it is desirable to have a formula for finding the derivative at a tabular point other than x_0. For example, by setting $s = 1$ in (2.2.1) we obtain

$$f'(x_1) \approx \frac{1}{h}\left[\mu\delta f_0 + \delta^2 f_0 + \frac{1}{3}\mu\delta^3 f_0 + \frac{1}{12}\delta^4 f_0 - \frac{1}{20}\mu\delta^5 f_0 + \cdots\right].$$

$$(2.2.5)$$

If we neglect differences of third and higher order and express $\mu \delta f_0$ and $\delta^2 f_0$ in terms of ordinates, we find that

$$f'(x_1) \approx \frac{1}{2h}(3f_1 - 4f_0 + f_{-1}).$$ (2.2.6)

In a similar manner, neglecting differences of fifth and higher order we obtain

$$f'(x_1) \approx \frac{1}{12h}(3f_2 + 10f_1 - 18f_0 + 6f_{-1} - f_{-2}).$$ (2.2.7)

Proceeding in a similar manner we may obtain the following useful formulas:

$$f'(x_{-1}) \approx \frac{1}{2h}(-f_1 + 4f_0 - 3f_{-1}),$$ (2.2.8)

$$f'(x_{-1}) \approx \frac{1}{12h}(f_2 - 6f_1 + 18f_0 - 10f_{-1} - 3f_{-2}),$$ (2.2.9)

$$f'(x_2) \approx \frac{1}{12h}(25f_2 - 48f_1 + 36f_0 - 16f_{-1} + 3f_{-2}),$$ (2.2.10)

$$f'(x_{-2}) \approx \frac{1}{12h}(-3f_2 + 16f_1 - 36f_0 + 48f_{-1} - 25f_{-2}).$$ (2.2.11)

We note that formulas (2.2.3), (2.2.6), and (2.2.8) may be described as three-point formulas for the derivatives, whereas formulas (2.2.4), (2.2.7), (2.2.9), (2.2.10), and (2.2.11) are five-point formulas for the derivatives. Formulas involving more ordinates could be obtained by retaining more differences in (2.2.1). It will be noted that the symmetric formulas (2.2.3) and (2.2.4) are simpler than the others, and it can be shown that they are also more accurate. For this reason they should be preferred whenever possible.

If the derivative is desired at a tabulated point in a table which is not too close to the beginning or end of the table, it will always be possible to choose the desired point as x_0 and use points on either side of x_0 as in formulas (2.2.3) and (2.2.4). If the derivative is desired at a tabulated point very near the beginning or end of the table, however, one of the other formulas would be necessary. For example, to find the derivative at the first table entry by a five-point formula, we could use formula (2.2.11) with x_0 chosen as the third argument in the table.

It has been pointed out earlier that in interpolating near the beginning or end of a table it is appropriate to use Newton's forward or backward interpolation formula. We might therefore expect to obtain approximate formulas for derivatives by differentiating either of these formulas. Such formulas would, of course, involve the ordinary forward or backward differences instead of central differences as in (2.2.1).

Such formulas might be convenient if these differences were available. If these differences are expressed in terms of ordinates, we obtain exactly the same formulas as were derived earlier in this section except that the notation is different, that is, the abscissas and ordinates are numbered from a different origin. For these reasons we omit any further discussion of such formulas.

In all of the foregoing discussion we have assumed that the abscissas are uniformly spaced. If this is not the case, then we may differentiate Lagrange's interpolation formula (1.6.1) with respect to x yielding

$$f'(x) \approx \sum_{i=0}^{n} f_i l_i'(x) \qquad (2.2.12)$$

where, as usual, $f_i = f(x_i)$, and $l_i(x)$ is given by (1.6.3).

Formulas (2.2.3), (2.2.4), and (2.2.6) to (2.2.11) may be obtained from (2.2.12) by specializing to the case of uniformly spaced abscissas.

Following is an example of the use of some of these formulas.

Example 1. Given the following table of $f(x) = \sin x$, find the derivative of $\sin x$ at $x = 0.5$ and $x = 0.3$.

x	0.3	0.4	0.5	0.6	0.7
$\sin x$	0.29552	0.38942	0.47943	0.56464	0.64422

Here $h = 0.1$ and we can use formulas (2.2.3) and (2.2.4) for $x_0 = 0.5$. From (2.2.3), $f'(0.5) \approx 0.8761$. From (2.2.4), $f'(0.5) \approx 0.8775$. The true value is 0.87758. To calculate $f'(0.3)$ we may use formula (2.2.8) with $x_0 = 0.4$ and formula (2.2.11) with $x_0 = 0.5$. From (2.2.8), $f'(0.3) \approx 0.9584$ and from (2.2.11), $f'(0.3) \approx 0.9552$. The true value is 0.95534.

2.3 NUMERICAL INTEGRATION

To obtain formulas for approximating the value of the integral of a function over an interval from a to b, we may break up the interval from a to b into a number of smaller subintervals and approximate $f(x)$ by a polynomial over each of these subintervals. These polynomials are easily integrated, and the results can be combined to give an approximation to the desired integral.

We first seek to develop formulas to accomplish the integration over one of these subintervals over which $f(x)$ is approximated by a polynomial. Whether the abscissas are uniformly spaced or not, we can always use

Lagrange's interpolation formula to write down the interpolating polynomial in the form

$$I(x) = f_0 l_0(x) + f_1 l_1(x) + \cdots + f_n l_n(x),$$

where $l_i(x)$ are given by equation (1.6.3). Then

$$\int_a^b I(x)\, dx = f_0 \int_a^b l_0(x)\, dx + f_1 \int_a^b l_1(x) + \cdots + f_n \int_a^b l_n(x).$$

$$(2.3.1)$$

This formula is to be used as an approximation for $\int_a^b f(x)\, dx$. Since each $\int_a^b l_i(x)\, dx$ is a number which depends only on the abscissas $x_0, x_1, \cdots, x_n$ used and is independent of the functional values $f_0, f_1, \cdots, f_n$ we observe that the approximate integration formula is expressed as a linear combination of the functional values involved. Thus in order to derive an approximate integration formula we have only to determine the constants which appear as multipliers of the desired functional values. Although these constants could be determined by actually evaluating the integrals of the Lagrangian coefficients which appear, this is usually rather tedious.

We proceed to illustrate other methods which are more convenient for the evaluation of these constants, at least in the case in which the abscissas are uniformly spaced. First let us find a formula involving only two functional values f_0 and f_1 corresponding to x_0 and $x_1 = x_0 + h$ and giving an approximation to $\int_{x_0}^{x_1} f(x)\, dx$. We might use Newton's forward-difference formula to approximate $f(x)$ in the form

$$f_s \approx f_0 + s\, \Delta f_0,$$

where, as usual, $s = (x - x_0)/h$. Then

$$\int_{x_0}^{x_1} f(x)\, dx \approx \int_0^1 (f_0 + s\, \Delta f_0) h\, ds$$

$$= h f_0 + \frac{1}{2} h\, \Delta f_0$$

$$= \frac{h}{2} (f_0 + f_1).$$

$$(2.3.2)$$

This is the basic formula of the trapezoidal rule.

Next let us find an approximate formula for $\int_{x_{-1}}^{x_1} f(x)\, dx$ which involves the three functional values f_{-1}, f_0, f_1 corresponding to $x_{-1} = x_0 - h$, x_0, $x_1 = x_0 + h$. Clearly, Stirling's central difference formula is appropriate here. Thus we write approximately

$$f_s \approx f_0 + s\mu\delta f_0 + \frac{s^2}{2}\delta^2 f_0.$$

Then

$$\int_{x_{-1}}^{x_1} f(x)\, dx \approx \int_{-1}^{1} \left(f_0 + s\mu\delta f_0 + \frac{s^2}{2}\delta^2 f_0 \right) h\, ds$$

$$= 2hf_0 + \frac{h}{3}\delta^2 f_0$$

$$= 2hf_0 + \frac{h}{3}(f_1 - 2f_0 + f_{-1})$$

$$= \frac{h}{3}(f_{-1} + 4f_0 + f_1). \tag{2.3.3}$$

This is the well-known formula of Simpson's rule.

Instead of using a single polynomial to approximate $f(x)$ over the entire range (a, b), we may divide (a, b) into subranges and approximate $f(x)$ by a different polynomial over each subrange. If we subdivide (a, b) into n subranges of length h and apply the two-point formula (2.3.2) to each subrange, we obtain the so-called trapezoidal rule,

$$\int_a^b f(x)\, dx \approx h(\tfrac{1}{2}f_0 + f_1 + f_2 + \cdots + f_{n-1} + \tfrac{1}{2}f_n) \tag{2.3.4}$$

where $f_0 = f(a)$, $f_k = f(a + kh)$, $f_n = f(b)$, and $h = (b - a)/n$. This formula corresponds to replacing the graph of $f(x)$ by a series of straight-line segments joining the ends of adjacent ordinates and hence the area in question is replaced by a sum of trapezoids. This formula is a very simple one but its accuracy is not high. By choosing h small, however, we can get good results.

If we subdivide (a, b) into $n/2$ subranges of length $2h$, where n is even, and apply the three-point formula (2.3.3) to each subrange, we obtain Simpson's rule in the form

$$\int_a^b f(x)\, dx \approx \frac{h}{3}(f_0 + 4f_1 + 2f_2 + 4f_3 + \cdots$$

$$+ 4f_{n-3} + 2f_{n-2} + 4f_{n-1} + f_n) \tag{2.3.5}$$

where again $f_0 = f(a)$, $f_k = f(a + kh)$, $f_n = f(b)$, and $h = (b - a)/n$. This formula corresponds to replacing the graph of $f(x)$ by a parabola in each subrange. The accuracy of Simpson's rule is usually greater than that of the trapezoidal rule, and also its weighting coefficients are relatively simple. For these reasons it is perhaps one of the most widely used of all formulas of numerical integration. By taking h sufficiently small, we can get any desired accuracy, provided the number n of ordinates which are needed does not become so large as to introduce round-off errors as a serious source of error.

For calculations by hand or with a desk calculator, the use of a large number of ordinates entails a prohibitive amount of labor. In such cases we may wish to have more accurate integration formulas even if these may involve more complicated coefficients. On an electronic computer, however, calculations using a large number of ordinates present no serious problem (unless round-off considerations enter), so it is usually more convenient to use a simple formula like Simpson's rule with a small value of h than it is to use a more complicated and more accurate formula with a larger value of h. Hence these more complicated formulas are not used as much as they once were.

Because a need for hand calculation may sometimes arise, however, we give without proof two celebrated formulas involving respectively four and seven ordinates. Newton's three-eighths rule may be written in the form

$$\int_{x_0}^{x_3} f(x)\, dx \approx \frac{3h}{8}\,(f_0 + 3f_1 + 3f_2 + f_3). \qquad (2.3.6)$$

A celebrated formula notable for the simplicity of its coefficients is Weddle's rule:

$$\int_{x_{-3}}^{x_3} f(x)\, dx \approx \frac{3h}{10}\,(f_{-3} + 5f_{-2} + f_{-1} + 6f_0 + f_1 + 5f_2 + f_3).$$

$$(2.3.7)$$

Both of these formulas may be applied to the evaluation of an integral over an interval (a, b) by dividing in $n/3$ subranges of length $3h$ or $n/6$ subranges of length $6h$ respectively. In the former n must be a multiple of 3, and in the latter n must be a multiple of 6.

Example 2. Use the data of example 1 to calculate $\int_{0.3}^{0.7} \sin x\, dx$ by the trapezoidal rule and by Simpson's rule, using $h = 0.1$.

Using the trapezoidal rule we find that

$$\int_{0.3}^{0.7} \sin x\, dx \approx 0.1[\tfrac{1}{2}(0.29552) + 0.38942 + 0.47943$$

$$+\ 0.56464 + \tfrac{1}{2}(0.64422)]$$

$$=\ 0.190336 \doteq 0.19034.$$

Simpson's rule gives

$$\int_{0.3}^{0.7} \sin x \, dx \approx \frac{0.1}{3} \, [0.29552 + 4(0.38942) + 2(0.47943)$$

$$+ \, 4(0.56464) + 0.64422]$$

$$= 1.1904947 \doteq 0.19049.$$

The true value is $\cos 0.3 - \cos 0.7 = 0.19050.$

2.4 INTEGRATION FORMULAS BY THE METHOD OF UNDETERMINED COEFFICIENTS

All the foregoing formulas of integration are said to be of closed type because they involve the ordinates at the ends of the interval of integration. Formulas of open type which involve ordinates at interior points of the interval of integration but do not involve the ordinates at the ends of the interval may also be obtained. Such formulas may be obtained as before by dividing the interval of integration in n equal parts by inserting $n - 1$ equally spaced abscissas and approximating $f(x)$ by the polynomial of degree $n - 2$ which coincides with $f(x)$ at the $n - 1$ interior points, and approximating the desired integral by integrating the resultant polynomial. Open formulas are used principally in the numerical integration of differential equations.

As has been noted, open formulas may be obtained by proceeding in a manner similar to that followed in deriving the closed formulas. There is another method, however, the method of undetermined coefficients, which can be used to derive many formulas of integration, whether closed or open. We illustrate this method by using it to derive a useful open formula. This method may be used to derive integration formulas involving any specified ordinates (and in addition any specified values of derivatives) of the integrand. For example, suppose that, as usual, x_0, x_1, x_2, x_3, x_4 denote uniformly spaced abscissas with spacing h. We seek a formula of the form

$$\int_{x_0}^{x_4} f(x) \, dx \approx A_1 f_1 + A_2 f_2 + A_3 f_3.$$

This is clearly an open formula since it does not involve f_0 and f_4. Since there are three constants to be determined, we may impose three conditions on this formula. We shall require that the formula give the exact value of the integral when $f(x)$ is a polynomial of zeroth, first, or second degree. There will, in general, be an error if $f(x)$ is a polynomial of higher degree. Clearly, the constant coefficients A_1, A_2, A_3 will not be altered by a change in the origin of coordinates. We therefore choose $x_2 = 0$ so that $x_0 = -2h$, $x_1 = -h$, $x_3 = h$, $x_4 = 2h$. Imposing the condition that the formula shall be exact when $f(x) = 1$, x, and x^2, we find that

$$\int_{-2h}^{2h} 1 \cdot dx = 4h = A_1 + A_2 + A_3,$$

$$\int_{-2h}^{2h} x \, dx = 0 = -hA_1 + 0 \cdot A_2 + hA_3,$$

$$\int_{-2h}^{2h} x^2 \, dx = \frac{16h^3}{3} = h^2 A_1 + 0 \cdot A_2 + h^2 A_3.$$

From the second equation we see that $A_1 = A_3$, and from the third equation we obtain $A_1 = A_3 = 8h/3$. The first equation then yields $A_2 = -4h/3$. The final formula becomes

$$\int_{x_0}^{x_4} f(x) \, dx = \frac{4h}{3} \, (2f_1 - f_2 + 2f_3). \qquad (2.4.1)$$

It is a simple matter to verify that this formula is also exact for $f(x) = x^3$ but not for $f(x) = x^4$. Thus we obtain in a certain sense, a bonus, in that the formula is exact for polynomials of degree one higher than might be expected on the basis of the number of conditions which could be imposed for the determination of A_1, A_2, and A_3.

Formulas (2.3.2), (2.3.3), and (2.3.6) could be derived by the method of undetermined coefficients, but the method used in the previous section is probably simpler. Formula (2.3.7) could not be derived in this way as it is a rather ingenious modification of the formula which would result by imposing the condition that the formula be exact for $f(x) = 1, x, \cdots, x^6$. (See, e.g., Hildebrand [12].) The method of undetermined coefficients is very useful if we want to derive a formula of integration involving ordinates different from those which appear in the standard formulas of integration. We may include values of first and higher derivatives in such formulas if this is desirable. We may then impose as many conditions as there are constants appearing in the desired formula. It should also be mentioned that the method may also be used to derive appropriate formulas for derivatives as well. Indeed all of the formulas of Section 2.2 could be obtained in this way.

2.5   ERROR ESTIMATES

Since all of the formulas of differentiation and integration have been derived on the assumption that $f(x)$ could be approximated by a polynomial of low degree, it is clear that they will be exact whenever $f(x)$

coincides with the interpolating polynomial used, but in other cases there will be an error introduced. For example, in deriving Simpson's rule (2.3.3) we approximated $f(x)$ by a polynomial of degree 2, and so if $f(x)$ is such a polynomial, the integration formula will be exact. But it is easily verified that the formula is also exact if $f(x) = x^3$, and hence it is exact for any third degree polynomial. However, if $f(x) = x^4$, we find that the error introduced is given by

$$E = \int_{-h}^{h} x^4 \, dx - \frac{h}{3}(+h^4 + 4 \cdot 0 + h^4) = \frac{2h^5}{5} - \frac{2h^5}{3} = -\frac{4h^5}{15}.$$

We note that if $f(x) = x^4$, then $f^{iv}(x) = 4!$ It follows at once that if $f(x) = x^4/4!$ then $f^{iv}(x) = 1$. If we apply Simpson's rule to the function $f(x) = x^4/4!$, we find at once that the error is $-h^5/90$.

We might guess that the error introduced when integrating by Simpson's rule any function $f(x)$ having at least four continuous derivatives would be

$$E = -\frac{h^5}{90} f^{iv}(\xi), \tag{2.5.1}$$

where ξ is some value in the range of the integration.

This is indeed a special case of a more general result concerning the error term in formulas of numerical integration. Each of the formulas of integration which have been derived in this chapter is exact for polynomials up to a certain degree but is not exact for polynomials of higher degree. If $E(f)$ denotes the error in a particular formula of integration, there is a number n depending on the formula in question such that $E(x^m) = 0$ for $m \leq n$ but $E(x^{n+1}) \neq 0$. For a large class of integration formulas which includes formulas (2.3.2), (2.3.3), (2.3.6), and (2.4.1), discussed in this chapter, it can be shown that if $f(x)$ has a derivative or order $n + 1$ in the range involved in the formula, then the error is given by

$$E(f) = f^{(n+1)}(\xi) E\left[\frac{x^{n+1}}{(n+1)!}\right] \tag{2.5.2}$$

where ξ lies between the greatest and least values of x involved in the integration formula (see Milne [19]).

In Simpson's rule, $n = 3$, and formula (2.5.1) follows at once from formula (2.5.2) since we have just shown that

$$E\left(\frac{x^4}{4!}\right) = -\frac{h^5}{90}.$$

By applying formula (2.5.2) in a similar manner to the integration formulas (2.3.2), (2.3.6), and (2.4.1), we can obtain the error terms for these formulas. For convenience of reference we list these formulas with their error terms:

$$\int_{x_0}^{x_1} f(x)\, dx = \frac{h}{2}\,(f_0 + f_1) - \frac{h^3}{12} f''(\xi), \tag{2.5.3}$$

$$\int_{x_{-1}}^{x_1} f(x)\, dx = \frac{h}{3}\,(f_{-1} + 4f_0 + f_1) - \frac{h^5}{90} f^{iv}(\xi), \tag{2.5.4}$$

$$\int_{x_0}^{x_3} f(x)\, dx = \frac{3h}{8}\,(f_0 + 3f_1 + 3f_2 + f_3) - \frac{3h^5}{80} f^{iv}(\xi), \tag{2.5.5}$$

$$\int_{x_0}^{x_4} f(x)\, dx = \frac{4h}{3}\,(2f_1 - f_2 + 2f_3) + \frac{14h^5}{45} f^{iv}(\xi). \tag{2.5.6}$$

Since Weddle's rule is obtained by modifying another formula in an ingenious fashion, the expression for its error consists of two terms. It may be written in the form

$$\int_{x_{-3}}^{x_3} f(x)\, dx = \frac{3h}{10}\,(f_{-3} + 5f_{-2} + f_{-1} + 6f_0 + f_1 + 5f_2 + f_3)$$

$$- \frac{h^7}{140} f^{vi}(\xi) - \frac{9h^9}{1400} f^{viii}(\xi). \tag{2.5.7}$$

It should be noted that the formulas such as (2.5.4), (2.5.6), and (2.5.7), which involve an even number of subintervals, may be written either in a symmetric form involving ordinates on either side of x_0 as in (2.5.4) and (2.5.7) or in a nonsymmetric form as in (2.5.6). The form will be the same in either case—only the numbering of the ordinates will be changed.

For formulas (2.3.4) and (2.3.5), which were obtained by application of formulas (2.3.2) and (2.3.3) over a series of subranges, the error terms become $-(nh^3/12)f''(\xi)$ for (2.3.4) and $-(nh^5/180)f^{iv}(\xi)$ for (2.3.5).

It is also of interest to observe that formula (2.5.2) may be used to find the error terms for many of the differentiation formulas of Section 2.2. For convenience of reference we list the following differentiation formulas with their error terms.

Three-point formulas:

$$f'(x_{-1}) = \frac{1}{2h}\,(-f_1 + 4f_0 - 3f_{-1}) + \frac{h^2}{3} f'''(\xi),$$

$$f'(x_0) = \frac{1}{2h}\,(f_1 = f_{-1}) - \frac{h^2}{6} f'''(\xi),$$

$$f'(x_1) = \frac{1}{2h}\,(3f_1 - 4f_0 + f_{-1}) + \frac{h^2}{3} f'''(\xi).$$

Five-point formulas:

$$f'(x_{-2}) = \frac{1}{12h}(-3f_2 + 16f_1 - 36f_0 + 48f_{-1} - 25f_{-2}) + \frac{h^4}{5}f^{\mathrm{v}}(\xi),$$

$$f'(x_{-1}) = \frac{1}{12h}(f_2 - 6f_1 + 18f_0 - 10f_{-1} - 3f_{-2}) - \frac{h^4}{20}f^{\mathrm{v}}(\xi),$$

$$f'(x_0) = \frac{1}{12h}(-f_2 + 8f_1 - 8f_{-1} + f_{-2}) + \frac{h^4}{30}f^{\mathrm{v}}(\xi),$$

$$f'(x_1) = \frac{1}{12h}(3f_2 + 10f_1 - 18f_0 + 6f_{-1} - f_{-2}) - \frac{h^4}{20}f^{\mathrm{v}}(\xi),$$

$$f'(x_2) = \frac{1}{12h}(25f_2 - 48f_1 + 36f_0 - 16f_{-1} + 3f_{-2}) + \frac{h^4}{5}f^{\mathrm{v}}(\xi).$$

It should be pointed out that each ξ lies between the extreme values of the abscissas involved in that formula. An examination of these formulas reveals that when the derivative is to be calculated at the central point, not only is the formula simpler than others involving the same ordinates but also the error term is smaller. Thus the central formula should be chosen whenever a choice is possible.

chapter 3 Roots of equations

3.1 INTRODUCTION

The solution of transcendental equations or algebraic equations of degree higher than two is usually impractical by direct analytical methods. To find the roots of such an equation the first step is usually to find some approximation to the root by rough graphical methods or otherwise from known properties of the roots of the equation. Thus if we seek the roots of the equation

$$f(x) = 0$$

we might plot the function

$$y = f(x)$$

and determine approximately where the graph crosses the x-axis. Having found an approximate value of a root, we then make use of some recurrence relation to generate a sequence of successive approximations which, under suitable conditions, will converge to the root. By this means we may obtain the value of the root to any desired accuracy.

In this chapter we discuss some of the methods for carrying out this procedure for one equation in one unknown. We also indicate how these methods can be applied to the solution of two simultaneous equations.

3.2 GENERAL ITERATIVE METHODS

We wish to consider the problem of finding a real root of the real equation

$$f(x) = 0. \tag{3.2.1}$$

We can always rewrite (3.2.1) in the form

$$x = F(x) \tag{3.2.2}$$

and indeed often in many different ways. If we have found an approximation z_0 to a root α of (3.2.1), we can use the recurrence relation

$$z_{k+1} = F(z_k) \tag{3.2.3}$$

to generate a sequence of approximations to α. The convergence or
divergence of this sequence of approximations may depend on the particular form chosen for $F(x)$. To study this situation we note that since α
is a root of (3.2.1) we have $F(\alpha) = \alpha$ and consequently

$$\alpha - z_{k+1} = F(\alpha) - F(z_k) = (\alpha - z_k)F'(\xi_k) \tag{3.2.4}$$

where ξ_k lies between z_k and α, if we assume that $F(x)$ possesses a continuous derivative over that range. If the sequence of approximations z_k
converges to α, then $F'(\xi_k) \approx F'(\alpha)$ for sufficiently large k, say for $k \geq k_0$.
For such k we find that

$$\alpha - z_k \approx (\alpha - z_{k_0})[F'(\alpha)]^{k-k_0}$$

and consequently $\alpha - z_k \to 0$ as $k \to \infty$, only if $|F'(\alpha)| < 1$.

Thus in order that the iteration converge to $x = \alpha$, it is necessary
that $|F'(x)| < 1$ in a neighborhood of $x = \alpha$.

It is also clear that if $|F'(\alpha)| < 1$ and if the initial approximation is
sufficiently near to α, the sequence of iterates will indeed converge to α.
In the special case in which $F'(\alpha) = 0$, the nature of the convergence
depends on the behavior of the higher derivatives of $F(x)$ hear $x = \alpha$.

Example 1. Find the real root of $x^3 - 2x - 5 = 0$.

A rough graph of the function $f(x) = x^3 - 2x - 5$ shows that the only
real root of the equation $x^3 - 2x - 5 = 0$ lies between 2 and 3 and is near
2. If we rewrite the equation in the form

$$x = \frac{x^3 - 5}{2}$$

we may try the recurrence formula

$$z_{k+1} = \frac{z_k^3 - 5}{2}.$$

If we start with $z_0 = 2$, we obtain the sequence $z_1 = 1.5$, $z_2 = -0.8125$,
$z_3 \doteq -2.7682, \cdots$. If we start with $z_0 = 2.1$, we obtain the sequence
$z_1 = 2.1305$, $z_2 \doteq 2.3352$, $z_3 \doteq 3.8671, \cdots$. It is clear that neither of these
sequences is converging and the reason is easily found. We have written
the equation in the form (3.2.2) with

$$F(x) = \frac{x^3 - 5}{2}.$$

Now $F'(x) = 3x^2/2$, which is 6 when $x = 2$. Another possible way of writing the equation in the form (3.2.2) is to choose

$$F(x) = \frac{5}{x^2 - 2}.$$

But again when x is near 2, $F'(x)$ is considerably larger than 1. If, however, we write the equation in the form

$$x = (2x + 5)^{1/3},$$

choosing $F(x) = (2x + 5)^{1/3}$, we find that

$$F'(x) = \frac{2}{3(2x + 5)^{2/3}} \approx 0.16 < 1$$

when $x = 2$. We therefore expect convergence if we use the recurrence formula

$$z_{k+1} = (2z_k + 5)^{1/3}.$$

If we start with $z_0 = 2$, we obtain the sequence $z_1 \doteq 2.0801$, $z_2 \doteq 2.0924$, $z_3 \doteq 2.0942$, $z_4 \doteq z_5 \doteq 2.0945$ when four decimal places are retained. The true value is 2.094551 to six places.

3.3 METHOD OF FALSE POSITION (*REGULA FALSI*)

Suppose that we have found an approximation to a root of $f(x) = 0$ by graphical or other means as indicated in Section 3.1. One of the oldest and most generally applicable methods for improving the approximation is the method of false position. If we have found two values of x, say $x = a$ and $x = b$, for which $f(a)$ and $f(b)$ have opposite signs, we can be certain that there is at least one root of $f(x) = 0$ between $x = a$ and $x = b$ because the graph of $f(x)$ must cross the x-axis between the two points. We may then replace the actual curve $f(x)$ between the two points by a straight line and take the point c where this line crosses the x-axis as an approximation to the root of the equation. The typical situation is shown in Fig. 3.1 and from the geometry of that figure we have

$$-\frac{f(a)}{c - a} = \frac{f(b) - f(a)}{b - a}$$

so that

$$c = a - \frac{b - a}{f(b) - f(a)} f(a). \tag{3.3.1}$$

Since $f(a)$ and $f(b)$ are of opposite signs, $f(c)$ must be opposite in sign to one of them, and so we may apply the same procedure again for a still better approximation to the root α.

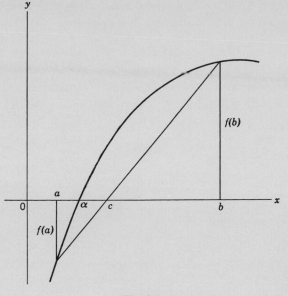

Fig. 3.1.

We see that at each step we are using linear inverse interpolation as
described in Section 1.7. It is clear that the procedure is certain to converge, although the rate of convergence may be slow.

It is instructive to express the method of false position in the form of a
recurrence formula of the type

$$z_{k+1} = z_k - \frac{f(z_k)}{\gamma_k} . \tag{3.3.2}$$

In such a recurrence formula the ideal choice of γ_k would be a value that
makes $z_{k+1} = \alpha$. To achieve this desirable result we would have to choose

$$\gamma_k = \frac{0 - f(z_k)}{\alpha - z_k} .$$

This is seen to be the slope of the secant joining $P_k[z_k, f(z_k)]$ and $(\alpha, 0)$.
Unfortunately this slope is not known unless the root α is already known,
which it is not. We should choose γ_k in such a way that this situation is
approximated at each stage of the calculation. In the method of false
position, we see from (3.3.1) that γ_k is to be chosen as the slope of the
secant joining P_k and the most recently determined point at which the
ordinate differs in sign from that at P_k.

We note that (3.3.2) is a special case of (3.2.3) in which we have written

$$F(x) = x - \varphi(x)f(x) \tag{3.3.3}$$

where $\varphi(x)$ is a function such that $\varphi(z_k) = 1/\gamma_k$. The explicit definition of a function $\varphi(x)$ which assumes the chosen value $1/\gamma_k$ is obviously unnecessary here.

Example 2.   Find the real root of $x^3 - 2x - 5 = 0$ by the method of false position.

If we start with $z_0 = 2.0$ and $z_1 = 2.2$, the next four iterates are shown in Table 3.1.

TABLE 3.1

z_k	$f(z_k)$	γ_k	$-f(z_k)/\gamma_k$
2.0	−1.0		
2.2	1.248	11.24	−0.111
2.089	−0.0618	11.80	0.0052
2.0942	−0.00392	11.83	0.00033
2.0945	−0.000575	11.83	0.00005
2.09455			

As in this example, γ_k often changes slowly after the first few steps. There would be some saving of labor if from some stage onward γ_k were assigned a constant value instead of being recalculated at each stage. The rate of convergence would be reduced only slightly if this were done.

In Table 3.1, z_4 was obtained by interpolation based on z_3 and z_1, following the preceding description of the method. If, however, the last two abscissas available are used, then z_4 may be obtained by extrapolation based on z_3 and z_2. Here, $\gamma_3 = 11.13$ and $z_4 = 2.09455$, which is a slightly better approximation. It can be shown that choice of γ_k as the slope of the secant $P_{k-1}P_k$ will yield a more rapidly convergent sequence if the sequence does converge. Unfortunately, the convergence of the resulting sequence cannot be guaranteed if extrapolation is required.

To study the convergence situation for the general recurrence formula (3.3.2), we observe that since $f(\alpha) = 0$ we have

$$\alpha - z_{k+1} = \alpha - z_k - \frac{f(\alpha) - f(z_k)}{\gamma_k}$$

$$= (\alpha - z_k)\left[1 - \frac{f'(\xi_k)}{\gamma_k}\right] \tag{3.3.4}$$

where ξ_k is between z_k and α. In order that $z_k \to \alpha$, it will be necessary that $1 - [f'(\xi_k)/\gamma_k]$ be smaller in magnitude than unity. This means that for convergence of z_k to α we shall have to have

$$0 < \frac{f'(\alpha)}{\gamma_k} < 2$$

for sufficiently large k.

Since the error in z_{k+1} is in general approximately proportional to the error in z_k as is shown by (3.3.4), we call the method under discussion a first-order process. Formula (3.2.4) shows that the method of Section 3.2 is in general also a first-order process.

3.4 NEWTON-RAPHSON METHOD

In formula (3.3.2), a reasonable choice for γ_k would be the slope of the tangent to the graph of $f(x)$ at $P_k[z_k, f(z_k)]$. The recursion formula then becomes

$$z_{k+1} = z_k - \frac{f(z_k)}{f'(z_k)}. \qquad (3.4.1)$$

This is the basic formula of the Newton-Raphson method. Formula (3.4.1) is a special case of formula (3.2.3) with

$$F(x) = x - \frac{f(x)}{f'(x)}.$$

Since $f(\alpha) = 0$, it is clear that $F(\alpha) = \alpha$. Moreover,

$$F'(x) = 1 - \frac{f'(x)}{f'(x)} + \frac{f(x)f''(x)}{[f'(x)]^2} = \frac{f(x)f''(x)}{[f'(x)]^2}$$

so that $F'(\alpha) = 0$. Thus, if $z_k \to \alpha$, the convergence is more rapid than for the methods of Sections 3.2 and 3.3. In other words, the Newton-Raphson method is a process of higher than first-order. To investigate the behavior of the error $\alpha - z_k$ more closely, we first expand $f(x)$ about the iterate z_k using Taylor's series with a remainder,

$$f(x) = f(z_k) + (x - z_k)f'(z_k) + \tfrac{1}{2}(x - z_k)^2 f''(\xi_k)$$

where ξ_k lies between z_k and α, under the assumption that $f''(x)$ is continuous in that interval. Next we set $x = \alpha$, note that $f(\alpha) = 0$, and solve for $f(z_k)$, obtaining

$$f(z_k) = -(\alpha - z_k)f'(z_k) - \tfrac{1}{2}(\alpha - z_k)^2 f''(\xi_k).$$

We substitute this into (3.4.1) and obtain

$$\alpha - z_{k+1} = \alpha - z_k - \frac{(\alpha - z_k)f'(z_k) + \frac{1}{2}(\alpha - z_k)^2 f''(\xi_k)}{f'(z_k)}$$

$$= -\tfrac{1}{2}(\alpha - z_k)^2 \frac{f''(\xi_k)}{f'(z_k)}.$$

If $z_k \to \alpha$, then for sufficiently large k we have

$$\alpha - z_{k+1} \approx -\tfrac{1}{2}(\alpha - z_k)^2 \frac{f''(\alpha)}{f'(\alpha)}.$$

We note that the error in z_{k+1} is approximately proportional to the square of the error in z_k, when k is large. We say that the Newton-Raphson method is a second-order process. It appears that the number of correct decimal places will be approximately doubled at each stage.

It must be emphasized that the Newton-Raphson method will not always produce a convergent sequence. Difficulties are likely to be encountered if $f'(x) = 0$ near a root or if the graph of $f(x)$ has inflection points between z_k and α. If a trial root is sufficiently close to α, convergence will occur provided $f'(\alpha) \neq 0$.

Since the Newton-Raphson method is a second-order process whereas the method of false position is a first-order process, one might think that the former would always be the more advantageous method to use. It should be noted, however, that in the Newton-Raphson method each stage of the iteration requires the calculation of two quantities, namely $f(z_k)$ and $f'(z_k)$. If we were to advance the subscript of z_k once for each evaluation required, we would conclude that the equivalent order of the Newton-Raphson process is only $\sqrt{2} = 1.414$. For the method of false position, only one new evaluation is required at each stage. If we use the modified method in which γ_k is chosen as the slope of the secant $P_{k-1}P_k$ at each stage, we can show that the order of the process is $\frac{1}{2}(\sqrt{5} + 1) = 1.618$. Thus, in this sense, the modified method of false position may be said to be superior to the Newton-Raphson method. The method of false position would also be preferred whenever the derivative of the function $f(x)$ is either difficult or impossible to compute. Where the derivative is easily found, the Newton-Raphson method is a very satisfactory procedure.

Example 3.   Find the real root $x^3 - 2x - 5 = 0$ by the Newton-Raphson method.

Since $f(x) = x^3 - 2x - 5$, we have at once that $f'(x) = 3x^2 - 2$. If we start with $z_0 = 2.0$, the next three iterates are shown in Table 3.2.

TABLE 3.2

z_k	$f(z_k)$	$f'(z_k)$	$-f(z_k)/f'(z_k)$
2.0	−1.0	10.0	0.10
2.10	0.061	11.23	−0.0054
2.0946	0.000542	11.162	−0.00004856
2.09455144			

The last value is correct to six decimal places.

As an interesting application of the Newton-Raphson method, we derive an iterative procedure for finding the square root of a number A. To find the square root of A we have only to solve the equation $x^2 - A = 0$. Applying formula (3.4.1) to this equation we find at once that

$$z_{k+1} = z_k - \frac{z_k^2 - A}{2z_k}$$

or

$$z_{k+1} = \frac{1}{2}\left(z_k + \frac{A}{z_k}\right).$$

This is the required iteration formula for the square root, and it provides a very convenient and rapid means of calculation. When square roots are needed in the course of a calculation on an electronic computer, this is the method which is most frequently used.

3.5 SIMULTANEOUS EQUATIONS

The methods of the previous sections may be extended to the solution of two or more simultaneous equations.

Suppose that we wish to solve the two simultaneous equations

$$f(x, y) = 0, \qquad g(x, y) = 0. \tag{3.5.1}$$

These equations may be rewritten in the form

$$x = F(x, y), \qquad y = G(x, y) \tag{3.5.2}$$

and usually in many different ways. If by graphical or other means we can find an approximate solution (x_0, y_0), we may then use the recurrence formulas

$$x_{k+1} = F(x_k, y_k), \qquad y_{k+1} = G(x_k, y_k) \tag{3.5.3}$$

to obtain a sequence of points (x_k, y_k). It can be shown that if the partial derivatives of F and G satisfy the conditions

$$|F_x| + |F_y| < 1, \qquad |G_x| + |G_y| < 1$$

near the solution (α, β), and if (x_0, y_0) is sufficiently close to (α, β), then the sequence of points (x_k, y_k) will converge to the point (α, β).

We may also derive an analogue of the Newton-Raphson method for two simultaneous equations. If (α, β) is a solution we may expand $f(\alpha, \beta)$ and $g(\alpha, \beta)$ about the point (x_k, y_k) by means of Taylor's series:

$$0 = f(\alpha, \beta) = f(x_k, y_k) + (\alpha - x_k)f_x(x_k, y_k) + (\beta - y_k)f_y(x_k, y_k) + \cdots,$$

$$0 = g(\alpha, \beta) = g(x_k, y_k) + (\alpha - x_k)g_x(x_k, y_k) + (\beta - y_k)g_y(x_k, y_k) + \cdots.$$

(Note that in these equations the subscript k is an integer but the subscripts x and y denote partial differentiation with respect to x and y.) Replacing (α, β) by the approximation (x_{k+1}, y_{k+1}), writing $\Delta x_k = x_{k+1} - x_k$ and $\Delta y_k = y_{k+1} - y_k$, and neglecting all nonlinear terms in Δx_k and Δy_k, we obtain the equations

$$\Delta x_k f_x(x_k, y_k) + \Delta y_k f_y(x_k, y_k) = -f(x_k, y_k),$$

$$\Delta x_k g_x(x_k, y_k) + \Delta y_k g_y(x_k, y_k) = -g(x_k, y_k).$$

These simultaneous linear equations may now be solved for Δx_k and Δy_k, and these corrections are then added to x_k and y_k to obtain the next approximations x_{k+1} and y_{k+1}.

3.6 APPLICATION TO POLYNOMIAL EQUATIONS

Although the specific example solved in Sections 3.2–3.4 was a polynomial equation, the methods of these sections are not restricted to equations of this type but may be applied to any algebraic or transcendental equation. Since the solution of such equations introduces no new difficulties, a numerical example was not included.

The Newton-Raphson method is particularly convenient for polynomial equations because the polynomial and its derivative can be evaluated readily by the process of synthetic substitution which will now be explained.

We consider a polynomial equation $f(x) = 0$ where

$$f(x) = a_0 x^n + a_1 x^{n-1} + \cdots + a_{n-1}x + a_n. \tag{3.6.1}$$

Let us divide $f(x)$ by a linear factor $x - z$. We obtain a quotient $b_0 x^{n-1} + b_1 x^{n-2} + \cdots + b_{n-1}$ and a remainder R. We may write

$$f(x) = (x - z)(b_0 x^{n-1} + b_1 x^{n-2} + \cdots + b_{n-1}) + R. \tag{3.6.2}$$

It should be noted that the coefficients $b_0, b_1, \cdots, b_{n-1}$ and R depend on z. If we set $x = z$ in (3.6.2) we obtain

$$R = f(z). \tag{3.6.3}$$

Thus $f(z)$ is the remainder on division of $f(x)$ by $x - z$. To obtain a convenient method for the calculation of $f(z)$ we proceed to introduce the idea of synthetic division in the following way. If we equate the co-efficients of x^n, x^{n-1}, $\cdots$, x, x^0 in (3.6.1) and (3.6.2) we obtain

$$a_0 = b_0, \qquad a_1 = b_1 - zb_0, \qquad a_2 = b_2 - zb_1, \cdots,$$

$$a_{n-1} = b_{n-1} - zb_{n-2}, \qquad a_n = R - zb_{n-1}.$$

These relations may be rewritten in the form

$$b_0 = a_0, \qquad b_1 = a_1 + zb_0, \qquad b_2 = a_2 + zb_1, \cdots,$$

$$b_{n-1} = a_{n-1} + zb_{n-2}, \qquad R = a_n + zb_{n-1},$$

or more compactly

$$b_k = a_k + zb_{k-1}, \qquad k = 0, 1, 2, \cdots, n$$

$$b_{-1} = 0, \qquad R = b_n. \tag{3.6.4}$$

If the quotient in (3.6.2) is again divided by $x - z$ we have

$$b_0 x^{n-1} + b_1 x^{n-2} + \cdots + b_{n-2} x + b_{n-1} =$$

$$(x - z)(c_0 x^{n-2} + c_1 x^{n-3} + \cdots + c_{n-2}) + R'. \tag{3.6.5}$$

Consequently

$$f(x) = (x - z)^2 (c_0 x^{n-2} + c_1 x^{n-3} + \cdots + c_{n-2}) + R'(x - z) + R.$$

It follows that

$$f'(z) = R'.$$

Thus $f'(z)$ is the remainder on dividing the quotient in (3.6.2) by $x - z$. It is also evident that the c's in (3.6.5) are related to the b's as the b's are related to the a's and hence

$$c_k = b_k + zc_{k-1}, \qquad k = 0, 1, 2, \cdots, n - 1$$

$$c_{-1} = 0, \qquad R' = c_{n-1}. \tag{3.6.6}$$

For actual calculation it is convenient to arrange the entries in the following form:

a_0	a_1	a_2	a_3	$\cdots$	a_{n-2}	a_{n-1}	a_n	$\lfloor z$
	zb_0	zb_1	zb_2	$\cdots$	zb_{n-3}	zb_{n-2}	zb_{n-1}	
b_0	b_1	b_2	b_3	$\cdots$	b_{n-2}	b_{n-1}	b_n	
	zc_0	zc_1	zc_2	$\cdots$	zc_{n-3}	zc_{n-2}		
c_0	c_1	c_2	c_3	$\cdots$	c_{n-2}	c_{n-1}		

The coefficients of the equation are written in order in the first row, zero coefficients being supplied where a power of x is missing, and the value of the argument is shown at the extreme right. The b_k are calculated in order by adding the two numbers above them. The c_k are found similarly.

Example 4. For $f(x) = x^3 - 2x - 5$, evaluate $f(2)$ and $f'(2)$ by synthetic division.

$$
\begin{array}{rrrrl}
1 & 0 & -2 & -5 & \quad \lfloor 2 \\
  & 2 & 4 & 4 & \\
\hline
1 & 2 & 2 & -1 = f(2) & \\
  & 2 & 8 & & \\
\hline
1 & 4 & 10 = f'(2) & &
\end{array}
$$

The values agree with those shown in the example of Section 3.4.

If one of the roots of the polynomial equation $f(x) = 0$ is to be found using the Newton-Raphson procedure, starting with the initial approximation z, the next approximation z_1 is

$$z_1 = z - \frac{b_n}{c_{n-1}}.$$

The process will be repeated with z replaced by z_1. This procedure for applying the Newton-Raphson method with the polynomial and its derivative evaluated by synthetic division is sometimes called the Birge-Vieta method.

When we have found a root of the equation so that $R = b_n$ is effectively reduced to zero, then $b_0, b_1, \cdots, b_{n-1}$ are (approximately) the coefficients of the reduced polynomial equation, of degree $n - 1$, whose roots are the remaining roots of $f(x) = 0$.

The procedure just described can also be applied to the problem of finding the complex roots of polynomial equations provided a complex starting value is used. Since the calculations involve complex arithmetic, however, they are likely to become very tedious. If the coefficients of the equation are all real, it is well known that the roots occur in conjugate complex pairs. To each such pair of roots will correspond a real quadratic factor $x^2 + px + q$ of $f(x)$. We now explain the Bairstow method in which a sequence of successive approximations to a quadratic factor is generated.

If the polynomial with real coefficients

$$f(x) = a_0 x^n + a_1 x^{n-1} + \cdots + a_{n-1} x + a_n$$

is divided by the quadratic expression $x^2 + px + q$, we obtain

$$f(x) = a_0 x^n + a_1 x^{n-1} + \cdots + a_{n-1} x + a_n$$

$$= (x^2 + px + q)(b_0 x^{n-2} + b_1 x^{n-3} + \cdots + b_{n-3} x + b_{n-2}) + Rx + S.$$

$$(3.6.7)$$

Now both R and S are functions of p and q. The condition that $x^2 + px + q$ be a factor of $f(x)$ is that

$$R = R(p, q) = 0, \qquad S = S(p, q) = 0. \tag{3.6.8}$$

We are therefore confronted with the problem of solving two simultaneous equations for p and q. In Section 3.5 an analogue of the Newton-Raphson method was described for doing this. If Δp and Δq are the corrections to be added to the trial values p and q, the equations to be solved are

$$\Delta p \frac{\partial R}{\partial p} + \Delta q \frac{\partial R}{\partial q} + R = 0$$

$$\Delta p \frac{\partial S}{\partial p} + \Delta q \frac{\partial S}{\partial q} + S = 0. \tag{3.6.9}$$

We need a simple procedure for the evaluation of R and S and the necessary derivatives.

If we equate coefficients of like powers of x in the two members of (3.6.7), we obtain

$$a_0 = b_0, \qquad a_1 = b_1 + pb_0, \qquad a_2 = b_2 + pb_1 + qb_0,$$

$$a_3 = b_3 + pb_2 + qb_1, \cdots, \qquad a_k = b_k + pb_{k-1} + qb_{k-2}, \cdots,$$

$$a_{n-2} = b_{n-2} + pb_{n-3} + qb_{n-4}, \qquad a_{n-1} = R + pb_{n-2} + qb_{n-3},$$

$$a_n = S + qb_{n-2}. \tag{3.6.10}$$

If we set

$$b_{-1} = b_{-2} = 0,$$

$$R = b_{n-1},$$

$$S = b_n + pb_{n-1}, \tag{3.6.11}$$

then we obtain from (3.6.10)

$$b_k = a_k - pb_{k-1} - qb_{k-2}, \qquad k = 0, 1, 2, \cdots, n. \tag{3.6.12}$$

Thus if the b's are calculated from (3.6.12) we obtain R and S.

It can be shown (see Hildebrand [12]) that the necessary derivatives require the calculation of the following quantities:

$$c_{-1} = c_{-2} = 0,$$

$$c_k = b_k - pc_{k-1} - qc_{k-2}, \qquad k = 0, 1, 2, \cdots, n-2 \qquad (3.6.13)$$

$$\bar{c}_{n-1} = 0 - pc_{n-2} - qc_{n-3}.$$

If the first of equations (3.6.9) is multiplied by p and subtracted from the second of these equations, the equations for the determination of Δp and Δq finally reduce to

$$c_{n-2} \Delta p + c_{n-3} \Delta q = b_{n-1}$$

$$\bar{c}_{n-1} \Delta p + c_{n-2} \Delta q = b_n. \qquad (3.6.14)$$

The calculations can be conveniently arranged as follows:

a_0	b_0	c_0
a_1	b_1	c_1
a_2	b_2	c_2
.	.	.
.	.	.
.	.	.
a_{n-4}	b_{n-4}	c_{n-4}
a_{n-3}	b_{n-3}	c_{n-3}
a_{n-2}	b_{n-2}	c_{n-2}
a_{n-1}	b_{n-1}	$\bar{c}_{n-1}$
a_n	b_n	

Each element in the b-column (including b_n) and each element in the c-column (except the last one $\bar{c}_{n-1}$) is calculated by subtracting from the element to its left p times the last calculated element above it and q times the next-to-last element above it. The element $\bar{c}_{n-1}$ is calculated in the same way except that the element to its left is replaced by zero.

To solve the equations (3.6.14) it is convenient to compute

$$D = c_{n-2}^2 - \bar{c}_{n-1}c_{n-3},$$

$$D_p = b_{n-1}c_{n-2} - b_n c_{n-3}, \qquad D_q = b_n c_{n-2} - b_{n-1}\bar{c}_{n-1},$$

from which we obtain

$$\Delta p = \frac{D_p}{D}, \qquad \Delta q = \frac{D_q}{D}.$$

Example 5.   Find the roots of the quartic equation

$$x^4 - 7x^3 + 32x^2 - 31x + 25 = 0.$$

We attempt to find a quadratic factor of the form $x^2 + px + q$. We start with the approximation $p = q = 0$. The first three stages in applying the Bairstow method appear as shown in Table 3.3. Thus this iteration gives $p = -0.999975$ and $q = 0.999973$ which are very close to the true values of $p = -1$ and $q = 1$.

If we solve the corresponding quadratic equation

$$x^2 - 0.999975x + 0.999973 = 0$$

we find that $x = 0.499988 \pm 0.866017i$ which are very close to the true

TABLE 3.3

$p, q =$	0, 0		−0.8, 0.8		−0.99, 0.99	
1	1	1	1	1	1	1
−7	−7	−7	−6.20	−5.40	−6.01	−5.02
32	32	32	26.24	21.08	25.0601	19.1003
−31	−31	0	−5.08	21.18	−0.2406	23.8791
25	25		−0.02		−0.0477	
$D =$	1024		559		484.7	
$D_p, D_q =$	−817, 824		−107, 107		−4.835, 4.834	
$\Delta p, \Delta q =$	−0.8, 0.8		−0.19, 0.19		−0.009975, 0.009973	

roots $(1 \pm i\sqrt{3})/2$. The other roots of the original quartic equation can be found by solving the quadratic equation corresponding to the quotient obtained by dividing the original equation by the quadratic factor just found. The first three entries in the b-column in the previous scheme provide approximations to the coefficients of this quotient. Thus when $p = -0.99$ and $q = 0.99$ we obtain the quotient $x^2 - 6.01x + 25.0601$ which is very close to the true factor $x^2 - 6x + 25$. If we carried the calculation out for $p = -0.999975$ and $q = 0.999973$ we would find the factor $x^2 - 6.000025x + 25.000152$. The corresponding roots are $3.000013 \pm 4.000010i$ which are very close to the true roots $3 \pm 4i$.

3.7 CHARACTER OF THE ROOTS OF A POLYNOMIAL EQUATION

In this section we consider a polynomial equation

$$f(x) = a_0x^n + a_1x^{n-1} + \cdots + a_{n-1}x + a_n = 0, \qquad (3.7.1)$$

all of whose coefficients are real. Then it is well known that its roots may be real or complex and that the complex roots occur in complex conjugate pairs. Before applying the methods of the previous section for the calculation of the roots of an equation, it is frequently convenient to obtain some preliminary information concerning the character and location of the roots.

A convenient procedure for obtaining such information is provided by Descartes' Rule of Signs which we shall now explain. We observe the signs of the coefficients of the equation (3.7.1) written in order a_0, $a_1, \cdots, a_n$. If a_{i-1} and a_i have opposite signs, we say that they present a variation of sign. We proceed to count the number of variations of sign in the sequence of coefficients. If some of the coefficients are zero, they are disregarded in counting the number of variations. We may then state the classical theorem known as

DESCARTES' RULE OF SIGNS. The number of positive real roots of the equation (3.7.1) with real coefficients is never greater than the number of variations of sign in the sequence of its coefficients $a_0, a_1, \cdots, a_n$, and, if it is less, then it is less by an even integer.

A proof of this result can be found in any standard textbook on the theory of equations. (See, e.g., Uspensky [18, pp. 121–124].)

By replacing x by $-x$ in equation (3.7.1), we may obtain information concerning the number of negative real roots.

Example 6. Use Descartes' rule of signs to obtain information concerning the roots of the equation

$$f(x) = x^6 - 2x^3 + x^2 - 3x - 1 = 0.$$

There are three variations of sign, and so there may be one or three positive real roots. Changing x into $-x$ we have

$$f(-x) = x^6 + 2x^3 + x^2 + 3x - 1.$$

There is just one variation of sign, and so there is exactly one negative real root. The total number of real roots does not exceed four, and so there are at least two complex roots.

In many dynamical problems we encounter motions which can be described by formulas of the type constant $\cdot\, e^{\lambda t}$, where λ is often obtained as a root of a polynomial equation with real coefficients. Such a motion is stable if the exponent λ has no positive real part. To determine whether such a motion is stable, we have only to determine whether any of the roots of the corresponding polynomial equation have real parts that are positive. For a system to be stable, it is necessary that none of the roots has a positive real part. We therefore seek necessary and sufficient conditions on the coefficients of the polynomial equation so that the real parts of all of its roots are negative.

For a cubic equation

$$a_0\lambda^3 + a_1\lambda^2 + a_2\lambda + a_3 = 0, \tag{3.7.2}$$

the conditions can be obtained from well-known elementary properties of the roots. We assume that $a_0 > 0$, since this can always be achieved by dividing the equation by -1 if necessary. Let $\lambda_1, \lambda_2, \lambda_3$ denote the roots of the equation (3.7.2). Then, since the left side of (3.7.2) is equal to

$$a_0(\lambda - \lambda_1)(\lambda - \lambda_2)(\lambda - \lambda_3),$$

we have

$$\lambda_1 + \lambda_2 + \lambda_3 = -\frac{a_1}{a_0} \tag{3.7.3}$$

$$\lambda_1\lambda_2 + \lambda_2\lambda_3 + \lambda_3\lambda_1 = \frac{a_2}{a_0} \tag{3.7.4}$$

$$\lambda_1\lambda_2\lambda_3 = -\frac{a_3}{a_0}. \tag{3.7.5}$$

To obtain necessary conditions on the coefficients, we assume that the real parts of $\lambda_1, \lambda_2, \lambda_3$ are all negative. In case the roots are all real and negative, it is at once obvious from (3.7.3)–(3.7.5) that $a_1 > 0$, $a_2 > 0$, $a_3 > 0$. In case two of the roots, say λ_2 and λ_3, are complex, then $\lambda_2 = \alpha + i\beta$, $\lambda_3 = \alpha - i\beta$, and hence $\lambda_2\lambda_3 = \alpha^2 + \beta^2 > 0$ and $\lambda_2 + \lambda_3 = 2\alpha < 0$. Moreover, λ_1 is real and negative. Hence from (3.7.3) we have $a_1 > 0$ and from (3.7.5) $a_3 > 0$. Now (3.7.4) may be rewritten in the form

$$\lambda_1(\lambda_2 + \lambda_3) + \lambda_2\lambda_3 = \frac{a_2}{a_0},$$

and it is clear that $a_2 > 0$. Thus for all the roots to have negative real parts it is necessary that $a_1 > 0$, $a_2 > 0$, $a_3 > 0$ when $a_0 > 0$. These conditions are not sufficient, however.

To obtain an additional necessary and sufficient condition we assume $a_0 > 0$, $a_1 > 0$, $a_2 > 0$, $a_3 > 0$. Then one of the roots, say λ_1, must be real and negative. Suppose that a_3 is very large compared to a_1 and a_2; (3.7.2) becomes approximately $a_0\lambda^3 + a_3 = 0$ and hence $\lambda_1 \approx -(a_3/a_0)^{1/3}$, $\lambda_2 \approx -(a_3/a_0)^{1/3}\omega$, $\lambda_3 \approx -(a_3/a_0)^{1/3}\omega^2$ where $\omega = (-1 + i\sqrt{3})/2$, one of the cube roots of unity. Thus λ_2 and λ_3 have positive real parts. Now if we diminish a_3, keeping a_1 and a_2 fixed, eventually the real parts of λ_2 and λ_3 will become negative, and we pass through a value of a_3 for which the real parts are zero and hence λ_2 and λ_3 are pure imaginary. If we write $\lambda_2 = \beta i$, substitute the value in (3.7.2), and equate real and imaginary parts, we obtain

$$-a_0\beta^3 + a_2\beta = 0$$

$$-a_1\beta^2 + a_3 = 0.$$

Eliminating β we obtain

$$\frac{a_3}{a_1} = \frac{a_2}{a_0}$$

or

$$a_3 = \frac{a_1 a_2}{a_0}.$$

Regarding a_0, a_1, and a_2 fixed, we observe that the roots are continuous functions of a_3. Hence λ_2 and λ_3 will have a positive real part if

$$a_3 a_0 > a_1 a_2$$

and a negative real part if

$$a_3 a_0 < a_1 a_2.$$

Thus we have shown that necessary and sufficient conditions that all the roots have negative real parts are $a_1 > 0$, $a_2 > 0$, $a_3 > 0$, $a_1 a_2 - a_0 a_3 > 0$.

For equations of higher degree, a convenient procedure for determining when all of the roots have a negative real part has been given by Routh. We make $a_0 > 0$ and arrange the coefficients of (3.7.1) in two rows thus:

$$a_0 \quad a_2 \quad a_4 \quad a_6 \quad a_8 \quad \cdots$$

$$a_1 \quad a_3 \quad a_5 \quad a_7 \quad a_9 \quad \cdots.$$

We then form a new row by cross multiplication in the following manner:

$$a_1 a_2 - a_0 a_3, \quad a_1 a_4 - a_0 a_5, \quad a_1 a_6 - a_0 a_7, \quad a_1 a_8 - a_0 a_9, \quad \cdots.$$

Next we form a fourth row by operating on the last two rows in exactly the same manner. Proceeding in this manner from row to row, the number of terms in each row will gradually decrease and we stop when no term is left. (Note that the first two rows are, of course, finite, because there are only a finite number of coefficients in the polynomial equation.) Then for the real parts of all the roots to be negative, it is necessary and sufficient that the terms of the first column should all be positive.

To formulate the foregoing rule for the calculation of the various rows we denote the first two rows as

$$\alpha_{00} \quad \alpha_{10} \quad \alpha_{20} \quad \alpha_{30} \quad \alpha_{40} \quad \cdots$$
$$\alpha_{01} \quad \alpha_{11} \quad \alpha_{21} \quad \alpha_{31} \quad \alpha_{41} \quad \cdots.$$

Then the third row is

$$\alpha_{02} \quad \alpha_{12} \quad \alpha_{22} \quad \alpha_{32} \quad \alpha_{42} \quad \cdots$$

where

$$\alpha_{i2} = - \begin{vmatrix} \alpha_{00} & \alpha_{i+1,0} \\ \alpha_{01} & \alpha_{i+1,1} \end{vmatrix}, \qquad i = 0, 1, 2, \cdots.$$

In general the jth row is

$$\alpha_{0j} \quad \alpha_{1j} \quad \alpha_{2j} \quad \alpha_{3j} \quad \alpha_{4j} \quad \cdots$$

where

$$\alpha_{ij} = - \begin{vmatrix} \alpha_{0,j-2} & \alpha_{i+1,j-2} \\ \alpha_{0,j-1} & \alpha_{i+1,j-1} \end{vmatrix}, \qquad i = 0, 1, 2, \cdots.$$

Then for the real parts of all the roots of a polynomial equation of degree n to be negative, it is necessary and sufficient that $\alpha_{0j} > 0$, $j = 0, 1, 2, \cdots, n$.

The so-called test determinants T_j which essentially appear in the first column of the scheme above may be written down explicitly in the following form:

$$T_0 = \alpha_{00} = a_0, \qquad T_1 = \alpha_{01} = a_1, \qquad T_2 = \alpha_{02} = \begin{vmatrix} a_1 & a_0 \\ a_3 & a_2 \end{vmatrix},$$

$$T_3 = \alpha_{03} = \begin{vmatrix} a_1 & a_0 & 0 \\ a_3 & a_2 & a_1 \\ a_5 & a_4 & a_3 \end{vmatrix}, \qquad T_4 = \frac{\alpha_{04}}{a_1} = \begin{vmatrix} a_1 & a_0 & 0 & 0 \\ a_3 & a_2 & a_1 & a_0 \\ a_5 & a_4 & a_3 & a_2 \\ a_7 & a_6 & a_5 & a_4 \end{vmatrix},$$

and so on. Any coefficient whose subscript exceeds n, the degree of the equation under consideration, is to be replaced by zero. It may be remarked that if $T_{n-1} = 0$, then the nth degree equation has either a pair of purely imaginary roots or a pair of equal and opposite real roots.

For example, $n = 3$ for the cubic equation, and we have

$$T_0 = a_0, \qquad T_1 = a_1, \qquad T_2 = \begin{vmatrix} a_1 & a_0 \\ a_3 & a_2 \end{vmatrix} = a_1 a_2 - a_0 a_3,$$

$$T_3 = \begin{vmatrix} a_1 & a_0 & 0 \\ a_3 & a_2 & a_1 \\ 0 & 0 & a_3 \end{vmatrix} = a_3 T_2.$$

It is easily seen that the positivity of these quantities is equivalent to the conditions previously obtained.

An alternative discussion of the Routh procedure may be found in Frazer, Duncan, and Collar [8, pp. 154–155].

chapter 4 Simultaneous linear equations and matrices

4.1 LINEAR EQUATIONS, VECTORS, AND MATRICES

Many problems in engineering, physics, applied mathematics, and other fields lead to systems of simultaneous linear equations. For example, in solving an elliptic partial differential equation, such as Laplace's equation, we frequently cover the region under study with a rectangular net and seek to find the values of the solution at the lattice points of the net. If we replace the differential equation by an approximating difference equation, we are led to a system of simultaneous linear equations in a large number of unknowns. In problems in many fields, including aircraft structural analysis, the complicated interactions between the various quantities under study can be represented by systems of linear equations.

A system of n linear equations in n unknowns may be written in the form

$$a_{11}x_1 + a_{12}x_2 + \cdots + a_{1n}x_n = b_1$$
$$a_{21}x_1 + a_{22}x_2 + \cdots + a_{2n}x_n = b_2 \qquad (4.1.1)$$
$$\cdots \cdots \cdots \cdots \cdots \cdots \cdots \cdots$$
$$a_{n1}x_1 + a_{n2}x_2 + \cdots + a_{nn}x_n = b_n.$$

In order to introduce a convenient notation for writing such systems and for studying them, we proceed to define vectors and matrices.

The reader is familiar with the concept of a vector in 2-space and in 3-space. Such vectors have two or three components respectively. This concept may be generalized to n-space if we define a vector to be a set of n real numbers which may be written in the form

$$\mathbf{x} = \begin{bmatrix} x_1 \\ x_2 \\ \cdot \\ \cdot \\ \cdot \\ x_n \end{bmatrix}. \qquad (4.1.2)$$

Indeed we may permit the x_i to be complex numbers. We remind the reader that a real number is a special case of a complex number in which the imaginary part is zero. In Sections 4.1 to 4.8 we shall consider only vectors with real components; in Sections 4.9 to 4.16 the vectors may have complex components. The vector in equation (4.1.2) is called a column vector. If n numbers are arranged in a horizontal array,

$$\mathbf{x} = (x_1, x_2, \cdots, x_n), \qquad (4.1.3)$$

$\mathbf{x}$ is called a row vector. Lower-case letters such as $\mathbf{x}$, $\mathbf{y}$, $\mathbf{z}$ or $\mathbf{a}$, $\mathbf{b}$, $\mathbf{c}$ will be used to designate vectors. The quantities x_i are called the components of $\mathbf{x}$, whereas n is called the dimension of the vector $\mathbf{x}$. One-dimensional vectors are called scalars.

It will be recalled that in 2-space and 3-space vectors are equal if and only if their components are equal, and that the operation of vector addition of two vectors is accomplished by adding corresponding components. Multiplication of a vector by a scalar means that each component is multiplied by the same real number.

If these concepts are generalized to n-space, we are led to the following formal definitions. Two vectors $\mathbf{x}$ and $\mathbf{y}$ are equal if and only if their components are equal, that is $x_i = y_i$ for $i = 1, 2, \cdots, n$. The sum of two vectors, $\mathbf{x}$ and $\mathbf{y}$, is denoted by $\mathbf{x} + \mathbf{y}$ and is defined to be

$$\mathbf{x} + \mathbf{y} = \begin{bmatrix} x_1 + y_1 \\ x_2 + y_2 \\ \cdot \\ \cdot \\ \cdot \\ x_n + y_n \end{bmatrix}. \qquad (4.1.4)$$

Addition is commutative and associative. In other words, $\mathbf{x} + \mathbf{y} = \mathbf{y} + \mathbf{x}$

and $\mathbf{x} + (\mathbf{y} + \mathbf{z}) = (\mathbf{x} + \mathbf{y}) + \mathbf{z}$. Multiplication of a vector $\mathbf{x}$ by a scalar c_1 is defined by means of the relation

$$c_1\mathbf{x} = \mathbf{x}c_1 = \begin{bmatrix} c_1x_1 \\ c_1x_2 \\ \cdot \\ \cdot \\ \cdot \\ c_1x_n \end{bmatrix}. \tag{4.1.5}$$

In real 2-space and 3-space the length of a vector $\mathbf{x}$ has an obvious geometric meaning, and this length, denoted by $|\mathbf{x}|$, can be computed as the square root of the sum of the squares of the components of $\mathbf{x}$. In addition, the scalar product or dot product of two vectors $\mathbf{x}$ and $\mathbf{y}$ is defined to be $|\mathbf{x}|\,|\mathbf{y}|\cos\theta$ where θ is the angle between the two vectors. This dot product can be shown to be equal to $x_1y_1 + x_2y_2$ in 2-space or $x_1y_1 + x_2y_2 + x_3y_3$ in 3-space.

These notions can be generalized to n-space. The inner product or scalar product of two vectors $\mathbf{x}$ and $\mathbf{y}$ is written $(\mathbf{x}, \mathbf{y})$ and is defined by the relation

$$(\mathbf{x}, \mathbf{y}) = \sum_{i=1}^{n} x_iy_i. \tag{4.1.6}$$

This is a scalar function of $\mathbf{x}$ and $\mathbf{y}$. We call

$$\sqrt{(\mathbf{x}, \mathbf{x})} = \left(\sum_{i=1}^{n} x_i^2 \right)^{1/2}$$

the length of the vector $\mathbf{x}$, and denote it by $|\mathbf{x}|$. It is clear that the length of a vector is zero if and only if all of its components x_i are zero. The vector whose components are all zero is called the zero vector and is denoted by $\mathbf{0}$. Thus $|\mathbf{0}| = 0$ and $|\mathbf{x}| > 0$ if $\mathbf{x} \neq \mathbf{0}$.

In 2-space and 3-space, two vectors are said to be orthogonal if the angle θ between them is 90°, that is, if their dot product is zero. Thus in n-space, two vectors $\mathbf{x}$ and $\mathbf{y}$ are said to be orthogonal if and only if $(\mathbf{x}, \mathbf{y}) = 0$.

Thus far we have assumed that the vectors have real components. To generalize the definition (4.1.6) for vectors with complex components, we have only to replace y_i by $\bar{y}_i$, the complex conjugate of y_i. We shall need this form of (4.1.6) in Section 4.11.

If $c_1, c_2, \cdots, c_m$ are scalars, then the vector

$$\mathbf{y} = c_1\mathbf{x}^1 + c_2\mathbf{x}^2 + \cdots + c_m\mathbf{x}^m$$

is said to be a linear combination of the vectors $x^1, x^2, \cdots, x^m$. Note that we have used superscripts to distinguish different vectors; the notation must not be confused with the familiar notation used for powers or exponents.

Vectors $x^1, x^2, \cdots, x^m$ are called linearly dependent if there exist scalar constants $c_1, c_2, \cdots, c_m$, not all zero, such that the equation

$$c_1 x^1 + c_2 x^2 + \cdots + c_m x^m = 0$$

holds. Otherwise the vectors $x^1, x^2, \cdots, x^m$ are said to be linearly independent. This may also be expressed by saying that the vectors $x^1, x^2, \cdots, x^m$ are linearly independent if and only if any relation of the form

$$c_1 x^1 + c_2 x^2 + \cdots + c_m x^m = 0$$

implies that $c_1 = c_2 = \cdots = c_m = 0$.

If the vectors $x^1, x^2, \cdots, x^m$ are linearly dependent, at least one of them will be a linear combination of the others, for at least one of the constants, say c_k, is different from zero and so

$$x^k = -\frac{c_1}{c_k} x^1 - \cdots - \frac{c_{k-1}}{c_k} x^{k-1} - \frac{c_{k+1}}{c_k} x^{k+1} - \cdots - \frac{c_m}{c_k} x^m.$$

Next we introduce the concept of a matrix. An array of mn real (or complex) numbers written in the form

$$A = \begin{bmatrix} a_{11} & a_{12} & \cdots & a_{1n} \\ a_{21} & a_{22} & \cdots & a_{2n} \\ \cdot & \cdot & \cdots & \cdot \\ a_{m1} & a_{m2} & \cdots & a_{mn} \end{bmatrix} \tag{4.1.7}$$

will be called a matrix. The quantities a_{ij} are called the elements of A. The matrix has m rows and n columns. We refer to $a_{i1}, a_{i2}, \cdots, a_{in}$ as the ith row of A and to $a_{1j}, a_{2j}, \cdots, a_{mj}$ as the jth column. Matrices will be denoted by upper case letters such as X, Y, Z or A, B, C. The shorthand notation

$$A = (a_{ij}) \tag{4.1.8}$$

is often convenient. If $m = n$, the matrix is square. Here n is called the order of the matrix.

Two matrices are equal if and only if their elements are equal. The sum of two matrices A and B is denoted by $A + B$ and is defined by

$$A + B = (a_{ij} + b_{ij}). \tag{4.1.9}$$

Multiplication of a matrix A by a scalar c_1 is defined by the relation

$$c_1 A = A c_1 = (c_1 a_{ij}).$$ \hfill (4.1.10)

The determinant associated with a square matrix A is one whose elements are those of the matrix (without disarrangement) and is denoted by $|A|$ or $|a_{ij}|$. This determinant is a scalar quantity which is a function of the elements a_{ij}. It may be defined by forming all possible products consisting of one element from each row and each column, affixing an appropriate sign to each product, and adding. The order of a determinant is the number of rows and columns of the associated square matrix. To describe a more convenient procedure for the evaluation of a determinant, we begin with a determinant of order 2. The definition here is

$$\begin{vmatrix} a_{11} & a_{12} \\ a_{21} & a_{22} \end{vmatrix} = a_{11}a_{22} - a_{12}a_{21}.$$

The value of a determinant of order 3 may be written in terms of determinants of order 2 by expanding the determinant in terms of the elements of any column (or of any row). For example, we have

$$\begin{vmatrix} a_{11} & a_{12} & a_{13} \\ a_{21} & a_{22} & a_{23} \\ a_{31} & a_{32} & a_{33} \end{vmatrix} = a_{11} \begin{vmatrix} a_{22} & a_{23} \\ a_{32} & a_{33} \end{vmatrix} - a_{12} \begin{vmatrix} a_{21} & a_{23} \\ a_{31} & a_{33} \end{vmatrix} + a_{13} \begin{vmatrix} a_{21} & a_{22} \\ a_{31} & a_{32} \end{vmatrix}$$

\hfill (4.1.11)

where the expansion is in terms of the first row. The determinantal coefficients of $\pm a_{ij}$ in the foregoing expansion are called minors and the coefficients of the a_{ij} are known as cofactors.

In general, the expansion of a determinant of order n in terms of the elements of any column (or of any row) will involve determinants of order $n - 1$, and so determinants of any order can be evaluated inductively. If in the matrix A we delete the ith row and jth column, the determinant whose elements are the remaining elements of A is called the minor of a_{ij}. The cofactor A_{ij} of the element a_{ij} is obtained by multiplying the minor of a_{ij} by $(-1)^{i+j}$. The rule for evaluating the determinant $|A|$ in terms of the elements of the ith row may then be written

$$|A| = \sum_{k=1}^{n} a_{ik} A_{ik}.$$ \hfill (4.1.12)

For reference we state some of the elementary properties of determinants:

(a) If two columns (or two rows) of a determinant are interchanged, the value of the determinant is changed in sign.

(*b*) If two columns (or two rows) of a determinant are identical, the value of the determinant is zero.

(*c*) If every element of a column (or a row) is multiplied by the same number, the determinant is multiplied by that number.

(*d*) If the rows and columns of a determinant are interchanged without changing the order in which they occur, the value of the determinant is unchanged.

(*e*) If to the elements of any column (or row) are added the corresponding elements of any other column (or row), each multiplied by the same arbitrary number, the value of the determinant is unchanged.

(*f*) The sum of products of each element of a row (or column) by the cofactor of the corresponding element of another row (or column) is zero. Thus we have

$$\sum_{k=1}^{n} a_{ik}A_{jk} = 0 \qquad i \neq j$$

$$\sum_{k=1}^{n} a_{ki}A_{kj} = 0 \qquad i \neq j.$$

If we combine these results with (4.1.12) and the corresponding result for columns, we may write the following relations:

$$\sum_{k=1}^{n} a_{ik}A_{jk} = |A|\,\delta_{ij},$$

$$\sum_{k=1}^{n} a_{ki}A_{kj} = |A|\,\delta_{ij},$$

$$(4.1.13)$$

where δ_{ij} denotes the Kronecker delta which takes the value 1 when $i = j$ and 0 when $i \neq j$.

4.2 MATRIX MULTIPLICATION

To introduce the concept of matrix multiplication, we begin by considering a linear transformation of a vector **x** into a vector **y**. Such a linear transformation may be written in the form

$$y_i = \sum_{j=1}^{n} a_{ij}x_j, \qquad i = 1, 2, \cdots, n \qquad (4.2.1)$$

where the coefficients a_{ij} are real (or complex) quantities. If we write the relation between **x** and **y** given by (4.2.1) in the form

$$\mathbf{y} = A\mathbf{x}, \qquad (4.2.2)$$

then (4.2.1) and (4.2.2) define the multiplication of a vector **x** by a square matrix A. In other words, the vector by matrix product A**x** is a vector **y** whose components are given by (4.2.1). For example, the linear transformation given by

$$y_1 = 3x_1 + 2x_2$$

$$y_2 = 2x_1 - 4x_2$$

may be written in the form

$$\begin{bmatrix} y_1 \\ y_2 \end{bmatrix} = \begin{bmatrix} 3 & 2 \\ 2 & -4 \end{bmatrix} \begin{bmatrix} x_1 \\ x_2 \end{bmatrix}.$$

Next we wish to define the product of a matrix by a matrix. We consider a second linear transformation

$$\mathbf{x} = B\mathbf{z} \tag{4.2.3}$$

which converts the components of **z** into the components of **x**. We wish to express the components of **y** in terms of the components of **z**, where, as above, **y** = A**x**. We may write (4.2.3) in the form

$$x_j = \sum_{k=1}^{n} b_{jk} z_k, \qquad j = 1, 2, \cdots, n. \tag{4.2.4}$$

If we substitute (4.2.4) into (4.2.1) we obtain

$$y_i = \sum_{j=1}^{n} a_{ij} \left(\sum_{k=1}^{n} b_{jk} z_k \right)$$

$$= \sum_{k=1}^{n} \left(\sum_{j=1}^{n} a_{ij} b_{jk} \right) z_k. \tag{4.2.5}$$

If we now introduce a new matrix $C = (c_{ik})$ defined by

$$c_{ik} = \sum_{j=1}^{n} a_{ij} b_{jk}, \qquad i, k = 1, 2, \cdots, n, \tag{4.2.6}$$

we may write

$$\mathbf{y} = C\mathbf{z}.$$

Since formally

$$\mathbf{y} = A\mathbf{x} = A(B\mathbf{z}) = (AB)\mathbf{z},$$

we are led to define the product of B by A as

$$C = AB, \tag{4.2.7}$$

where C is determined by (4.2.6). Note carefully the order in which the product is written. The product AB is referred to either as B premultiplied by A or as A postmultiplied by B.

To illustrate how the matrix product defined in (4.2.7) is formed we consider the transformations

$$\begin{bmatrix} y_1 \\ y_2 \end{bmatrix} = \begin{bmatrix} 3 & 2 \\ 2 & -4 \end{bmatrix} \begin{bmatrix} x_1 \\ x_2 \end{bmatrix}$$

and

$$\begin{bmatrix} x_1 \\ x_2 \end{bmatrix} = \begin{bmatrix} 1 & -2 \\ 2 & 1 \end{bmatrix} \begin{bmatrix} z_1 \\ z_2 \end{bmatrix}.$$

We may express y_1 and y_2 in terms of z_1 and z_2 in the following way:

$$y_1 = 3x_1 + 2x_2 = 3(z_1 - 2z_2) + 2(2z_1 + z_2) = [3(1) + 2(2)]z_1$$
$$+ [3(-2) + 2(1)]z_2 = 7z_1 - 4z_2$$

$$y_2 = 2x_1 - 4x_2 = 2(z_1 - 2z_2) - 4(2z_1 + z_2) = [2(1) - 4(2)]z_1$$
$$+ [2(-2) - 4(1)]z_2 = -6z_1 - 8z_2.$$

In matrix notation this can be written as

$$\begin{bmatrix} y_1 \\ y_2 \end{bmatrix} = \begin{bmatrix} 3 & 2 \\ 2 & -4 \end{bmatrix} \begin{bmatrix} 1 & -2 \\ 2 & 1 \end{bmatrix} \begin{bmatrix} z_1 \\ z_2 \end{bmatrix}$$

$$= \begin{bmatrix} 7 & -4 \\ -6 & -8 \end{bmatrix} \begin{bmatrix} z_1 \\ z_2 \end{bmatrix}.$$

We note that the element in the first row and first column of the product matrix is the sum of the products of corresponding elements from the first row of the left matrix and the first column of the right matrix. The other elements of the product are found similarly.

It is important to point out that matrix multiplication is not commutative. In other words, in general

$$AB \neq BA.$$

It is a simple matter to construct examples to exhibit this behavior. For example, if

$$A = \begin{bmatrix} 1 & -1 \\ 2 & 3 \end{bmatrix}, \qquad B = \begin{bmatrix} 2 & -3 \\ 1 & -1 \end{bmatrix},$$

then

$$AB = \begin{bmatrix} 1 & -2 \\ 7 & -9 \end{bmatrix}, \qquad BA = \begin{bmatrix} -4 & -11 \\ -1 & -4 \end{bmatrix}.$$

If $AB = BA$, we shall say that A and B commute.

It is easily shown directly from the definition that matrix multiplication is associative. In other words, for all A, B, and C we have

$$(AB)C = A(BC).$$

We remark that in determinant theory it is shown that the determinant of a product of two matrices is equal to the product of the determinants of the multiplied matrices: $|AB| = |A|\,|B|$.

We give an additional example to illustrate matrix multiplication.

Example 1. Find the product AB of the matrices

$$A = \begin{bmatrix} 4 & 2 & -1 \\ 3 & -7 & 1 \\ 2 & 4 & -3 \end{bmatrix}, \quad B = \begin{bmatrix} 2 & 3 & 2 \\ -3 & 0 & -1 \\ 1 & 5 & 1 \end{bmatrix}.$$

The element in the ith row and jth column of AB is obtained by adding the products of corresponding elements of the ith row of A and the jth column of B. For example, the element in the second row and third column is

$$(3)(2) + (-7)(-1) + (1)(1) = 14.$$

Carrying out the calculation of the other elements in a similar fashion, we find that

$$AB = \begin{bmatrix} 1 & 7 & 5 \\ 28 & 14 & 14 \\ -11 & -9 & -3 \end{bmatrix}.$$

In this discussion of matrix multiplication we have restricted ourselves to square matrices. But, the rule for forming the elements of the product matrix which is given by (4.2.6) is also applicable to rectangular matrices provided the number of columns of matrix A equals the number of rows of matrix B. Thus if A is an $m \times n$ matrix and B is an $n \times p$ matrix, then C will be an $m \times p$ matrix, and in (4.2.6) i will vary from 1 to m while k ranges from 1 to p.

Example 2. Find the product CD of the matrices

$$C = \begin{bmatrix} 4 & 2 & -1 \\ 3 & -7 & 1 \end{bmatrix}, \quad D = \begin{bmatrix} 2 & 3 & 2 & 1 \\ -3 & 0 & -1 & -2 \\ 1 & 5 & 1 & 3 \end{bmatrix}.$$

Since C is a 2×3 matrix and D is a 3×4 matrix, the product can be formed and is a 2×4 matrix. Proceeding as in example 1 we easily find that

$$CD = \begin{bmatrix} 1 & 7 & 5 & -3 \\ 28 & 14 & 14 & 20 \end{bmatrix}.$$

4.3 TRANSPOSE, INVERSE, AND ADJOINT MATRICES

If we interchange the rows and columns of a matrix A, we obtain the transpose matrix which we shall denote by A^T. The notation A' is also used by many authors. Thus if

$$A = \begin{bmatrix} a_{11} & a_{12} & \cdots & a_{1n} \\ a_{21} & a_{22} & \cdots & a_{2n} \\ \cdot & \cdot & \cdot \cdot \cdot & \cdot \\ a_{m1} & a_{m2} & \cdots & a_{mn} \end{bmatrix} = (a_{ij}),$$

then

$$A^T = \begin{bmatrix} a_{11} & a_{21} & \cdots & a_{m1} \\ a_{12} & a_{22} & \cdots & a_{m2} \\ \cdot & \cdot & \cdot \cdot \cdot & \cdot \\ a_{1n} & a_{2n} & \cdots & a_{mn} \end{bmatrix} = (a_{ji}). \tag{4.3.1}$$

The following rule for a transpose product is of interest:

$$(AB)^T = B^T A^T. \tag{4.3.2}$$

To prove this we note that the element in the ith row and jth column of the matrix $(AB)^T$ is equal to the element in the jth row and ith column of the matrix AB by the definition of a transpose matrix. By (4.2.6) this element is seen to be

$$\sum_{k=1}^{n} a_{jk} b_{ki}.$$

Since this may be rewritten in the form

$$\sum_{k=1}^{n} b_{ki} a_{jk},$$

and since the b_{ki} are the elements of the ith row of B^T, and a_{jk} are the elements of the jth column of A^T, it follows that this expression is the element in the ith row and jth column of the matrix $B^T A^T$.

A matrix A is said to be symmetric if and only if

$$A = A^T.$$

This condition may also be written as

$$a_{ij} = a_{ji}.$$

A square matrix A is said to be a diagonal matrix if all the elements other than those on the principal diagonal are zero, that is, if $a_{ij} = 0$ for $i \neq j$. If in a diagonal matrix all the elements on the principal diagonal are 1, the matrix is called the unit matrix or identity matrix and denoted by I. Thus

$$I = \begin{bmatrix} 1 & 0 & \cdots & 0 \\ 0 & 1 & \cdots & 0 \\ \cdots & \cdots & \cdots & \cdots \\ 0 & 0 & \cdots & 1 \end{bmatrix}. \tag{4.3.3}$$

From the definition of multiplication in (4.2.6) we see at once that

$$AI = IA = A. \tag{4.3.4}$$

For example, it is clear that

$$\begin{bmatrix} 3 & 2 \\ 2 & -4 \end{bmatrix}\begin{bmatrix} 1 & 0 \\ 0 & 1 \end{bmatrix} = \begin{bmatrix} 1 & 0 \\ 0 & 1 \end{bmatrix}\begin{bmatrix} 3 & 2 \\ 2 & -4 \end{bmatrix} = \begin{bmatrix} 3 & 2 \\ 2 & -4 \end{bmatrix}.$$

A square matrix A is said to be nonsingular if its determinant is not equal to zero. Otherwise it is, of course, singular.

We now introduce the concept of an inverse matrix. The inverse of the square matrix A is denoted by A^{-1} and is defined by the relation

$$AA^{-1} = I. \tag{4.3.5}$$

For example, if

$$A = \begin{bmatrix} 3 & 2 \\ 1 & -1 \end{bmatrix}$$

and if

$$A^{-1} = \begin{bmatrix} \frac{1}{5} & \frac{2}{5} \\ \frac{1}{5} & -\frac{3}{5} \end{bmatrix}$$

then clearly

$$\begin{bmatrix} 3 & 2 \\ 1 & -1 \end{bmatrix}\begin{bmatrix} \frac{1}{5} & \frac{2}{5} \\ \frac{1}{5} & -\frac{3}{5} \end{bmatrix} = \begin{bmatrix} 1 & 0 \\ 0 & 1 \end{bmatrix}.$$

It is at once clear that if A^{-1} exists, then A is nonsingular. For if A were singular, then $|A| = 0$. But this is impossible because from $AA^{-1} = I$ it follows that $|A|\,|A^{-1}| = 1$.

We therefore assume that A is nonsingular and show how to construct the inverse matrix. We first define the adjoint matrix as the transpose of the matrix of the cofactors of A. It will be denoted by adj (A). Then

$$\text{adj}\,(A) = \begin{bmatrix} A_{11} & A_{21} & \cdots & A_{n1} \\ A_{12} & A_{22} & \cdots & A_{n2} \\ \cdot & \cdot & \cdots & \cdot \\ A_{1n} & A_{\mathfrak{g}n} & \cdots & A_{nn} \end{bmatrix}. \tag{4.3.6}$$

Example 3. Find the adjoint of the matrix

$$A = \begin{bmatrix} 2 & 0 & 7 \\ -1 & 4 & 5 \\ 3 & 2 & 1 \end{bmatrix}.$$

First we calculate the cofactors of A. For example

$$A_{12} = - \begin{vmatrix} -1 & 5 \\ 3 & 1 \end{vmatrix} = 16.$$

The adjoint matrix is found to be

$$\text{adj}\,(A) = \begin{bmatrix} -6 & 14 & -28 \\ 16 & -19 & -17 \\ -14 & -4 & 8 \end{bmatrix}.$$

Before defining the inverse of A, we first show that if $C = \text{adj}\,(A)$, then

$$AC = |A|\,I. \tag{4.3.7}$$

The element in the ith row and jth column of AC is by (4.2.6) given by

$$\sum_{k=1}^{n} a_{ik} A_{jk} = a_{i1} A_{j1} + a_{i2} A_{j2} + \cdots + A_{in} A_{jn}.$$

But from the rules (4.1.13) for expansion of determinants this is known to be $|A|$ if $i = j$ and 0 if $i \neq j$. This proves (4.3.7).

The reader may wish to verify equation (4.3.7) for the matrix A of example 3. It will be found that

$$A\,\text{adj}\,(A) = \begin{bmatrix} 2 & 0 & 7 \\ -1 & 4 & 5 \\ 3 & 2 & 1 \end{bmatrix} \begin{bmatrix} -6 & 14 & -28 \\ 16 & -19 & -17 \\ -14 & -4 & 8 \end{bmatrix}$$

$$= \begin{bmatrix} -110 & 0 & 0 \\ 0 & -110 & 0 \\ 0 & 0 & -110 \end{bmatrix} = -110 \begin{bmatrix} 1 & 0 & 0 \\ 0 & 1 & 0 \\ 0 & 0 & 1 \end{bmatrix}.$$

We note that $|A| = -110$.

In a similar manner we can also prove that

$$CA = |A| I. \tag{4.3.8}$$

Now we see at once that the inverse A^{-1} is given by

$$A^{-1} = \frac{1}{|A|} C = \frac{1}{|A|} \operatorname{adj}(A) \tag{4.3.9}$$

for

$$AA^{-1} = A \frac{1}{|A|} C = \frac{1}{|A|} AC = I.$$

Moreover we also note that

$$A^{-1}A = I \tag{4.3.10}$$

which follows from (4.3.8)

Example 4. Find the inverse of the matrix A of example 3.

The adjoint of A was found in example 3. The determinant is $|A| = 2(-6) + 7(-14) = -110$. Hence the inverse matrix is

$$A^{-1} = -\tfrac{1}{110} \operatorname{adj}(A) = \begin{bmatrix} \frac{8}{55} & -\frac{7}{55} & \frac{14}{15} \\[4pt] \frac{8}{55} & \frac{19}{110} & \frac{17}{110} \\[4pt] \frac{7}{55} & \frac{2}{55} & -\frac{4}{55} \end{bmatrix}.$$

It is easily verified that the product of A and A^{-1} is I.

We remark that a matrix A is called an orthogonal matrix if $A^{-1} = A^T$. An example of an orthogonal matrix is furnished by the matrix whose rows are the direction cosines of three mutually perpendicular axes referred to three fixed mutually perpendicular axes. One such matrix is

$$A = \begin{bmatrix} \dfrac{1}{\sqrt{2}} & \dfrac{1}{\sqrt{2}} & 0 \\[10pt] \dfrac{1}{2} & -\dfrac{1}{2} & \dfrac{1}{\sqrt{2}} \\[10pt] \dfrac{1}{2} & -\dfrac{1}{2} & -\dfrac{1}{\sqrt{2}} \end{bmatrix}.$$

We leave it to the reader to show that $AA^T = I$.

4.4 SOLUTION OF LINEAR EQUATIONS

We began this chapter by introducing a system of n linear equations in n unknowns. With the notation and rules for operating on matrices which have been developed, the system of equations (4.1.1) may be written in the more convenient form

$$Ax = b \qquad (4.4.1)$$

where A is a square matrix of order n and x and b are column vectors. If we assume that A is nonsingular and if we premultiply this equation by the inverse matrix A^{-1}, we obtain

$$A^{-1}Ax = A^{-1}b,$$

or, on using (4.3.10),

$$x = A^{-1}b, \qquad (4.4.2)$$

which gives formally the solution of the equations. If we make use of (4.3.9), we have

$$x = \frac{1}{|A|} \operatorname{adj}(A)b. \qquad (4.4.3)$$

On taking account of the definition of adj (A) given in (4.3.6), we can write

$$x_i = \frac{1}{|A|} \sum_{k=1}^{n} A_{ki} b_k, \qquad i = 1, 2, \cdots, n.$$

We note that the sum appearing in this formula is just the expansion of the determinant of the matrix obtained by replacing the ith column of A by the column vector b. If we denote this determinant by D_i and $|A|$ by D, we have

$$x_i = \frac{D_i}{D}, \qquad i = 1, 2, \cdots, n \qquad (4.4.4)$$

which is the familiar Cramer's rule.

For example if $n = 3$, the equations represented by (4.4.1) may be written out at length in the form

$$a_{11}x_1 + a_{12}x_2 + a_{13}x_3 = b_1$$
$$a_{21}x_1 + a_{22}x_2 + a_{23}x_3 = b_2$$
$$a_{31}x_1 + a_{32}x_2 + a_{33}x_3 = b_3.$$

In this case

$$D = \begin{vmatrix} a_{11} & a_{12} & a_{13} \\ a_{21} & a_{22} & a_{23} \\ a_{31} & a_{32} & a_{33} \end{vmatrix}$$

and

$$x_1 = \frac{1}{D} \begin{vmatrix} b_1 & a_{12} & a_{13} \\ b_2 & a_{22} & a_{23} \\ b_3 & a_{32} & a_{33} \end{vmatrix}, \qquad x_2 = \frac{1}{D} \begin{vmatrix} a_{11} & b_1 & a_{13} \\ a_{21} & b_2 & a_{23} \\ a_{31} & b_3 & a_{33} \end{vmatrix},$$

$$x_3 = \begin{vmatrix} a_{11} & a_{12} & b_1 \\ a_{21} & a_{22} & b_2 \\ a_{31} & a_{32} & b_3 \end{vmatrix}.$$

Thus in (4.4.4) we have a set of formulas which might be used to find the solution of the system of equations (4.1.1), and in (4.3.9) and (4.3.6) we have a specific method for the calculation of the inverse matrix. In both cases the evaluation of a number of determinants is required. Unfortunately, unless n is quite small, the evaluation of determinants is a very tedious and inefficient procedure, and so the methods just mentioned for solution of equations and inversion of matrices are very undesirable. In the following four sections we proceed to describe alternative methods which are to be preferred for such calculations. The methods to be described are suitable both for desk calculators and for high speed electronic computing machines.

Before proceeding to these alternative methods, we mention briefly the situation if A is singular. We first introduce the notion of rank. When A is nonsingular, the value of its associated determinant is, by definition, not zero. In this case, if the determinant is of order n, it is said to be of rank n. In the contrary case in which A is singular, the associated determinant has the value zero and the order of the nonvanishing minor of highest order is said to be the rank of the determinant. To define the rank of an $m \times n$ matrix we note that we can set up determinants by striking out (if necessary) certain rows and columns from the matrix. The determinant of highest order that can be so formed has an order equal to the lesser of the two numbers m and n if m and n are unequal, or equal to their common value if m and n are equal. The highest rank of the determinants of highest order is said to be the rank of the matrix.

In addition to the matrix A associated with the system (4.1.1) we shall be interested in the augmented matrix obtained by adjoining the column vector b at the right of the matrix A, thus forming a matrix of n rows and $n + 1$ columns.

The nonsingularity of the matrix A is equivalent to the statement that the rank of A is n and in this case we saw that the system (4.1.1) possesses a unique solution given by (4.4.4).

If A is singular, there are two possibilities:

(a) If the rank of the augmented matrix is greater than the rank of A, the system (4.1.1) has no solutions.

(b) If the ranks of the augmented matrix and of the matrix A are both equal to $n - r$, there are an infinite number of solutions expressible in terms of r arbitrary parameters.

In the following sections we shall be concerned with the case in which A is nonsingular.

4.5 GAUSSIAN ELIMINATION

A simple and convenient method for obtaining the solution of the system (4.1.1) is Gauss's method of systematic elimination. We first divide the first equation by a_{11}. The resulting equation is multiplied by a_{21} and subtracted from the second equation of (4.1.1), thus eliminating x_1 from this equation. In a similar manner x_1 is eliminated from all succeeding equations. The system (4.1.1) then takes the form

$$x_1 + a_{12}'x_2 + a_{13}'x_3 + \cdots + a_{1n}'x_n = b_1'$$
$$a_{22}'x_2 + a_{23}'x_3 + \cdots + a_{2n}'x_n = b_2'$$
$$\cdots \cdots \cdots \cdots \cdots \cdots \cdots \cdots \quad (4.5.1)$$
$$a_{n2}'x_2 + a_{n3}'x_3 + \cdots + a_{nn}'x_n = b_n'.$$

Next we divide the modified second equation which appears in (4.5.1) by a_{22}' and use the result to eliminate x_2 from the succeeding equations. By repeating this procedure, we successively eliminate $x_3, x_4, \cdots, x_{n-1}$. If the determinant of the coefficients is not equal to zero, we obtain a system of equations equivalent to the original system except for the effects of any round-offs committed and which is of the form

$$x_1 + a_{12}''x_2 + a_{13}''x_3 + \cdots + a_{1n}''x_n = b_1''$$
$$x_2 + a_{23}''x_3 + \cdots + a_{2n}''x_n = b_2''$$
$$\cdots \cdots \cdots \cdots \cdots \cdots \cdots \cdots \quad (4.5.2)$$
$$x_{n-1} + a_{n-1,n}''x_n = b_{n-1}''$$
$$x_n = b_n''.$$

The solution is completed by working backward from the last equation to obtain successively $x_n, x_{n-1}, \cdots, x_2, x_1$.

It is instructive to describe this elimination procedure in the language of matrix operations. We have already noted that the system (4.1.1) can be written in the more convenient form

$$A\mathbf{x} = \mathbf{b}. \tag{4.5.3}$$

The operation of eliminating the unknown x_1 from the equations is equivalent to multiplying the matrix equation (4.5.3) on the left by the matrix L_1 where

$$L_1 = \begin{bmatrix} \dfrac{1}{a_{11}} & 0 & \cdots & 0 & 0 \\[2ex] -\dfrac{a_{21}}{a_{11}} & 1 & \cdots & 0 & 0 \\[1ex] \cdot & \cdot & \cdot\ \cdot\ \cdot & \cdot & \cdot \\[1ex] -\dfrac{a_{n1}}{a_{11}} & 0 & \cdots & 0 & 1 \end{bmatrix}. \tag{4.5.4}$$

Such a matrix, in which every element above the principal diagonal is zero, is called a lower triangular matrix. We note also that L_1 has all its off-diagonal nonzero elements in the first column. It is easily seen that if both sides of (4.5.3) are premultiplied by L_1, the result is the same as (4.5.1).

Similarly we see that the elimination of x_2 from the remaining equations is equivalent to multiplication by another lower triangular matrix L_2, all of whose off-diagonal nonzero elements are in the second column and which indeed differs from the identity matrix only in the second column. The successive elimination of $x_3, \cdots, x_{n-1}$ is equivalent to successive multiplication by lower triangular matrices $L_3, \cdots, L_{n-1}$. Making the coefficient of x_n equal to one is also equivalent to multiplication by a lower triangular matrix L_n. The resulting system (4.5.2) clearly involves an upper triangular matrix, that is, a matrix in which all elements below the principal diagonal are zero. It may be written in the form

$$U\mathbf{x} = \mathbf{b}'', \tag{4.5.5}$$

where U is an upper triangular matrix.

It is readily verified that the product of lower triangular matrices is again a lower triangular matrix, so that the reduction of (4.5.3) to the form (4.5.5) is actually accomplished by multiplication by a single lower triangular matrix L where,

$$L = L_n L_{n-1} \cdots L_2 L_1.$$

Thus $U = LA$ and $\mathbf{b}'' = L\mathbf{b}$.

We have already noted that the equation (4.5.5), or equivalently the system (4.5.2) can be solved by a step-by-step procedure obtaining successively $x_n, x_{n-1}, \cdots, x_2, x_1$.

It should also be noted that the elimination procedure is a convenient one for the inversion of a matrix. If A^{-1} is the inverse of a matrix A, then

$$AA^{-1} = I. \tag{4.5.6}$$

If I_i denotes the vector consisting of the ith column of I and if A_i^{-1} is similarly related to A^{-1}, then it follows from (4.5.6) that

$$AA_i^{-1} = I_i, \qquad i = 1, 2, \cdots, n.$$

Thus to find each column of A^{-1}, we have only to solve a system of equations of the same form as (4.5.3). If L denotes the lower triangular matrix such that $LA = U$ is upper triangular, we obtain from (4.5.6) that

$$UA^{-1} = LI = L. \tag{4.5.7}$$

Thus the elements of A^{-1} are obtained by a simple step-by-step procedure, involving "back substitution" just as in the solution of (4.5.2). It is also worth noting that the inversion of an upper triangular matrix is particularly simple, involving, as it does, merely this simple step-by-step procedure without the necessity of introducing L (which is, of course, I here).

In the preceding discussion it has been assumed that the equations are operated on in the order in which they are given, without rearranging them. It may happen that at some stage of the procedure the diagonal element which is used as a "pivot" to eliminate a variable from the subsequent equations is zero. Consequently, it is impossible to use it as a divisor in the elimination process. This difficulty may be overcome by rearranging the equations so as to place a nonzero element in this position. More frequently it may happen that at some stage of the calculation a pivot element is small but not exactly zero. If a small element is used as a divisor, it, of course, yields large quotients and may very well introduce large errors into the calculated results. It is desirable to rearrange the equations in such a manner as to avoid division by small diagonal elements. One way in which this may be done is by searching for the largest element in the column involved at each stage and using this largest element as "pivot" for the elimination of the corresponding unknown. In solving large systems of equations, the large number of arithmetic operations involved may introduce considerable round-off error into the solutions. Indeed these round-off errors may grow to the point that the solutions become meaningless; searching for the largest pivots as described previously is an effective way to minimize such errors. Unfortunately many matrix inversion codes employed on electronic computers use straightforward elimination without searching for the largest pivots because it is simpler to write a code in this way; the results obtained when such codes are used to solve large systems are often unsatisfactory. It is strongly recommended that this procedure of searching for largest pivots be incorporated in matrix inversion codes which make use of elimination methods.

Example 5.   Find the solution of the following system of equations by the method of elimination:

$$3x_1 + 2x_2 + 7x_3 = 4$$

$$2x_1 + 3x_2 + x_3 = 5$$

$$3x_1 + 4x_2 + x_3 = 7.$$

We shall use the method without rearranging the equations. The first equation is divided by 3 and used to eliminate x_1 from the succeeding equations. On rounding all entries to four decimals, we obtain

$$x_1 + 0.6667x_2 + 2.3333x_3 = 1.3333$$

$$1.6666x_2 - 3.6666x_3 = 2.3334$$

$$1.9999x_2 - 5.9999x_3 = 3.0001.$$

Next we divide the second equation by 1.6666 and use it to eliminate x_2 from the third equation. If we also divide the resulting third equation by the coefficient of x_3, we obtain,

$$x_1 + 0.6667x_2 + 2.3333x_3 = 1.3333$$

$$x_2 - 2.2000x_3 = 1.4001$$

$$x_3 = -0.1250.$$

By working backward in this system we find that $x_3 = -0.1250$, $x_2 = 1.1251$, and $x_1 = 0.8749$.

Since the coefficients in these equations were such simple numbers, all calculations could have been carried out exactly, using rational numbers, and we would have found $x_3 = -\frac{1}{8}$, $x_2 = \frac{9}{8}$, and $x_1 = \frac{7}{8}$. But in most practical problems, the coefficients will be given to a certain number of decimal places and the calculations will be carried out with rounded numbers. We preferred to illustrate this situation in our calculations.

It is instructive to observe that the elimination of x_1 could have been accomplished by multiplying the matrix equation on the left by the matrix L_1 where

$$L_1 = \begin{bmatrix} \frac{1}{3} & 0 & 0 \\ -0.6667 & 1 & 0 \\ -1 & 0 & 1 \end{bmatrix}$$

as in equation (4.5.4). In a similar way the elimination of x_2 could be effected by multiplication by the matrix

$$L_2 = \begin{bmatrix} 1 & 0 & 0 \\ 0 & \dfrac{1}{1.6666} & 0 \\ 0 & -1.2 & 1 \end{bmatrix}.$$

Finally, making the coefficient of x_3 equal to unity could be done by multiplication by the matrix

$$L_3 = \begin{bmatrix} 1 & 0 & 0 \\ 0 & 1 & 0 \\ 0 & 0 & -\dfrac{1}{1.6} \end{bmatrix}.$$

Thus we see that the reduction to upper triangular form is equivalent to multiplication of the original matrix equation on the left by the matrix

$$L = L_3 L_2 L_1 = \begin{bmatrix} \dfrac{1}{3} & 0 & 0 \\ -0.4 & \dfrac{1}{1.6666} & 0 \\ 0.125 & 0.75 & -\dfrac{1}{1.6} \end{bmatrix}.$$

4.6 GAUSS-JORDAN ELIMINATION

The elimination method described in the preceding section may be modified in a convenient fashion. At the kth stage, we use the kth equation to eliminate x_k from the preceding equations as well as from the following equations. This reduces the matrix A to a diagonal matrix (one having nonzero elements on the principal diagonal only) which is indeed the identity matrix I. Thus the solution of the equations is obtained without the necessity of a back substitution.

In the language of matrix operations, this procedure is equivalent to multiplying the system $A\mathbf{x} = \mathbf{b}$ sequentially by matrices, each of which differs from the identity only in a single column.

The first stage of the Gauss and Gauss-Jordan eliminations are identical both consisting in multiplying A by L_1 given by (4.5.4) and yielding (4.5.1). At the second stage, however, the Gauss-Jordan method requires multiplication by the matrix

$$
J_2 =
\begin{bmatrix}
1 & -\dfrac{a_{12}'}{a_{22}'} & 0 & \cdots & 0 \\[2ex]
0 & \dfrac{1}{a_{22}'} & 0 & \cdots & 0 \\[2ex]
0 & -\dfrac{a_{32}'}{a_{22}'} & 1 & \cdots & 0 \\[1ex]
\cdot & \cdot & \cdot & \cdot & \cdot \\[1ex]
0 & -\dfrac{a_{n2}'}{a_{22}'} & 0 & \cdots & 1
\end{bmatrix},
\tag{4.6.1}
$$

whereas the matrix L_2 required in the Gaussian elimination is the same as (4.6.1) with the element in the first row, second column, replaced by 0. We note that J_2 differs from the identity matrix only in the second column. The successive elimination of $x_3, x_4, \cdots, x_n$ is equivalent to successive multiplication by matrices $J_3, J_4, \cdots, J_n$, which are such that J_k differs from the identity matrix only in the kth column. It will be convenient to define J_1 to be identical with L_1. Thus the system (4.5.3) is reduced to the form

$$\mathbf{x} = J_n J_{n-1} \cdots J_2 J_1 \mathbf{b}.$$

From this it follows that

$$J_n J_{n-1} \cdots J_2 J_1 A = I$$

so that

$$A^{-1} = J_n J_{n-1} \cdots J_2 J_1.$$

Thus the inverse matrix is generated by applying the successive transformations represented by $J_1, J_2, \cdots, J_n$ to the identity matrix. This is a very effective method for calculating the inverse of a matrix. It lends itself very well to programming on a high-speed electronic computer, since the procedure is a very iterative one because the operations performed are of the same form at each stage of the operation.

4.7 THE CROUT METHOD OF ELIMINATION

A convenient method for carrying out the Gaussian elimination described in section 4.5 was devised by Crout [3]. In this method the recording of the intermediate equations or arrays is avoided, and only the final values of the coefficients which appear in (4.5.2) together with such auxiliary data as are necessary for their calculation are written down. These auxiliary data are placed in the positions which would be occupied by zeros or ones in the array (4.5.2). The values of the x_i are obtained by carrying out the back solution as in the Gaussian elimination method.

We first write down the augmented matrix of the system of equations $Ax = b$. For convenience in writing the formulas needed in the Crout method we shall denote the elements of the column vector b by $a_{i,n+1}$. The augmented matrix of the system then takes the form

$$M = \begin{bmatrix} a_{11} & a_{12} & a_{13} & \cdots & a_{1n} & a_{1,n+1} \\ a_{21} & a_{22} & a_{23} & \cdots & a_{2n} & a_{2,n+1} \\ a_{31} & a_{32} & a_{33} & \cdots & a_{3n} & a_{3,n+1} \\ \cdot & \cdot & \cdot & \cdot & \cdot & \cdot \\ a_{n1} & a_{n2} & a_{n3} & \cdots & a_{nn} & a_{n,n+1} \end{bmatrix}. \tag{4.7.1}$$

The next step in the Crout procedure then consists of writing down a modified matrix of the same dimensions,

$$M' = \begin{bmatrix} a_{11}' & a_{12}' & a_{13}' & \cdots & a_{1n}' & a_{1,n+1}' \\ a_{21}' & a_{22}' & a_{23}' & \cdots & a_{2n}' & a_{2,n+1}' \\ a_{31}' & a_{32}' & a_{38}' & \cdots & a_{3n}' & a_{3,n+1}' \\ \cdot & \cdot & \cdot & \cdot & \cdot & \cdot \\ a_{n1}' & a_{n2}' & a_{n3}' & \cdots & a_{nn}' & a_{n,n+1}' \end{bmatrix} \tag{4.7.2}$$

by following the procedure which is described below. From this matrix is obtained a solution column vector x whose elements are the required values of $x_1, x_2, \cdots, x_n$, that is

$$x = \begin{bmatrix} x_1 \\ x_2 \\ \cdot \\ \cdot \\ \cdot \\ x_n \end{bmatrix}. \tag{4.7.3}$$

Each entry in (4.7.2) and (4.7.3) is obtained from previously calculated data by a continuous sequence of operations which can be carried out without the tabulation of intermediate data.

We now describe in detail how the elements of (4.7.2) are to be obtained.

1. The elements of the first column of M' are identical with the corresponding elements of M.

2. The elements of the first row of M' (excepting a_{11}') are each obtained by dividing the corresponding element of M by a_{11}. Thus

$$a_{i1}' = a_{i1}, \qquad i = 1, 2, \cdots, n$$

$$a_{1j}' = a_{1j}/a_{11}, \qquad j = 2, 3, \cdots, n + 1.$$

3. Next the remaining elements of the second column are each calculated by subtracting from the corresponding element of M the product of the element in the first column of the corresponding row of M' and the element at the head of the second column of M'. Thus

$$a_{i2}' = a_{i2} - a_{i1}'a_{12}', \qquad i = 2, 3, \cdots, n.$$

4. Next the elements in the second row to the right of the principal diagonal are each calculated by subtracting from the corresponding element of M the product of the element in the first column of the second row of M' and the element at the head of the corresponding column of M', followed by a division by the diagonal element in the second row of M'. Thus

$$a_{2j}' = (a_{2j} - a_{21}'a_{1j}')/a_{22}', \qquad j = 3, 4, \cdots, n + 1.$$

5. The remaining elements in the third column are calculated by the formula

$$a_{i3}' = a_{i3} - a_{i1}'a_{13}' - a_{i2}'a_{23}', \qquad i = 3, 4, \cdots, n.$$

The procedure is similar to that in 3, except that there are two product terms to be subtracted. Note that the elements entering into the products are taken from the row and column in which the element being calculated lies.

6. The elements in the third row to the right of the principal diagonal are calculated by a procedure similar to 5, followed by a division by the diagonal element in the third row of M'. Thus

$$a_{3j}' = (a_{3j} - a_{31}'a_{1j}' - a_{32}'a_{2j}')/a_{33}', \qquad j = 4, 5, \cdots, n + 1.$$

7. The procedure just described is continued calculating alternately the remaining elements of the successive columns and rows until the array is filled.

8. The rule for obtaining each element of M' may be described as follows:

(a) Each element on or below the principal diagonal of M' is obtained by subtracting from the corresponding element of M the products of elements of M' in the row to the left and in the column above the desired element, taking the products in order, that is, first in row by first in column, second in row by second in column, etc.

(b) Each element to the right of the principal diagonal of M' is calculated by the procedure described in a, followed by a division by the diagonal element in its row of M'.

When all the elements of M' have been obtained, the elements of the solution column x are determined in the order $x_n, x_{n-1}, \cdots, x_2, x_1$, from foot to head. The element x_n is identical with $a'_{n,n+1}$. x_{n-1} is obtained by subtracting from $a'_{n-1,n+1}$, the product of x_n and $a'_{n-1,n}$. Each succeeding element x_i is obtained by subtracting from the corresponding element $a'_{i,n+1}$ the products of the previously found x_j and the corresponding elements of the ith row of M'. (Only elements to the right of the principal diagonal will enter into this calculation.)

The preceding instructions are completely described by the equations

$$a_{ij}' = a_{ij} - \sum_{k=1}^{j-1} a_{ik}'a_{kj}' \qquad\qquad i \geq j \qquad\qquad (4.7.4)$$

$$a_{ij}' = \frac{1}{a_{ii}'}\left[a_{ij} - \sum_{k=1}^{i-1} a_{ik}'a_{kj}'\right] \qquad i < j \qquad\qquad (4.7.5)$$

$$x_i = a'_{i,n+1} - \sum_{k=i+1}^{n} a_{ik}'x_k. \qquad\qquad\qquad (4.7.6)$$

In these equations, i ranges from 1 to n and j ranges from 1 to $n + 1$.

In many practical problems leading to systems of linear equations, it turns out that the matrix A of the system is symmetric. By considering the steps in the calculation of M', it is easily seen that pairs of elements in M' which are symmetrically situated with respect to the principal diagonal are identical except for division by the diagonal element. Thus considerable labor may be saved, because each element below the diagonal can be recorded as the dividend involved in the calculation of the symmetrically placed element before the required division by the diagonal element is performed.

It is easily seen that the elements to the right of the principal diagonal in M' are just the elements which appear in corresponding positions of the augmented matrix of (4.5.2) obtained by Gaussian elimination. The other elements of M' are necessary intermediate data tabulated in spaces which would normally be occupied by ones and zeros.

We see that a_{kk}' is the number by which the kth equation would be divided in Gaussian elimination before that equation is used to eliminate x_k from the succeeding equations. Moreover, all of the other operations in the calculation of M' leave the value of the determinant of A unchanged. Consequently the value of the determinant of the original coefficient matrix A is the product of the diagonal elements of M', namely, $a_{11}'a_{22}' \cdots a_{nn}'$. Thus the Crout method furnishes a convenient method for the evaluation of any numerical determinant.

The final solution can be checked by substitution back into the original equations. It is often desirable, however, to carry on a continuous check of the calculations as they are performed. This can be done by adjoining to the right of M a check column, each of whose elements is the sum of the elements in the corresponding row of M. The check column in M' is obtained from the check column in M in exactly the same manner as is any column to the right of the diagonal and is calculated along with each row of M'. The check consists in the fact that each element in the check column of M' should exceed by unity the sum of the elements in its row of M' lying to the right of the diagonal element. If we also calculate a set of x's corresponding to the new right-hand column, each of these new x's will exceed by unity the corresponding original x values.

Example 6.   Find the solution of the system of equations of example 3 using the Crout method.   Carry a check column.

The original augmented matrix with check column is

$$
\begin{array}{cccc|c}
3 & 2 & 7 & 4 & 16 \\
2 & 3 & 1 & 5 & 11 \\
3 & 4 & 1 & 7 & 15.
\end{array}
$$

The modified matrix is found to be

$$
\begin{array}{cccc|c}
3 & 0.6667 & 2.3333 & 1.3333 & 5.3333 \\
2 & 1.6666 & -2.2000 & 1.4001 & 0.2000 \\
3 & 1.9999 & -1.6001 & -0.1250 & 0.8749
\end{array}
$$

if we use equations (4.7.4) and (4.7.5) or the preceding rules 1 to 8. Thus the first column of the original matrix is copied without change. The elements of the first row (except 3) are divided by 3, the diagonal element. Next, the remaining elements of the second column are calculated. They are $3 - 2(0.6667) = 1.6666$ and $4 - 3(0.6667) = 1.9999$. Then the elements in the second row to the right of the principal diagonal are computed. For example, the fourth element in the second row is $[5 - 2(1.3333)]/1.6666 = 1.4001$. The other two are found similarly. Next, the remaining element of the third column is seen to be $1 - 3(2.3333) - 1.9999(-2.2000) = -1.6001$. Finally, the elements in the third row to the right of the principal diagonal are calculated. For example, the fifth element in the third row is $[15-3(5.3333)-1.9999(0.2000)]/(-1.6000)$ $= 0.8749$. The other one is found similarly. To get the solutions of the system we first observe that $x_3 = -0.1250$ which appears as the fourth element of the third row. Using the other entries in the fourth column we find that $x_2 = 1.4001 - (-2.2000)x_3 = 1.1251$ and $x_1 = 1.3333 - 2.3333x_3 - 0.6667x_2 = 0.8749$. The corresponding values of the check solutions are found in the same way from the fifth column to be 0.8749, 2.1248, and 1.8753. As expected, they are seen to be approximately one greater than the corresponding solutions of the system.

The computational error check indicates errors in the fourth decimal place which are undoubtedly due to round-off errors. We could secure greater accuracy by carrying more decimals in the calculations or more conveniently by an iterative procedure which will now be described.

If we denote the approximate solutions of the system (4.4.1) by $\bar{x}_1, \cdots,$ $\bar{x}_n$, substitution of these values into the left members of (4.1.1) yields right-hand members $\bar{b}_1, \bar{b}_2, \cdots, \bar{b}_n$ which should be close to $b_1, b_2, \cdots, b_n$. Then

$$a_{11}\bar{x}_1 + a_{12}\bar{x}_2 + \cdots + a_{n1}\bar{x}_n = \bar{b}_1$$
$$\cdots \cdots \cdots \cdots \cdots \cdots \cdots \cdots \cdots \cdots \qquad (4.7.7)$$
$$a_{n1}\bar{x}_1 + a_{n2}\bar{x}_2 + \cdots + a_{nn}\bar{x}_n = \bar{b}_n.$$

Now the true solutions satisfy (4.1.1). If we let

$$\delta x_k = x_k - \bar{x}_k, \qquad \delta b_k = b_k - \bar{b}_k \qquad (4.7.8)$$

we obtain by subtraction

$$a_{11}\,\delta x_1 + a_{12}\,\delta x_2 + \cdots + a_{n1}\,\delta x_n = \delta b_1$$
$$\cdots \cdots \cdots \cdots \cdots \cdots \cdots \cdots \cdots \cdots \qquad (4.7.9)$$
$$a_{n1}\,\delta x_1 + a_{n2}\,\delta x_2 + \cdots + a_{nn}\,\delta x_n = \delta b_n.$$

Thus we see that the corrections $\delta x_1, \cdots, \delta x_n$ satisfy a set of equations which differ from (4.1.1) only in that each b_k is replaced by the residual δb_k. The Crout method is particularly convenient in this situation since we have only to calculate a new right-hand column leaving all other columns unchanged.

There is no certainty that this iteration procedure will converge, but in many cases it does so and provides an efficient method for improving the accuracy of a solution by successive iteration, carrying along more and more significant figures only in the calculation of the residuals.

In example 4 the residuals corresponding to the approximate solutions obtained are found to be

$$\delta b_1 = +0.0001, \qquad \delta b_2 = -0.0001, \qquad \delta b_3 = -0.0001.$$

The approximate corrections are found to be

$$\delta x_3 = 0, \quad \delta x_2 = -0.0001, \quad \delta x_1 = +0.0001,$$

yielding the improved values

$$x_3 = -0.1250, \quad x_2 = 1.1250, \quad x_1 = 0.8750.$$

These happen to be exactly correct.

The Crout method also provides a convenient method for the calculation of the inverse matrix. As noted in section 4.5, each column of the inverse is obtained by solving a system of equations in which the right-hand members are a column of the identity matrix. Thus in place of a single column containing the elements $a_{i,n+1}$, in (4.7.1) we insert the square array

$$
\begin{matrix}
1 & 0 & \cdots & 0 \\
0 & 1 & \cdots & 0 \\
\cdot & \cdot & \cdot & \cdot \cdot \\
0 & 0 & \cdots & 1
\end{matrix}
\tag{4.7.10}
$$

and treat each column of this array as we treated the rightmost column in the Crout procedure. If $x_1^{(j)}, x_2^{(j)}, \cdots, x_n^{(j)}$ denote the solutions corresponding to the jth column of (4.7.10), the inverse matrix A^{-1} is

$$
\begin{matrix}
x_1^{(1)} & x_1^{(2)} & \cdots & x_1^{(n)} \\
x_2^{(1)} & x_2^{(2)} & \cdots & x_2^{(n)} \\
\cdot & \cdot & \cdot & \cdot \\
x_n^{(1)} & x_n^{(2)} & \cdots & x_n^{(n)}.
\end{matrix}
$$

A check column can be included if desired, and the rules given for its use apply as stated.

The determination of the inverse matrix is particularly desirable when the system (4.1.1) or (4.4.1) is to be solved for many distinct sets of right-hand members for, since $\mathbf{x} = A^{-1}\mathbf{b}$ by (4.4.2), each solution $\mathbf{x}$ is obtained by a matrix multiplication of the column vector consisting of the right-hand members of the system by the inverse matrix.

Example 7. Find the inverse of the matrix

$$
A = \begin{bmatrix} 3 & 2 & 7 \\ 2 & 3 & 1 \\ 3 & 4 & 1 \end{bmatrix}
$$

using the Crout method.

The original array takes the form

$$
\begin{array}{cccccc}
3 & 2 & 7 & 1 & 0 & 0 \\
2 & 3 & 1 & 0 & 1 & 0 \\
3 & 4 & 1 & 0 & 0 & 1.
\end{array}
$$

The modified array is found to be

$$
\begin{array}{cccccc}
3 & 0.6667 & 2.3333 & 0.3333 & 0 & 0 \\
2 & 1.6666 & -2.2000 & -0.4000 & -0.6000 & 0 \\
3 & 1.9999 & -1.6001 & 0.1250 & 0.7499 & -0.6250
\end{array}
$$

and the inverse matrix is

$$
\begin{array}{ccc}
0.1250 & -3.2497 & 2.3750 \\
-0.1250 & 2.2498 & -1.3750 \\
0.1250 & 0.7499 & -0.6250.
\end{array}
$$

4.8 GAUSS-SEIDEL ITERATION

Many practical problems lead to systems of linear equations which can be ordered in such a way that the coefficient of x_k in the kth equation is large in magnitude compared with all other coefficients in that equation. In other words, the elements not on the principal diagonal of the matrix are smaller than the elements on this diagonal. Indeed, in many problems, such as the solution of elliptic partial differential equations by difference methods, the linear equations which arise have the property that many of the off-diagonal elements are zero and the nonzero elements are located near the principal diagonal. To solve such systems of equations, it is convenient to rewrite them in the form

$$
x_1 = \frac{1}{a_{11}}(b_1 - a_{12}x_2 - a_{13}x_3 - \cdots - a_{1n}x_n)
$$

$$
x_2 = \frac{1}{a_{22}}(b_2 - a_{21}x_1 - a_{23}x_3 - \cdots - a_{2n}x_n) \qquad (4.8.1)
$$

$$
\cdot \quad \cdot \quad \cdot \quad \cdot \quad \cdot \quad \cdot \quad \cdot \quad \cdot \quad \cdot \quad \cdot \quad \cdot
$$

$$
x_n = \frac{1}{a_{nn}}(b_n - a_{n1}x_1 - a_{n2}x_2 - \cdots - a_{n,n-1}x_{n-1}).
$$

We may start with an initial approximation of zero for each of the x_i. If the unknowns in the right-hand members of (4.8.1) are replaced by zero, we obtain the approximation

$$
x_1^{(1)} = \frac{b_1}{a_{11}}, \; x_2^{(1)} = \frac{b_2}{a_{22}}, \; \cdots, \; x_n^{(1)} = \frac{b_n}{a_{nn}}
$$

where the superscript (1) denotes that this is the first (nontrivial) approximation. These values are again substituted into the right-hand members of (4.8.1) obtaining second approximations $x_i^{(2)}$, $i = 1, 2, \cdots, n$. This substitution procedure is repeated until the approximations in successive cycles agree to the desired accuracy. The iteration may or may not converge.

If the iterative procedure does converge, it may frequently be accelerated by replacing each unknown in each right-hand member by its most recently calculated approximation rather than by the approximation afforded by the preceding cycle. Here the rate of convergence depends on the order in which the x's are modified. If the equations are taken in the natural order as given in (4.8.1), this procedure is often called Gauss-Seidel iteration.

4.9 CHARACTERISTIC NUMBERS AND VECTORS OF A MATRIX

In many branches of applied mathematics, problems arise in which we need to find numbers λ and nonzero vectors $\mathbf{x}$ associated with a matrix A such that

$$Ax = \lambda x. \tag{4.9.1}$$

Examples which may be mentioned are problems in the dynamical theory of oscillations, problems of conditioned maxima and minima, problems of correlation between statistical variables, determination of principal axes of quadrics, and the solution of differential and other operational equations.

Equation (4.9.1) may be rewritten in the form

$$(A - \lambda I)\mathbf{x} = 0. \tag{4.9.2}$$

For example, if A is of order 3, equation (4.9.2) may be written out at length in the form

$$(a_{11} - \lambda)x_1 + a_{12}x_2 + a_{13}x_3 = 0$$

$$a_{21}x_1 + (a_{22} - \lambda)x_2 + a_{23}x_3 = 0$$

$$a_{31}x_1 + a_{32}x_2 + (a_{33} - \lambda)x_3 = 0.$$

It is clear that $\mathbf{x} = 0$ is always a solution of (4.9.2). But we are interested in finding nonzero vectors $\mathbf{x}$ which satisfy (4.9.1) or (4.9.2). According to Section 4.4 such nonzero solutions will exist only if

$$|A - \lambda I| = 0. \tag{4.9.3}$$

The left member of this equation is clearly a polynomial in λ, and it is called the characteristic polynomial (or characteristic function) of the matrix A. Equation (4.9.3) is called the characteristic, or secular, equation of the matrix A. The roots of the characteristic equation are called the characteristic numbers (or proper numbers, proper values, latent roots, eigenvalues) of the matrix A. The spectrum of the matrix is the set of its characteristic numbers. Corresponding to each characteristic number λ there is at least one nonzero vector **x** which satisfies (4.9.2). Any such vector is called a characteristic vector (proper vector, latent vector, eigenvector) associated with the characteristic number λ. Note that even if the elements of A are real, λ and **x** may be complex.

Example 8.   Find the characteristic numbers and the characteristic vectors of the matrix

$$A = \begin{bmatrix} -4 & -5 \\ 2 & 3 \end{bmatrix}.$$

The characteristic equation of A is

$$\begin{vmatrix} -4 - \lambda & -5 \\ 2 & 3 - \lambda \end{vmatrix} = 0$$

by equation (4.9.3). It is easily seen to reduce to

$$\lambda^2 + \lambda - 2 = 0$$

whose roots are clearly 1 and -2. Thus the characteristic values of A are 1 and -2. To find the characteristic vector corresponding to 1 we have to find a nonzero solution of the equation

$$A\mathbf{x} = \mathbf{x}$$

or

$$-4x_1 - 5x_2 = x_1$$
$$2x_1 + 3x_2 = x_2.$$

Both of these equations yield $x_1 = -x_2$. Hence $\begin{bmatrix} 1 \\ -1 \end{bmatrix}$ is a characteristic vector of A corresponding to the characteristic value 1. In the same way we find that $\begin{bmatrix} 5 \\ -2 \end{bmatrix}$ is a characteristic vector corresponding to the characteristic value -2.

It is clear that if **x** is a characteristic vector associated with λ, then for all $c \neq 0$, $c\mathbf{x}$ is also a characteristic vector associated with the same characteristic number λ. Moreover, if several characteristic vectors of a matrix correspond to some one characteristic number, any linear combination of them will also be a characteristic vector associated with the same characteristic number. It can be shown that the number of linearly independent characteristic vectors associated with the same characteristic number does not exceed the multiplicity of the number (as a zero of the characteristic polynomial). We might suppose that to a k-fold zero of the characteristic polynomial there correspond k linearly independent characteristic vectors. But this need not be true. Indeed the number of linearly independent vectors may be less than the multiplicity of the characteristic number.

This is exhibited by considering the matrix

$$A = \begin{bmatrix} 3 & 0 \\ 1 & 3 \end{bmatrix}.$$

Then $|A - \lambda I| = (\lambda - 3)^2$, so that $\lambda = 3$ in a double zero of the characteristic polynomial. The system of equations for determining the characteristic vector is

$$3x_1 = 3x_1$$
$$x_1 + 3x_2 = 3x_2.$$

Thus $x_1 = 0$ and so all the characteristic vectors of the matrix are $(0, x_2) = x_2(0, 1)$. So here only one linearly independent vector is associated with a double root.

The direct calculation of the characteristic function involves a large amount of labor, especially in the case of matrices of high order. If we write

$$\varphi(\lambda) = |A - \lambda I| = (-1)^n [\lambda^n - p_1 \lambda^{n-1} - p_2 \lambda^{n-2} - \cdots - p_n], \quad (4.9.4)$$

then

$$p_1 = a_{11} + a_{22} + \cdots + a_{nn}, \quad (4.9.5)$$
$$p_n = (-1)^{n-1} |A|. \quad (4.9.6)$$

To express the remaining p_k we need to introduce the notion of principal minor of a determinant. A principal minor of a determinant is a minor whose principal diagonal elements are on the principal diagonal of the determinant. With this definition the coefficient p_k is the sum of all the principal minors of order k of the determinant of the matrix A multiplied by $(-1)^{k-1}$. The number of such minors equals the number of combinations of n things taken k at a time. From well-known results in the theory of equations we have

$$\lambda_1 + \lambda_2 + \cdots + \lambda_n = p_1 = a_{11} + a_{22} + \cdots + a_{nn}, \quad (4.9.7)$$
$$\lambda_1 \lambda_2 \cdots \lambda_n = (-1)^{n-1} p_n = |A|. \quad (4.9.8)$$

The quantity $p_1 = a_{11} + a_{22} + \cdots + a_{nn}$ is called the trace of the matrix A and is denoted by $\mathrm{tr}(A)$.

Example 9. Find the characteristic function of the matrix

$$A = \begin{bmatrix} 2 & 1 & 3 \\ -1 & -2 & 4 \\ 3 & 1 & 6 \end{bmatrix}.$$

The characteristic function is

$$\varphi(\lambda) = -(\lambda^3 - p_1\lambda^2 - p_2\lambda - p_3)$$

where $p_1 = 2 - 2 + 6 = 6$ by equation (4.9.5) and $p_3 = |A| = 1$ by equation (4.9.6). To find p_2 we need the principal minors of order 2. We obtain at once

$$p_2 = -\left\{ \begin{vmatrix} 2 & 1 \\ -1 & -2 \end{vmatrix} + \begin{vmatrix} 2 & 3 \\ 3 & 6 \end{vmatrix} + \begin{vmatrix} -2 & 4 \\ 1 & 6 \end{vmatrix} \right\}$$

$$= -(-3 + 3 - 16) = 16.$$

Thus the characteristic function of A is

$$\varphi(\lambda) = -(\lambda^3 - 6\lambda^2 - 16\lambda - 1).$$

4.10 THE CAYLEY-HAMILTON THEOREM

Section 4.2 defines the product of two matrices A and B. If A is a square matrix, the product AA can be computed, and we denote it by A^2. In a similar manner we define the positive integral power of a matrix A by writing

$$\underbrace{AA \cdots A}_{n \text{ factors}} = A^n. \tag{4.10.1}$$

Since matrix multiplication obeys the associative law, how the parentheses in this product are placed makes no difference and so we omit them. From the definition it is clear that

$$A^m A^n = A^{m+n},$$

$$(A^m)^n = A^{mn}. \tag{4.10.2}$$

Thus powers of the same matrix are commutative.
We also define A^0 to be I.
An expression of the form

$$c_0 A^n + c_1 A^{n-1} + \cdots + c_n I,$$

where $c_0, c_1, \cdots, c_n$ are real (or complex) numbers, is called a matrix polynomial. This matrix polynomial may be regarded as the result of replacing the variable λ in an algebraic polynomial

$$c_0 \lambda^n + c_1 \lambda^{n-1} + \cdots + c_n$$

by the matrix A.

Since the powers of a matrix are commutative, the rules for operating with matrix polynomials are the same as those for operating with algebraic polynomials, at least insofar as addition and multiplication are concerned.

We now show that the following remarkable relation, known as the Cayley-Hamilton theorem, holds for any square matrix.

THEOREM (Cayley-Hamilton). If $\varphi(\lambda)$ is the characteristic polynomial [equation (4.9.4)] of the square matrix A, then $\varphi(A) = 0$. In other words, a square matrix satisfies its own characteristic equation.

To prove this result we consider the matrix B which is the adjoint of the matrix $A - \lambda I$. It is clear that each cofactor in the determinant $|A - \lambda I|$ is a polynomial in λ of degree not exceeding $n - 1$. Hence the adjoint matrix may be represented as an algebraic polynomial with matrix coefficients, that is, in the form

$$B = B_{n-1} + B_{n-2}\lambda + \cdots + B_0 \lambda^{n-1},$$

where $B_{n-1}, \cdots, B_0$ are matrices independent of λ. On making use of (4.3.8), we have

$$(B_{n-1} + B_{n-2}\lambda + \cdots + B_0 \lambda^{n-1})(A - \lambda I) = |A - \lambda I| \, I$$
$$= (-1)^n [\lambda^n - p_1 \lambda^{n-1} - p_2 \lambda^{n-2} - \cdots - p_n] \, I$$

with the notation of (4.9.4). This equation is equivalent to the system of equations

$$B_{n-1}A = (-1)^{n+1} p_n I$$
$$B_{n-2}A - B_{n-1} = (-1)^{n+1} p_{n-1} I$$
$$\cdots \cdots \cdots \cdots \cdots \cdots \cdots$$
$$B_0 A - B_1 = (-1)^{n+1} p_1 I$$
$$-B_0 = (-1)^n I.$$

If we multiply these equations on the right by $I, A, A^2, \cdots, A^{n-1}, A^n$, respectively, and add, we obtain on the left side a matrix all of whose elements are zero and on the right

$$(-1)^n [-p_n I - p_{n-1}A - p_{n-2}A^2 - \cdots - p_1 A^{n-1} + A^n] = \varphi(A).$$

Thus $\varphi(A) = 0$, as was to be proved.

The Cayley-Hamilton theorem may be used to express any power of a square matrix A of order n in terms of $I, A, A^2, \cdots, A^{n-1}$. Thus, from

$$\varphi(A) = (-1)^n[A^n - p_1 A^{n-1} - p_2 A^{n-2} - \cdots - p_{n-1}A - p_n I] = 0$$

we obtain

$$A^n = p_1 A^{n-1} + p_2 A^{n-2} + \cdots + p_{n-1}A + p_n I.$$

Then

$$A^{n+1} = A^n A = p_1 A^n + p_2 A^{n-1} + \cdots + p_{n-1}A^2 + p_n A$$
$$= p_1[p_1 A^{n-1} + p_2 A^{n-2} + \cdots + p_{n-1}A + p_n I]$$
$$+ p_2 A^{n-1} + \cdots + p_{n-1}A^2 + p_n A$$
$$= (p_1^2 + p_2)A^{n-1} + (p_1 p_2 + p_3)A^{n-2} + \cdots$$
$$+ (p_1 p_{n-1} + p_n)A + p_1 p_n I.$$

Proceeding in this way, we may express each of $A^{n+2}, A^{n+3}, \cdots$ in terms of $I, A, A^2, \cdots, A^{n-1}$.

For the matrix A of example 9, we saw that

$$\varphi(\lambda) = -(\lambda^3 - 6\lambda^2 - 16\lambda - 1).$$

Hence we have at once

$$A^3 = 6A^2 + 16A + I.$$

Then

$$A^4 = 6A^3 + 16A^2 + A = 52A^2 + 97A + 6I,$$

$$A^5 = 52A^3 + 97A^2 + 6A = 409A^2 + 838A + 52I,$$

and so on.

The Cayley-Hamilton theorem shows that for a given square matrix A there exists a polynomial (for example, the characteristic polynomial) for which the matrix A is a zero. But the characteristic polynomial is not the only such polynomial having this property; for if $\psi(\lambda)$ has such a property, so has any polynomial divisible by $\psi(\lambda)$. The polynomial of lowest degree having the property that the matrix A is a zero of it is called the minimum polynomial of the matrix A.

We now show that the characteristic polynomial is divisible by the minimum polynomial.

If we divide the characteristic polynomial $\varphi(\lambda)$ by the minimum polynomial $\psi(\lambda)$, we obtain a quotient $q(\lambda)$ and a remainder $r(\lambda)$; the degree of $r(\lambda)$ must be less than the degree of $\psi(\lambda)$. We have the relation

$$\varphi(\lambda) = \psi(\lambda)q(\lambda) + r(\lambda).$$

If we substitute A for λ in this equation, we obtain

$$r(A) = \varphi(A) - \psi(A)q(A) = 0.$$

Thus the matrix A is a zero of the polynomial $r(\lambda)$, contradicting the fact that $\psi(\lambda)$ is the minimum polynomial. It follows that $r(\lambda) \equiv 0$, and consequently $\psi(\lambda)$ divides $\varphi(\lambda)$.

It can also be shown that every characteristic number is a zero of the minimum polynomial. (See, e.g., Householder [14].)

4.11 PROPERTIES OF THE CHARACTERISTIC NUMBERS AND VECTORS OF A MATRIX

We first note that a matrix A and its transpose A^T have identical characteristic polynomials and hence identical spectra. This follows from the fact that

$$|A^T - \lambda I| = |A - \lambda I|$$

since a determinant is not altered when its rows and columns are interchanged.

Before obtaining further properties of the characteristic numbers and vectors, we need a property of the inner product. We now assume that the elements of a matrix A and the components of a vector $\mathbf{x}$ may be complex. We must remember that in the definition of the inner product given by equation (4.1.6), y_i must be replaced by $\bar{y}_i$, the complex conjugate of y_i. Thus

$$(\mathbf{x}, \mathbf{y}) = \sum_{i=1}^{n} x_i \bar{y}_i.$$

If A is a square matrix, we denote by $\bar{A}$ the matrix whose elements are the complex conjugates of the corresponding elements of A, and by A^* the transpose of $\bar{A}$. We have

$$A^* = \bar{A}^T. \tag{4.11.1}$$

We shall prove that for any vectors $\mathbf{x}$ and $\mathbf{y}$

$$(A\mathbf{x}, \mathbf{y}) = (\mathbf{x}, A^*\mathbf{y}). \tag{4.11.2}$$

It follows at once from the modified form of (4.1.6) and from (4.2.1) that

$$(A\mathbf{x}, \mathbf{y}) = \sum_{i=1}^{n}\left(\sum_{j=1}^{n} a_{ij} x_j\right)\bar{y}_i.$$

If we interchange the order of summation we find that

$$(A\mathbf{x}, \mathbf{y}) = \sum_{j=1}^{n} x_j \sum_{i=1}^{n} a_{ij}\bar{y}_i = \sum_{j=1}^{n} x_j \overline{\sum_{i=1}^{n} \bar{a}_{ij} y_i}$$

$$= (\mathbf{x}, A^*\mathbf{y})$$

since the element a_{ji}^* of A^* is equal to $\bar{a}_{ij}$.

We now consider a real square matrix. Since the characteristic polynomial will have real coefficients, the characteristic numbers that are not real will occur in complex conjugate pairs. If λ_r and λ_s denote distinct characteristic numbers of the matrix A, then $\bar{\lambda}_s$, the complex conjugate of λ_s, is also a characteristic number of A and hence also of A^T. Let $\mathbf{x}^r$ be the characteristic vector of A associated with λ_r and $\mathbf{y}^s$ the characteristic vector of A^T associated with $\bar{\lambda}_s$. We shall show that $\mathbf{x}^r$ and $\mathbf{y}^s$ are orthogonal.

We first note that

$$(A\mathbf{x}^r, \mathbf{y}^s) = (\lambda_r\mathbf{x}^r, \mathbf{y}^s) = \lambda_r(\mathbf{x}^r, \mathbf{y}^s).$$

On the other hand, since the matrix A is real, we have $A^* = A^T$ and hence from (4.11.2)

$$(A\mathbf{x}^r, \mathbf{y}^s) = (\mathbf{x}^r, A^T\mathbf{y}^s) = (\mathbf{x}^r, \bar{\lambda}_s\mathbf{y}^s) = \lambda_s(\mathbf{x}^r, \mathbf{y}^s).$$

It follows that

$$\lambda_r(\mathbf{x}^r, \mathbf{y}^s) = \lambda_s(\mathbf{x}^r, \mathbf{y}^s),$$

and since $\lambda_r \neq \lambda_s$ we find that $(\mathbf{x}^r, \mathbf{y}^s) = 0$, as was to be proved.

For a real symmetric matrix we now show that all its characteristic numbers are real. Let λ and $\mathbf{x}$ be a characteristic number and vector, respectively. Then we have

$$(A\mathbf{x}, \mathbf{x}) = (\lambda\mathbf{x}, \mathbf{x}) = \lambda(\mathbf{x}, \mathbf{x}).$$

On the other hand, since A is real and symmetric we have $A^* = A^T = A$, and hence from (4.11.2)

$$(A\mathbf{x}, \mathbf{x}) = (\mathbf{x}, A^T\mathbf{x}) = (\mathbf{x}, A\mathbf{x}) = (\mathbf{x}, \lambda\mathbf{x}) = \bar{\lambda}(\mathbf{x}, \mathbf{x}).$$

It follows that

$$\lambda(\mathbf{x}, \mathbf{x}) = \bar{\lambda}(\mathbf{x}, \mathbf{x}),$$

and since $(\mathbf{x}, \mathbf{x}) > 0$ we see that $\lambda = \bar{\lambda}$, that is, λ is real.

Since the characteristic numbers of a real symmetric matrix are always real, it follows that vectors with real components can always be taken as the characteristic vectors; the components will be found by solving a linear homogeneous system with real coefficients.

Since the transpose of a real symmetric matrix A is identical with A, the characteristic vectors of A^T are indentical with those of A. Remembering also that the characteristic numbers are real, we see that the result concerning orthogonality proved earlier is considerably simplified. We observe that for a real symmetric matrix the characteristic vectors associated with distinct characteristic numbers are orthogonal.

If A is a real symmetric matrix and $\mathbf{x}$ is a real vector, then

$$(A\mathbf{x}, \mathbf{x}) = \sum_{i,k=1}^{n} a_{ik} x_i x_k. \qquad (4.11.3)$$

This is seen to be a homogeneous polynomial of the second degree in the variables $x_1, x_2, \cdots, x_n$ and is called the quadratic form associated with the matrix A. The quadratic form is said to be positive-definite if its values are positive for any real values of $x_1, x_2, \cdots, x_n$ not all zero simultaneously.

We shall show that if the quadratic form associated with the matrix A is positive-definite, the characteristic numbers of A are all positive. Let $\mathbf{x}$ be a real characteristic vector associated with λ, a characteristic number of A. Now since the quadratic form is positive-definite, $(A\mathbf{x}, \mathbf{x}) > 0$. But since

$$(A\mathbf{x}, \mathbf{x}) = (\lambda\mathbf{x}, \mathbf{x}) = \lambda(\mathbf{x}, \mathbf{x}),$$

we find that

$$\lambda = \frac{(A\mathbf{x}, \mathbf{x})}{(\mathbf{x}, \mathbf{x})}.$$

Since both numerator and denominator of this fraction are positive, we see that $\lambda > 0$.

In order to give a simple criterion for recognizing when a quadratic form is positive-definite, we introduce the notion of the discriminant of the form. If A is the matrix associated with the form, the discriminant of the quadratic form is the determinant $\Delta_n = |A|$; here n denotes the order of the determinant, which is the number of rows (or columns) of A. We denote by Δ_{n-1} the discriminant of the quadratic form obtained from $(A\mathbf{x}, \mathbf{x})$ by setting $x_n = 0$. Δ_{n-2} denotes the discriminant of the quadratic form obtained by setting $x_n = x_{n-1} = 0$ and in general Δ_j denotes the discriminant of the quadratic form obtained by setting $x_n = x_{n-1} = \cdots = x_{j+1} = 0$. Then, it can be shown that a necessary and sufficient condition that the quadratic form be positive-definite is that all the discriminants $\Delta_1, \Delta_2, \cdots, \Delta_n$ shall be positive. (See, e.g., Frazer, Duncan, and Collar [8, pp. 30–32].)

Thus, for example, for a quadratic form involving four variables the associated matrix is

$$A = \begin{bmatrix} a_{11} & a_{12} & a_{13} & a_{14} \\ a_{21} & a_{22} & a_{23} & a_{24} \\ a_{31} & a_{32} & a_{33} & a_{34} \\ a_{41} & a_{42} & a_{43} & a_{44} \end{bmatrix}$$

where $a_{ij} = a_{ji}$. The quadratic form

$$(A\mathbf{x}, \mathbf{x}) = \sum_{i,j=1}^{4} a_{ij} x_i x_j$$

will be positive-definite if and only if

$$a_{11} > 0, \quad \begin{vmatrix} a_{11} & a_{12} \\ a_{21} & a_{22} \end{vmatrix} > 0, \quad \begin{vmatrix} a_{11} & a_{12} & a_{13} \\ a_{21} & a_{22} & a_{23} \\ a_{31} & a_{32} & a_{33} \end{vmatrix} > 0, \quad |A| > 0.$$

For complex matrices, instead of the quadratic form one deals with the Hermitian form, which may be written

$$(A\mathbf{x}, \mathbf{x}) = \sum_{i,j=1}^{n} a_{ij} x_i \bar{x}_j \qquad (4.11.4)$$

where it is assumed that $a_{ji} = \bar{a}_{ij}$. A matrix A for which $a_{ji} = \bar{a}_{ij}$ is called an Hermitian matrix and has associated with it an Hermitian form. We first note that all values of an Hermitian form are real. This is easily seen by noting that

$$(A\mathbf{x}, \mathbf{x}) = (\mathbf{x}, A^*\mathbf{x}) = (\mathbf{x}, A\mathbf{x}) = \overline{(A\mathbf{x}, \mathbf{x})}.$$

If all the values of an Hermitian form are positive, it is called positive-definite. It can be shown that the characteristic numbers of an Hermitian matrix are real and that if the associated Hermitian form is positive-definite the characteristic numbers are positive.

Two matrices A and B are said to be similar if there exists a nonsingular matrix C such that

$$B = C^{-1}AC. \qquad (4.11.5)$$

Matrix B is said to be obtained from matrix A by a similarity transformation.

We now show that similar matrices have the same characteristic function and consequently the same characteristic numbers. If A and B are similar matrices, we have

$$|B - \lambda I| = |C^{-1}AC - \lambda I| = |C^{-1}AC - \lambda C^{-1}IC|$$
$$= |C^{-1}| \, |A - \lambda I| \, |C| = |A - \lambda I|.$$

Moreover, if $\mathbf{x}$ and $\mathbf{y}$ are characteristic vectors of the matrices A and B, respectively, associated with the same characteristic number λ, we have

$$\mathbf{y} = C^{-1}\mathbf{x}.$$

For if $A\mathbf{x} = \lambda\mathbf{x}$, then

$$B\mathbf{y} = (C^{-1}AC)(C^{-1}\mathbf{x}) = C^{-1}A\mathbf{x} = C^{-1}\lambda\mathbf{x} = \lambda\mathbf{y}.$$

Since diagonal matrices are particularly convenient for calculation, it is of interest to inquire whether any matrix can be reduced to diagonal form by a similarity transformation. We state without proof some useful results in this direction. Further details may be found in Frazer, Duncan, and Collar [8, Chapter 3] and Faddeeva [5, Chapter 1].

First, suppose that all the characteristic numbers, $\lambda_1, \lambda_2, \cdots, \lambda_n$, of a matrix A are distinct. Then A will have n distinct linearly independent characteristic vectors. Moreover, if W is the matrix whose columns are the characteristic vectors, then

$$W^{-1}AW = \Lambda \tag{4.11.6}$$

where Λ is the diagonal matrix

$$\Lambda = \begin{bmatrix} \lambda_1 & 0 & \cdots & 0 \\ 0 & \lambda_2 & \cdots & 0 \\ \cdots\cdots\cdots\cdots\cdots \\ 0 & 0 & \cdots & \lambda_n \end{bmatrix}.$$

Thus A can be reduced to diagonal form by a similarity transformation.

If any of the characteristic numbers of a matrix are of multiplicity greater than one, but to each characteristic number there correspond as many linearly independent characteristic vectors as its multiplicity, the matrix may be reduced to diagonal form and equation (4.11.6) is again valid. This is the case, in particular, for real symmetric matrices. We have already noted that the characteristic vectors associated with distinct characteristic numbers of a real symmetric matrix are orthogonal. Now the linearly independent characteristic vectors associated with a single characteristic number of multiplicity greater than one can be chosen to be orthogonal. Consequently, for a real $n \times n$ symmetric matrix it is possible to find n orthogonal characteristic vectors.

For the general case of multiple characteristic numbers, transformation to diagonal form is not always possible by a similarity transformation. To describe the Jordan canonical form into which every matrix may be transformed by a similarity transformation, we first introduce the definition of a canonical box which is a matrix of the following form

$$T = \begin{bmatrix} \lambda_i & 0 & 0 & \cdots & 0 & 0 \\ 1 & \lambda_i & 0 & \cdots & 0 & 0 \\ 0 & 1 & \lambda_i & \cdots & 0 & 0 \\ \cdot & \cdot & \cdot & \cdots & \cdot & \cdot \\ 0 & 0 & 0 & \cdots & 1 & \lambda_i \end{bmatrix}.$$

All elements on the principal diagonal are λ_i. All elements on the first subdiagonal (i.e., the elements directly under the principal diagonal) are units. All other elements are zero.

A canonical box cannot be simplified by using a similarity transformation. Its minimum polynomial is identical with its characteristic polynomial and is $(\lambda - \lambda_i)^{m_i}$ where m_i is the order of the box. Thus the canonical box has the sole multiple characteristic number λ_i. It has only one linearly independent characteristic vector. An example exhibiting this was given in Section 4.9.

The Jordan canonical form is a quasi-diagonal matrix composed of canonical boxes:

$$
\begin{bmatrix}
T_1 & 0 & 0 & \cdots & 0 \\
0 & T_2 & 0 & \cdots & 0 \\
0 & 0 & T_3 & \cdots & 0 \\
\cdot & \cdot & \cdot & \cdots & \cdot \\
0 & 0 & 0 & \cdots & T_j
\end{bmatrix}
$$

Here each T_k is a canonical box and each 0 represents a matrix all of whose elements are zero. This notation exhibits the matrix in question partitioned into submatrices of which those on the principal diagonal are T_k and all other submatrices are zero matrices. For example, if

$$
T_1 = \begin{bmatrix} 2 & 0 & 0 \\ 1 & 2 & 0 \\ 0 & 1 & 2 \end{bmatrix}, \qquad T_2 = [-3], \qquad T_3 = \begin{bmatrix} 4 & 0 \\ 1 & 4 \end{bmatrix}
$$

the Jordan canonical form would be

$$
\begin{bmatrix}
T_1 & 0 & 0 \\
0 & T_2 & 0 \\
0 & 0 & T_3
\end{bmatrix}
=
\begin{bmatrix}
2 & 0 & 0 & 0 & 0 & 0 \\
1 & 2 & 0 & 0 & 0 & 0 \\
0 & 1 & 2 & 0 & 0 & 0 \\
0 & 0 & 0 & -3 & 0 & 0 \\
0 & 0 & 0 & 0 & 4 & 0 \\
0 & 0 & 0 & 0 & 1 & 4
\end{bmatrix}
$$

The λ_i appearing in the various boxes are characteristic numbers of the original matrix as well as of the canonical matrix. It is possible that the same number λ_i appear in several canonical boxes. The multiplicity of a characteristic number equals the sum of the orders of the boxes in which it appears as a diagonal element. The number of linearly independent characteristic vectors associated with it equals the number of boxes in which it appears. If each characteristic number appears in only one box, the minimum polynomial coincides with the characteristic polynomial. In the foregoing example, 2, −3, 4 are characteristic values of order 3, 1, and 2 respectively. Associated with each characteristic value is just one linearly independent characteristic vector.

We note that a diagonal matrix is a special case of the Jordan canonical form in which all of the canonical boxes are of order 1.

As already mentioned, every matrix can be brought into the Jordan canonical form by a similarity transformation. We omit any discussion of how this canonical form can actually be calculated for a given matrix. Our discussion is intended only to show what situations may occur with respect to the characteristic numbers and vectors of a matrix.

4.12 THE CALCULATION OF THE CHARACTERISTIC NUMBERS AND VECTORS OF A MATRIX

We turn now to a description of methods which may be used for the actual calculation of the characteristic numbers and characteristic vectors of a given matrix. We recall that the characteristic numbers are the zeros of the characteristic polynomial which is given by (4.9.4) in the form

$$\varphi(\lambda) = |A - \lambda I| = (-1)^n(\lambda^n - p_1\lambda^{n-1} - p_2\lambda^{n-2} - \cdots - p_n).$$

We might attempt to calculate the coefficients p_i in this polynomial by direct evaluation of the determinants entering into their definition, and then proceed to solve the equation $\varphi(\lambda) = 0$ to find the characteristic numbers. To find the characteristic vectors, we would then have to solve the set of linear equations (4.9.2) after substituting each characteristic number in turn for λ. Except for matrices of very low order, this method is not recommended since it involves a very large amount of labor and yields rather limited accuracy.

In many problems of applied mathematics, only a few characteristic numbers of greatest modulus (or absolute value) are required. In such a case an iterative method, sometimes called the power method, may be used conveniently to find the characteristic number of greatest modulus as well as its associated characteristic vector. This method is described in Section 4.13. If we want to find further characteristic numbers and vectors, we need a deflation procedure in which the original matrix is replaced by a matrix of lower order which does not have the known number and vector among its characteristic numbers and vectors. The deflation procedure is described in Section 4.14. Methods for obtaining all of the characteristic numbers and characteristic vectors of a real symmetric matrix are discussed in Section 4.15. Section 4.16 discusses this problem for the case of a real nonsymmetric matrix.

4.13 THE POWER METHOD

To describe the power method in a simple manner, we shall at first assume that the dominant characteristic number is real and that to each characteristic number correspond as many linearly independent characteristic vectors as its multiplicity. We recall that in this case the matrix may be reduced to diagonal form by a similarity transformation. We also recall that real symmetric matrices are included in this class of matrices.

Let $\lambda_1, \lambda_2, \cdots, \lambda_n$ be the characteristic numbers of the matrix A, arranged in order of diminishing modulus (some of them perhaps equal); let $\mathbf{x}^1, \mathbf{x}^2, \cdots, \mathbf{x}^n$ be the characteristic vectors corresponding to them. This set of vectors can be chosen to be linearly independent. Indeed if all the numbers λ_i are distinct, the $\mathbf{x}^i$ are determined up to a multiplicative constant; but if two or more of the characteristic numbers are equal, any linear combination of the characteristic vectors corresponding to these numbers is again a characteristic vector.

An arbitrary vector $\mathbf{y}$ may be represented uniquely in the form

$$\mathbf{y} = a_1\mathbf{x}^1 + a_2\mathbf{x}^2 + \cdots + a_n\mathbf{x}^n, \tag{4.13.1}$$

where the numbers a_i are constants. Some of these constants may be zero but we shall restrict the vector $\mathbf{y}$ by assuming that $a_1 \neq 0$.

We now form the sequence of vectors

$$A\mathbf{y}, A^2\mathbf{y}, \cdots, A^k\mathbf{y}, \cdots.$$

We call the vector $A^k\mathbf{y}$ the kth iterate of the vector $\mathbf{y}$ by the matrix A. It is clear that

$$A\mathbf{y} = a_1\lambda_1\mathbf{x}^1 + a_2\lambda_2\mathbf{x}^2 + \cdots + a_n\lambda_n\mathbf{x}^n, \tag{4.13.2}$$

and in general

$$A^k\mathbf{y} = a_1\lambda_1{}^k\mathbf{x}^1 + a_2\lambda_2{}^k\mathbf{x}^2 + \cdots + a_n\lambda_n{}^k\mathbf{x}^n. \tag{4.13.3}$$

Now if $|\lambda_1| > |\lambda_2| \geq |\lambda_3| \geq \cdots \geq |\lambda_n|$, ultimately the term $\lambda_1{}^k$ will dominate, and the vector $A^k\mathbf{y}$ will be essentially in the direction of $\mathbf{x}^1$. Since $A^k\mathbf{y}$ will be approximately $a_1\lambda_1{}^k\mathbf{x}^1$ and $A^{k+1}\mathbf{y}$ will be approximately $a_1\lambda_1^{k+1}\mathbf{x}^1$, we see that λ_1 is given approximately by the ratio of the lengths of $A^{k+1}\mathbf{y}$ and $A^k\mathbf{y}$ or of corresponding components of these vectors.

In carrying out the iterations in practice, it is desirable to compute the ratio for several of the components of $A^{k+1}\mathbf{y}$ and $A^k\mathbf{y}$. If these ratios agree reasonably well, their common value will be close to λ_1. The rapidity of the convergence of the iterative process depends on the magnitude of the ratio λ_2/λ_1 and may be very slow if this ratio is near to 1 in magnitude. In computing the iterates, it is usually convenient to normalize the vectors by dividing the components of the vectors being iterated by the first or largest component or by the length of the vector in order to avoid growth of the components. Thus if μ_k is the normalizing factor, we obtain a sequence $\bar{y}^k = \mu_k A^k y$, and to find λ_1 we must take the ratio of the components of the vectors $A\bar{y}^k$ and $\bar{y}^k$. In choosing the initial vector y, we may have the misfortune to choose a vector for which the coefficient a_1 in (4.13.1) is zero or very close to zero. In this case, at the first steps of the iteration the dominant term will depend on λ_2 if $a_2 \neq 0$. But even if a_1 is exactly zero, rounding errors will introduce the term dependent on λ_1. At first this term will have a very small coefficient, but this coefficient will grow as the iterations proceed, and satisfactory results may be obtained even with this unfortunate choice of y. If this does not happen we should start again with a different initial vector y.

Example 10. Find the characteristic number of largest modulus and the associated characteristic vector of the matrix

$$A = \begin{bmatrix} 2 & 3 & 2 \\ 4 & 3 & 5 \\ 3 & 2 & 9 \end{bmatrix}.$$

We choose as an initial vector, y, the vector all of whose components are unity and proceed to form the sequence of iterates $A^k y$:

$$\begin{bmatrix} 1 \\ 1 \\ 1 \end{bmatrix} \begin{bmatrix} 7 \\ 12 \\ 14 \end{bmatrix} \begin{bmatrix} 78 \\ 134 \\ 171 \end{bmatrix} \begin{bmatrix} 900 \\ 1569 \\ 2041 \end{bmatrix} \begin{bmatrix} 10589 \\ 18512 \\ 24207 \end{bmatrix} \begin{bmatrix} 125128 \\ 218927 \\ 286654 \end{bmatrix} \begin{bmatrix} 1480345 \\ 2590563 \\ 3393124 \end{bmatrix}.$$

If we take the ratios of the components of $A^6 y$ and $A^5 y$, we obtain

$$\frac{1480345}{125128} = 11.8306,$$

$$\frac{2590563}{218927} = 11.8330,$$

$$\frac{3393124}{286654} = 11.8370.$$

Any of these is a good approximation to the true value of λ_1 which is 11.8354. If we normalize the vectors $A^5 y$ and $A^6 y$ by dividing each component by the first component we obtain the vectors

$$\begin{bmatrix} 1 \\ 1.7496 \\ 2.2909 \end{bmatrix} \begin{bmatrix} 1 \\ 1.7500 \\ 2.2991 \end{bmatrix}.$$

Either of these vectors provides a good approximation to the characteristic vector associated with λ_1. We note that the convergence of the iterates is quite rapid in this example. This is because the other characteristic numbers are 3.0293 and -0.8646, which are well separated from λ_1. (This example stems from Aitken [1, p. 272].)

If the dominant characteristic value is multiple with multiplicity r, that is, $\lambda_1 = \lambda_2 = \cdots = \lambda_r$, $|\lambda_r| > |\lambda_{r+1}|$, then we have

$$A y = \lambda_1(a_1 x^1 + a_2 x^2 + \cdots + a_r x^r) + a_{r+1}\lambda_{r+1} x^{r+1} + \cdots + a_n\lambda_n x^n$$

and

$$A^k y = \lambda_1^k(a_1 x^1 + a_2 x^2 + \cdots + a_r x^r) + a_{r+1}\lambda_{r+1}^k x^{r+1} + \cdots + a_n\lambda_n^k x^n.$$

Since $a_1 x^1 + a_2 x^2 + \cdots + a_r x^r$ is again a characteristic vector, we see that, as before, λ_1 is given approximately by the ratio of corresponding components of the vectors $A^{k+1} y$ and $A^k y$. We obtain no information concerning the multiplicity of the characteristic number however, but we do obtain one characteristic vector corresponding to λ_1. Here, by starting with different initial vectors, we arrive, generally speaking, at different characteristic vectors.

Next, if $\lambda_1 = -\lambda_2$, $|\lambda_1| > |\lambda_3|$, we have

$$A y = \lambda_1(a_1 x^1 - a_2 x^2) + \lambda_3 a_3 x^3 + \cdots + \lambda_n a_n x^n,$$

$$A^2 y = \lambda_1^2(a_1 x^1 + a_2 x^2) + \lambda_3^2 a_3 x^3 + \cdots + \lambda_n^2 a_n x^n,$$

and generally

$$A^{2k} y = \lambda_1^{2k}(a_1 x^1 + a_2 x^2) + \lambda_3^{2k} a_3 x^3 + \cdots + \lambda_n^{2k} a_n x^n,$$

$$A^{2k+1} y = \lambda_1^{2k+1}(a_1 x^1 - a_2 x^2) + \lambda_3^{2k+1} a_3 x^3 + \cdots + \lambda_n^{2k+1} a_n x^n.$$

Here, two successive iterates cannot be used for the determination of λ_1. We observe, however, that λ_1^2 is given approximately by the ratio of corresponding components of the vectors $A^{2k+2} y$ and $A^{2k} y$ or of $A^{2k+1} y$ and $A^{2k-1} y$. Now neither of the vectors $A^{2k} y$ nor $A^{2k+1} y$ will approximate the characteristic vectors x^1 or x^2. But we can obtain these characteristic vectors if we consider the sequence of vectors $A^k\mathbf{y} + \lambda_1 A^{k-1}\mathbf{y}$ and $A^k\mathbf{y} - \lambda_1 A^{k-1}\mathbf{y}$ for we have

$$A^k\mathbf{y} + \lambda_1 A^{k-1}\mathbf{y}$$
$$= 2a_1\lambda_1{}^k\mathbf{x}^1 + a_3(\lambda_3 + \lambda_1)\lambda_3^{k-1}\mathbf{x}^3 + \cdots + a_n(\lambda_n + \lambda_1)\lambda_n^{k-1}\mathbf{x}^n$$

and

$$A^k\mathbf{y} - \lambda_1 A^{k-1}\mathbf{y}$$
$$= 2a_2(-\lambda_1)^k\mathbf{x}^2 + a_3(\lambda_3 - \lambda_1)\lambda_3^{k-1}\mathbf{x}^3 + \cdots + a_n(\lambda_n - \lambda_1)\lambda_n^{k-1}\mathbf{x}^n.$$

The first term is the dominant one in each case. The ratios of the components of these vectors will, respectively, approach the ratios of the components of the vectors $\mathbf{x}^1$ and $\mathbf{x}^2$ associated with the characteristic numbers λ_1 and λ_2.

If we relax the condition that the dominant characteristic number be real, and, if we assume that A is a real matrix, it follows that $\lambda_2 = \bar{\lambda}_1$, the complex conjugate of λ_1, and $\mathbf{x}^2 = \bar{\mathbf{x}}^1$. Thus the first two characteristic numbers are equal in magnitude. If we assume that $|\lambda_1| = |\lambda_2| > |\lambda_3|$, we can proceed in a manner quite similar to that described previously. If we choose an arbitrary vector

$$\mathbf{y} = a_1\mathbf{x}^1 + a_2\bar{\mathbf{x}}^1 + a_3\mathbf{x}^3 + \cdots + a_n\mathbf{x}^n, \qquad (4.13.4)$$

we have

$$A\mathbf{y} = a_1\lambda_1\mathbf{x}^1 + a_2\bar{\lambda}_1\bar{\mathbf{x}}^1 + a_3\lambda_3\mathbf{x}^3 + \cdots + a_n\lambda_n\mathbf{x}^n \qquad (4.13.5)$$

and

$$A^k\mathbf{y} = a_1\lambda_1{}^k\mathbf{x}^1 + a_2\bar{\lambda}_1{}^k\bar{\mathbf{x}}^1 + a_3\lambda_3{}^k\mathbf{x}^3 + \cdots + a_n\lambda_n{}^k\mathbf{x}^n. \qquad (4.13.6)$$

If the iteration proceeds far enough the terms involving $\lambda_3, \cdots, \lambda_n$ will be small compared to the first two, but the vector $A^k\mathbf{y}$ will never converge. To find λ_1, we follow a method suggested by Aitken [1, p. 277]. We let $\lambda_1 = re^{i\theta}$ so that $\bar{\lambda}_1 = re^{-i\theta}$. Then the dominant part of any component of $A^k\mathbf{y}$ may be written in the form

$$\mu_k = a_1 r^k e^{ik\theta}c + a_2 r^k e^{-ik\theta}\bar{c}$$

where c denotes the corresponding component of $\mathbf{x}^1$. If we recall that $e^{ik\theta} = \cos k\theta + i\sin k\theta$ we can write instead

$$\mu_k = r^k(c_1\cos k\theta + c_2\sin k\theta)$$

where c_1 and c_2 are constants independent of k. Alternatively this may be written in the form

$$\mu_k = r^k c_0 \cos(k\theta + \epsilon) \qquad (4.13.7)$$

where c_0 and ϵ are independent of k. The presence of the factor $\cos(k\theta + \epsilon)$ in (4.13.7) is what causes the failure to converge. Each component will exhibit an irregularly oscillating sign. By making use of μ_k, μ_{k+1}, μ_{k+2}, μ_{k+3}, however, we may eliminate c_0 and ϵ and determine r and θ, that is, λ_1. We first note that

$$\begin{vmatrix} \mu_k & \mu_{k+1} \\ \mu_{k+1} & \mu_{k+2} \end{vmatrix} = c_0 r^{2k+2} \begin{vmatrix} \cos(k\theta + \epsilon) & \cos[(k+1)\theta + \epsilon] \\ \cos[(k+1)\theta + \epsilon] & \cos[(k+2)\theta + \epsilon] \end{vmatrix}$$

$$= \tfrac{1}{2}c_0 r^{2k+2}(\cos 2\theta - 1). \tag{4.13.8}$$

If the equation (4.13.8), with $k + 1$ replacing k, is divided by equation (4.13.8), we obtain

$$r^2 = \frac{\begin{vmatrix} \mu_{k+1} & \mu_{k+2} \\ \mu_{k+2} & \mu_{k+3} \end{vmatrix}}{\begin{vmatrix} \mu_k & \mu_{k+1} \\ \mu_{k+1} & \mu_{k+2} \end{vmatrix}}. \tag{4.13.9}$$

In addition we observe that

$$r\mu_k + r^{-1}\mu_{k+2} = r^{k+1}c_0 \{\cos(k\theta + \epsilon) + \cos[(k+2)\theta + \epsilon]\}$$

$$= 2c_0 r^{k+1} \cos[(k+1)\theta + \epsilon] \cos\theta$$

$$= 2\mu_{k+1} \cos\theta$$

so that

$$\cos\theta = \frac{r\mu_k + r^{-1}\mu_{k+2}}{2\mu_{k+1}}. \tag{4.13.10}$$

Thus, we have equations for determining both r and θ, and from these both λ_1 and $\lambda_2 = \bar{\lambda}_1$ can be found.

We can find the components of the characteristic vectors associated with these characteristic numbers by considering the combination

$$A^{k+1}\mathbf{y} - \bar{\lambda}_1 A^k \mathbf{y} \tag{4.13.11}$$

which can be obtained easily from the sequence of iterates $A^k \mathbf{y}$. This is seen by considering the dominant part of $A^k \mathbf{y}$ given by equation (4.13.6). We have approximately

$$A^{k+1}\mathbf{y} - \bar{\lambda}_1 A^k \mathbf{y} = a_1(\lambda_1^{k+1} - \bar{\lambda}_1 \lambda_1^{k})\mathbf{x}^1$$

$$= a_1 \lambda_1^{k}(\lambda_1 - \bar{\lambda}_1)\mathbf{x}^1. \tag{4.13.12}$$

Thus we obtain a certain complex multiple of $\mathbf{x}^1$. We can obtain a normalized form for $\mathbf{x}^1$ with first component unity by dividing the other components through by this number.

Instead of using (4.13.9) and (4.13.10) to find r and θ and then computing $\lambda_1 = re^{i\theta}$, we may proceed in a simpler manner, although the results may be somewhat less accurate. The following procedure is suggested by Bodewig [2]. By considering only the dominant parts of (4.13.6), we have approximately

$$A^k \mathbf{y} = a_1 \lambda_1{}^k \mathbf{x}^1 + a_2 \bar{\lambda}_1{}^k \bar{\mathbf{x}}^1$$

$$A^{k+1} \mathbf{y} = a_1 \lambda_1^{k+1} \mathbf{x}^1 + a_2 \bar{\lambda}_1^{k+1} \bar{\mathbf{x}}^1$$

$$A^{k+2} \mathbf{y} = a_1 \lambda_1^{k+2} \mathbf{x}^1 + a_2 \bar{\lambda}_1^{k+2} \bar{\mathbf{x}}^1.$$

Clearly λ_1 and $\bar{\lambda}_1$ are roots of the quadratic equation

$$\lambda^2 + a\lambda + b = 0 \tag{4.13.13}$$

where $a = -\lambda_1 - \bar{\lambda}_1$, $b = \lambda_1 \bar{\lambda}_1$. Hence we have at once

$$A^{k+2} \mathbf{y} + aA^{k+1} \mathbf{y} + bA^k \mathbf{y} = 0. \tag{4.13.14}$$

If we substitute the various components of these vectors we obtain n equations for the determination of these two unknown numbers a and b. Any pair of the equations can be used and several pairs should be used to see if consistent values of a and b are obtained. If the values are not consistent, the iteration of $\mathbf{y}$ by A should be carried further. If the values of a and b are consistent, then λ_1 and $\bar{\lambda}_1$ are found as the roots of the equation (4.13.13).

Example 11. Find the two conjugate complex characteristic numbers and their characteristic vectors for the matrix

$$A = \begin{bmatrix} 3 & 1 & -2 \\ -3 & -2 & 2 \\ 4 & -2 & 2 \end{bmatrix}.$$

We choose as an initial vector $\mathbf{y}$, the vector all of whose components are unity and form the sequence of iterates $A^k \mathbf{y}$:

$$\begin{bmatrix} 1 \\ 1 \\ 1 \end{bmatrix} \begin{bmatrix} 2 \\ -3 \\ 4 \end{bmatrix} \begin{bmatrix} -5 \\ 8 \\ 22 \end{bmatrix} \begin{bmatrix} -51 \\ 43 \\ 8 \end{bmatrix} \begin{bmatrix} -126 \\ 83 \\ -274 \end{bmatrix} \begin{bmatrix} 253 \\ -336 \\ -1218 \end{bmatrix}$$

$$\begin{bmatrix} 2859 \\ -2523 \\ -752 \end{bmatrix} \begin{bmatrix} 7558 \\ -5035 \\ 14978 \end{bmatrix} \begin{bmatrix} -12317 \\ 17352 \\ 70258 \end{bmatrix} \begin{bmatrix} -160115 \\ 142763 \\ 56544 \end{bmatrix} \begin{bmatrix} -450670 \\ 307907 \\ -812898 \end{bmatrix}.$$

We observe that the signs of the components vary irregularly, which suggests the existence of a pair of conjugate complex characteristic numbers. If the characteristic numbers are $\lambda_1 = re^{i\theta}$ and $\lambda_2 = \bar{\lambda}_1 = re^{-i\theta}$, we can use (4.13.9) to calculate r^2 and (4.13.10) to find $\cos\theta$.

Using the first components of the vectors A^7y, A^8y, A^9y, and $A^{10}y$, we find from (4.13.9) that $r^2 = 14.7489$. Similarly, using the second and third components of these vectors we find that $r^2 = 14.7450$ and 14.7483, respectively. Averaging these values of r^2 and taking the square root, we obtain $r = 3.8402$. Now from (4.13.10) we obtain from the three sets of components the values $\cos\theta = 0.5142, 0.5142, 0.5140$. Thus we take $\cos\theta = 0.5141$. It follows that $\sin\theta = 0.8577$. We then have

$$\lambda_1 = r(\cos\theta + i\sin\theta) = 1.9742 + 3.2937i.$$

We then find that

$$A^{10}y - \bar{\lambda}_1 A^9 y = \begin{bmatrix} -450670 \\ 307907 \\ -812898 \end{bmatrix} - (1.9742 - 3.2937i) \begin{bmatrix} -160115 \\ 142763 \\ 56544 \end{bmatrix}$$

$$= \begin{bmatrix} -134570.9670 - 527370.7755i \\ 26064.2854 + 470218.4931i \\ -924527.1648 + 186238.9728i \end{bmatrix}.$$

If this vector is normalized by dividing the second and third components by the first, we obtain

$$x^1 = \begin{bmatrix} 1.0000 \\ -0.8490 - 0.1672i \\ 0.08844 - 1.7305i \end{bmatrix}.$$

If we use the alternative method for the calculation of λ_1, then from (4.13.14) we obtain

$$-450670 - 160115a - 12317b = 0$$

$$307907 + 142763a + 17352b = 0$$

$$-812898 + 56544a + 70258b = 0.$$

Solving these equations in pairs, we obtain for a the three values -3.9489, -3.9492, and -3.9494 or taking the average we may use $a = -3.9492$. Similarly for b we obtain 14.7450, 14.7485, and 14.7487 and we take the average, namely $b = 14.7474$. Substituting these values in (4.13.13) we have

$$\lambda^2 - 3.9492\lambda + 14.7474 = 0$$

from which we obtain

$$\lambda_1 = 1.9746 + 3.2937i,$$

which is almost the same as the value obtained by the other method.

If the matrix A is a complex matrix, the characteristic numbers and characteristic vectors will, in general, be complex. If complex arithmetic is used in place of real, the power method can still be used. If the modulus of the dominant characteristic value is not repeated, that is, if no other characteristic number lies on the circle with center at the origin on which the dominant number lies, the method will work with $A^k\mathbf{y}$ converging to $\mathbf{x}^1$, a complex vector, and the ratio of the components of $A^{k+1}\mathbf{y}$ and $A^k\mathbf{y}$ converging to λ_1.

The power method will be most successful when the modulus of one of the characteristic numbers is considerably greater than the modulus of any other characteristic number, for the convergence of the iteration procedure will be rapid. But when two or more characteristic numbers are nearly equal or exactly equal in modulus, the convergence of the procedure is usually slow or fails altogether. For these reasons, blind application of the method is to be avoided. It is a useful method provided it is used carefully and the results are watched.

When convergence is slow, it may be possible to accelerate the convergence by various devices. One method is based on the fact that if λ_1 is a characteristic number of the matrix A, then $\lambda_1{}^k$ is a characteristic number of the matrix A^k. Moreover, if λ_1 is the dominant characteristic number, $\lambda_1{}^k$ will be more dominant than λ_1. Using equation (4.9.7), we have

$$\mathrm{tr}(A^k) = \lambda_1{}^k + \lambda_2{}^k + \cdots + \lambda_n{}^k.$$

Successive powers of the matrix A: A^2, A^4, A^8, A^{16}, $\cdots$, are computed. For sufficiently large k, $\lambda_1{}^{2^k}$ will be the dominant term, and we have approximately

$$\lambda_1 = \sqrt[2^k]{\mathrm{tr}(A^{2^k})}. \tag{4.13.15}$$

To find approximately the characteristic vector $\mathbf{x}^1$, we have only to form $A^{2^k}\mathbf{y}$ where $\mathbf{y}$ is an arbitrary vector and k is sufficiently large. It would be desirable also to calculate $A\mathbf{x}^1$ as a check that k was sufficiently large.

Instead of extracting the root we might begin the usual iteration of an arbitrary vector using the constructed powers. For example, we might compute $A^8\mathbf{y}$ and then $A^{16}\mathbf{y} = A^8(A^8\mathbf{y})$. An approximate value of λ_1 might then be obtained as the ratio of the components of $A^{17}\mathbf{y}$ and $A^{16}\mathbf{y}$.

Another acceleration method is Aitken's δ^2-process, which is applicable only if λ_1, λ_2, λ_3 are all real and $|\lambda_1| > |\lambda_2| > |\lambda_3|$. We have seen that an approximation to λ_1 can be found by taking, for example, the ratio of any component of $A^{k+1}\mathbf{y}$ and $A^k\mathbf{y}$ where $\mathbf{y}$ is an arbitrary vector. We may thus obtain a sequence of numbers z_k which will approach λ_1. If the convergence of this sequence to λ_1 is slow, we may form from this sequence another sequence $P(z_k)$ where

$$P(z_k) = \frac{\begin{vmatrix} z_k & z_{k+1} \\ z_{k+1} & z_{k+2} \end{vmatrix}}{z_k - 2z_{k+1} + z_{k+2}}. \tag{4.13.16}$$

Then Aitken [1, p. 291], showed that the convergence of $P(z_k)$ to λ_1 will be much more rapid than that of z_k. Thus the error in using $P(z_k)$ as an approximation to λ_1 will be considerably less than the error would be if z_k, z_{k+1}, or z_{k+2} were used to approximate λ_1. A proof of this result may also be found in Faddeeva [5, p. 215]. The same procedure can be applied to the sequences for the components of the characteristic vector in order to compute them.

For practical computations the operation P possesses a very convenient property which may be expressed in the form

$$P(z_k + c) = c + P(z_k) \tag{4.13.17}$$

where c is any constant. Thus before employing the δ^2-process we can subtract any convenient constant from the numbers z_k, z_{k+1}, z_{k+2}. The most convenient constant is, of course, the part consisting of the digits which these numbers possess in common. Thus the δ^2-process can be applied to the later differing digits only.

Example 12. Apply Aitken's δ^2-process to improve the value of λ_1 found in example 10. In addition, improve the characteristic vector.

In example 10, using the ratio of the first components of $A^6\mathbf{y}$ and $A^5\mathbf{y}$ we found $z_5 = 11.8306$ as an approximation to λ_1. Similarly, using the vectors $A^5\mathbf{y}$, $A^4\mathbf{y}$ and $A^4\mathbf{y}$, $A^3\mathbf{y}$ we find $z_4 = 11.8168$, and $z_3 = 11.7657$. Using (4.13.16) and (4.13.17) we find a better approximation to λ_1 to be

$$11.7000 + \frac{\begin{vmatrix} 0.0656 & 0.1168 \\ 0.1168 & 0.1306 \end{vmatrix}}{0.0656 - 2(0.1168) + 0.1306} = 11.8357.$$

Use of the second and third components of these vectors yields the approximations 11.8352 and 11.8354, respectively. The average of the three approximations is 11.8354 which happens to be correct to four places of decimals.

Normalizing the last three iterates found in example 10, we find the following approximations to the characteristic vector $\mathbf{x}^1$:

$$\begin{bmatrix} 1.0000 \\ 1.7482 \\ 2.2861 \end{bmatrix} \quad \begin{bmatrix} 1.0000 \\ 1.7496 \\ 2.2909 \end{bmatrix} \quad \begin{bmatrix} 1.0000 \\ 1.7500 \\ 2.2921 \end{bmatrix}.$$

Applying the δ^2-process to each of the sequences of components we obtain a better approximation, namely

$$\mathbf{x}^1 = \begin{bmatrix} 1.0000 \\ 1.7502 \\ 2.2926 \end{bmatrix}.$$

Another method for improving the convergence of the power method has been suggested by Wilkinson [25, 26]. We observe that if λ_i is a characteristic number of the matrix A, then $\lambda_i - p$ is a characteristic number of the matrix $A - pI$ and that the associated characteristic vector is the same for A as for $A - pI$. By suitable choice of p it may be possible to make one of the characteristic numbers of $A - pI$, say $\lambda_1 - p$, dominant. This possibility exists because the largest of the ratios

$$\frac{\lambda_2 - p}{\lambda_1 - p}, \ldots, \frac{\lambda_n - p}{\lambda_1 - p}$$

can be made smaller than the largest of the ratios

$$\frac{\lambda_2}{\lambda_1}, \ldots, \frac{\lambda_n}{\lambda_1}.$$

If in applying the usual power method, that is, $p = 0$, convergence is slow, the iteration is continued using the matrix $A - pI$ with suitably chosen p. If it is known that all the characteristic numbers are positive or that the negative ones are very small relative to the positive ones, Wilkinson suggests choosing p somewhat larger than one-third of the approximate value of λ_1 found by the preceding iteration process. Another use of the method is in the calculation of the lowest characteristic number without calculating all the rest. If all the characteristic numbers are positive and if p is chosen equal to some upper bound for the numbers, the magnitudes are reversed and the least characteristic number of A becomes dominant in $A - pI$ so that iteration with $A - pI$ yields this characteristic number.

If the dominant characteristic number is multiple and has associated with it less independent characteristic vectors than its multiplicity, the problem becomes more difficult. Fortunately, this is not often encountered in practice. A discussion of this case has been given by Aitken [1, pp. 279–284].

4.14 DEFLATION

When one characteristic number and its associated characteristic vector have been found for a matrix A, in order to find further characteristic numbers and vectors we need to use some method of deflation to reduce the original problem to one in which the characteristic number and vector that have just been found are no longer present. Generally this will require a knowledge of the characteristic vector for the transposed matrix A^T as well as that for the matrix A.

Suppose that λ_1, the characteristic number of largest magnitude, has been found for matrix A and suppose that λ_1 is real. Then, of course, λ_1 is also the characteristic number of largest magnitude for A^T. Suppose that, as usual, the associated characteristic vectors have been found approximately from the sequence of iterates $A^k \mathbf{y}$ and $(A^T)^k \mathbf{y}$ of an arbitrary vector $\mathbf{y}$ by the matrices A and A^T. Let $\mathbf{x}^1$ and $\mathbf{y}^1$ denote these characteristic vectors of A and A^T. We saw in section 4.11 that $\mathbf{y}^1$ is orthogonal to all of the characteristic vectors of A other than $\mathbf{x}^1$. Moreover, since we can write

$$\mathbf{y}^1 = a_1 \mathbf{x}^1 + a_2 \mathbf{x}^2 + \cdots + a_n \mathbf{x}^n,$$

where $\mathbf{x}^2, \mathbf{x}^3, \cdots, \mathbf{x}^n$ are the other characteristic vectors of A, we have

$$(\mathbf{y}^1, \mathbf{y}^1) = a_1(\mathbf{x}^1, \mathbf{y}^1) + 0.$$

Since $(\mathbf{y}^1, \mathbf{y}^1) > 0$ it follows that $(\mathbf{x}^1, \mathbf{y}^1) \neq 0$ and so $\mathbf{x}^1$ and $\mathbf{y}^1$ can be normalized so that $(\mathbf{x}^1, \mathbf{y}^1) = 1$.

Now both $\mathbf{x}^1$ and $\mathbf{y}^1$ are column vectors. Let us denote their components by $x_1{}^1, x_2{}^1, \cdots, x_n{}^1$ and $y_1{}^1, y_2{}^1, \cdots, y_n{}^1$, respectively. The transpose of $\mathbf{y}^1$ is a row vector $(\mathbf{y}^1)^T$ and if we form the matrix product $\mathbf{x}^1(\mathbf{y}^1)^T$ we obtain a square $n \times n$ matrix which will be

$$\begin{bmatrix} x_1{}^1 y_1{}^1 & x_1{}^1 y_2{}^1 & \cdots & x_1{}^1 y_n{}^1 \\ x_2{}^1 y_1{}^1 & x_2{}^1 y_2{}^1 & \cdots & x_2{}^1 y_n{}^1 \\ \cdots \cdots \cdots \cdots \cdots \cdots \\ x_n{}^1 y_1{}^1 & x_n{}^1 y_2{}^1 & \cdots & x_n{}^1 y_n{}^1 \end{bmatrix}.$$

We remark that the matrix product $(\mathbf{y}^1)^T \mathbf{x}^1$ is a scalar, namely the inner product $(\mathbf{y}^1, \mathbf{x}^1)$ which is unity.

We next form the matrix

$$A_1 = A - \lambda_1 \mathbf{x}^1 (\mathbf{y}^1)^T. \tag{4.14.1}$$

We show that the matrix A_1 has the same characteristic numbers and vectors as the matrix A except for the first characteristic number, in place of which there is a characteristic number equal to zero. We have

$$\begin{aligned} A_1 \mathbf{x}^1 &= A\mathbf{x}^1 - \lambda_1 [\mathbf{x}^1 (\mathbf{y}^1)^T] \mathbf{x}^1 \\ &= \lambda_1 \mathbf{x}^1 - \lambda_1 \mathbf{x}^1 [(\mathbf{y}^1)^T \mathbf{x}^1] = \lambda_1 \mathbf{x}^1 - \lambda_1 \mathbf{x}^1 (\mathbf{y}^1, \mathbf{x}^1) \\ &= \lambda_1 \mathbf{x}^1 - \lambda_1 \mathbf{x}^1 = 0, \end{aligned}$$

since $(\mathbf{y}^1, \mathbf{x}^1) = 1$. Also, if $i \neq 1$, then

$$\begin{aligned} A_1 \mathbf{x}^i &= A\mathbf{x}^i - \lambda_1 [\mathbf{x}^1 (\mathbf{y}^1)^T] \mathbf{x}^i \\ &= \lambda_i \mathbf{x}^i - \lambda_1 \mathbf{x}^1 [(\mathbf{y}^1)^T \mathbf{x}^i] \\ &= \lambda_i \mathbf{x}^i - \lambda_1 \mathbf{x}^1 (\mathbf{y}^1, \mathbf{x}^i) = \lambda_i \mathbf{x}^i \end{aligned}$$

since $(\mathbf{y}^1, \mathbf{x}^i) = 0$ by the orthogonality property.

If we now apply the power method to the matrix A_1 we will obtain the dominant characteristic number among $\lambda_2, \cdots, \lambda_n$ together with the associated characteristic vector. Clearly, the method can be repeated after the second number and vector have been found.

It is possible to avoid the calculation of the matrix A_1 and of the sequence of iterates $A_1^k \mathbf{y}$ because these iterates can be obtained from the sequence $A^k \mathbf{y}$ by means of the formula

$$A_1^k \mathbf{y} = A^k \mathbf{y} - \lambda_1^k \mathbf{x}^1 (\mathbf{y}^1)^T \mathbf{y}. \tag{4.14.2}$$

To prove this formula, we need to introduce the so-called bilinear resolution of the matrix A.

If $\mathbf{x}^1, \mathbf{x}^2, \cdots, \mathbf{x}^n$ are characteristic vectors of A and $\mathbf{y}^1, \mathbf{y}^2, \cdots, \mathbf{y}^n$ are the characteristic vectors of A^T where $\mathbf{x}^i$ and $\mathbf{y}^i$ are associated with conjugate complex characteristic numbers, then we saw in Section 4.11 that

$$(\mathbf{y}^i)^T \mathbf{x}^j = (\mathbf{y}^i, \mathbf{x}^j) = 0 \quad \text{if} \quad i \neq j.$$

Moreover, if we proceed as earlier in the present section we easily see that these vectors can be normalized in such a way that

$$(\mathbf{y}^i)^T \mathbf{x}^i = (\mathbf{y}^i, \mathbf{x}^i) = 1.$$

Using these results it is easy to verify that

$$I = \mathbf{x}^1 (\mathbf{y}^1)^T + \mathbf{x}^2 (\mathbf{y}^2)^T + \cdots + \mathbf{x}^n (\mathbf{y}^n)^T.$$

If we multiply this equation on the left by A and remember that $A\mathbf{x}^i = \lambda_i\mathbf{x}^i$, we obtain

$$A = \lambda_1\mathbf{x}^1(\mathbf{y}^1)^T + \lambda_2\mathbf{x}^2(\mathbf{y}^2)^T + \cdots + \lambda_n\mathbf{x}^n(\mathbf{y}^n)^T. \qquad (4.14.3)$$

Using (4.14.1), we find at once that

$$A_1 = \lambda_2\mathbf{x}^2(\mathbf{y}^2)^T + \cdots + \lambda_n\mathbf{x}^n(\mathbf{y}^n)^T. \qquad (4.14.4)$$

If we multiply equation (4.14.3) repeatedly on the left by A, we obtain

$$A^k = \lambda_1{}^k\mathbf{x}^1(\mathbf{y}^1)^T + \lambda_2{}^k\mathbf{x}^2(\mathbf{y}^2)^T + \cdots + \lambda_n{}^k\mathbf{x}^n(\mathbf{y}^n)^T.$$

In a similar manner,

$$A_1{}^k = \lambda_2{}^k\mathbf{x}^2(\mathbf{y}^2)^T + \cdots + \lambda_n{}^k\mathbf{x}^n(\mathbf{y}^n)^T.$$

Thus

$$A_1{}^k = A^k - \lambda_1{}^k\mathbf{x}^1(\mathbf{y}^1)^T,$$

and equation (4.14.2) follows at once.

It is not even necessary to compute the whole sequence of iterates $A_1{}^k\mathbf{y}$. It is sufficient to calculate two consecutive iterates $A_1{}^m\mathbf{y}$ and $A_1^{m+1}\mathbf{y}$ by formula (4.14.2). Then λ_2 and $\mathbf{x}^2$ are determined in the same manner in which λ_1 and $\mathbf{x}^1$ were found. Usually we will choose a value of m less than the number of the iterate which was used in the determination of λ_1 and $\mathbf{x}^1$. Devices for improving the convergence, such as Aitken's δ^2-process, are, of course, still available.

Actually, it is inappropriate to use the same vector $\mathbf{y}$ for iterations by A_1 as was used for the iterations by A. Doing so in order to be able to use (4.14.2) produces results of low accuracy. If the approximation to the characteristic vector $\mathbf{x}^2$ thus obtained is used as a starting vector for iteration by A_1, however, the iteration will converge rapidly.

Example 13. For the matrix of example 10, find the characteristic number next in order of magnitude after λ_1. Also find the corresponding characteristic vector.

In example 12 we found $\lambda_1 = 11.8354$ and the characteristic vector

$$\mathbf{x}^1 = \begin{bmatrix} 1.0000 \\ 1.7502 \\ 2.2926 \end{bmatrix}.$$

Proceeding exactly as in examples 10 and 12 but using the transposed matrix A^T, we find the characteristic vector of A^T associated with λ_1 to be

$$\begin{bmatrix} 1.0000 \\ 0.8309 \\ 2.1706 \end{bmatrix}.$$

Normalizing this vector so that $(\mathbf{y}^1, \mathbf{x}^1) = 1$ we have

$$\mathbf{y}^1 = \begin{bmatrix} 0.1346 \\ 0.1118 \\ 0.2921 \end{bmatrix}.$$

Then we have

$$\mathbf{x}^1(\mathbf{y}^1)^T = \begin{bmatrix} 1 \\ 1.7502 \\ 2.2926 \end{bmatrix} (0.1346, \quad 0.1118, \quad 0.2921)$$

$$= \begin{bmatrix} 0.1346 & 0.1118 & 0.2921 \\ 0.2356 & 0.1957 & 0.5112 \\ 0.3086 & 0.2563 & 0.6697 \end{bmatrix}.$$

Using (4.14.1), we find that

$$A_1 = \begin{bmatrix} 0.4070 & 1.6768 & -1.4571 \\ 1.2116 & 0.6838 & -1.0503 \\ -0.6254 & -1.0334 & 1.0738 \end{bmatrix}.$$

Starting, as usual with the vector $\mathbf{y}$, all of whose components are unity, we obtain the sequence of iterates $A_1{}^k\mathbf{y}$:

$$\begin{bmatrix} 1 \\ 1 \\ 1 \end{bmatrix} \begin{bmatrix} 0.6267 \\ 0.8451 \\ -0.6120 \end{bmatrix} \begin{bmatrix} 2.5640 \\ 1.9800 \\ -1.9394 \end{bmatrix} \begin{bmatrix} 7.1895 \\ 6.4974 \\ -5.8014 \end{bmatrix} \begin{bmatrix} 22.2742 \\ 19.2469 \\ -17.6344 \end{bmatrix}$$

$$\begin{bmatrix} 67.0339 \\ 58.6699 \\ -53.3573 \end{bmatrix} \begin{bmatrix} 203.4074 \\ 177.3779 \\ 161.6575 \end{bmatrix}.$$

Taking the ratio of the first components of successive vectors we obtain, as approximations to λ_2, the numbers $z_3 = 3.0982$, $z_4 = 3.0095$, $z_5 = 3.0344$. Applying Aitken's δ^2-process yields the result 3.0289. Proceeding in a similar manner, using the second and third components of successive vectors, we obtain the approximations 3.0289 and 3.0288, respectively. These values for λ_2 are very close to the true value 3.0293. If we normalize each of the last three vectors $A_1{}^k\mathbf{y}$ and apply the δ^2-process to their components we obtain

$$\mathbf{x}^2 = \begin{bmatrix} 1.0000 \\ 0.8727 \\ -0.7950 \end{bmatrix}.$$

Considerable labor can be saved by using equation (4.14.2), but some loss of accuracy results. To apply this formula, we first calculate

$$\mathbf{x}^1(\mathbf{y}^1)^T \mathbf{y} = \mathbf{x}^1(\mathbf{y}^1)^T \begin{bmatrix} 1 \\ 1 \\ 1 \end{bmatrix} = \begin{bmatrix} 0.5383 \\ 0.9425 \\ 1.2346 \end{bmatrix}.$$

Then from (4.14.2) we easily obtain

$$A_1^4 \mathbf{y} = \begin{bmatrix} 22.8330 \\ 18.7551 \\ -17.6792 \end{bmatrix}, \qquad A_1^5 \mathbf{y} = \begin{bmatrix} 73.1874 \\ 52.0495 \\ -54.7681 \end{bmatrix}$$

which agree only approximately with the values obtained earlier. Taking the ratios of the components of these vectors, we obtain as approximations to λ_2 the values 3.2053, 2.7752, and 3.0979 with an average of 3.0261. These values are not as good as those previously obtained.

The power method, followed by deflation, is a useful method for finding the characteristic numbers and vectors of matrices, especially if only a few of these are needed. Blind application of the method is not recommended. Because of the many situations which can arise, it is necessary for the computer to observe carefully the behavior of the iterates. For matrices of low order, where the calculations can be carried out by hand or on a desk calculator, it can be used successfully. For matrices of high order, however, where it is desirable to use high-speed electronic computers, methods that will yield all of the characteristic numbers and vectors, no matter how they are distributed, are needed.

In Section 4.15 we describe briefly such methods for real symmetric matrices and in Section 4.16 give a very brief discussion of what can be done in the case of nonsymmetric matrices.

4.15 REAL SYMMETRIC MATRICES

We have seen that the characteristic numbers of a real symmetric matrix are all real and that such a matrix can always be reduced to diagonal form by a similarity transformation. Moreover, if W is the matrix whose columns are the characteristic vectors of the matrix A, then

$$W^{-1}AW = \Lambda \tag{4.15.1}$$

where Λ is the diagonal matrix whose principal diagonal elements are the characteristic numbers of A. It can be shown that W is an orthogonal matrix, that is, $W^T = W^{-1}$.

Hence, to find the characteristic numbers and vectors, it is only necessary to find an orthogonal matrix W which will reduce A to diagonal form according to equation (4.15.1). Unfortunately, for $n > 2$, there is no manageable expression for the general orthogonal matrix of order n.

A procedure for obtaining the set of characteristic numbers as the limiting set of diagonal elements of a sequence of matrices generated from A by means of a series of plane rotations was introduced by Jacobi [15] in 1846. Each step of the method is reminiscent of the familiar method in analytic geometry for removing the xy-term from the general second-degree equation of a conic section; this is accomplished by rotating the co-ordinate axes through a suitable angle.

To explain the form of a plane rotation we denote the rotation angle by φ and consider the rotation associated with the ith row and jth column. Then we define the matrix $U_{ij} = (u_{pq})$ in the following way:

$$u_{pp} = 1, \qquad\qquad p \neq i, j$$
$$u_{ii} = \cos\varphi, \qquad u_{ij} = -\sin\varphi,$$
$$u_{ji} = \sin\varphi, \qquad u_{jj} = \cos\varphi,$$
$$\text{all other } u_{pq} = 0.$$

In other words, the matrix U_{ij} has the following form

$$
\begin{bmatrix}
1 & & & & & & & & & & \\
& 1 & & & & & & & & & \\
& & \cdot & & & & & & & & \\
& & & \cdot & & & & & & & \\
& & & & \cdot & & & & & & \\
& & & & & 1 & & & & & \\
& & & & & & \cos\varphi & \cdots & -\sin\varphi & & \\
& & & & & & \cdot & 1 & \cdot & & \\
& & & & & & \cdot & & \cdot & \cdot & \cdot \\
& & & & & & \cdot & & & 1 & \cdot \\
& & & & & & \sin\varphi & \cdots & \cos\varphi & & \\
& & & & & & & & & 1 & \\
& & & & & & & & & & \cdot \\
& & & & & & & & & & & \cdot \\
& & & & & & & & & & & & \cdot \\
& & & & & & & & & & & & & 1
\end{bmatrix}
$$

Clearly U_{ij} is an orthogonal matrix. As in elementary analytic geometry, it can be shown that the angle φ can be chosen in such a manner that the elements $a_{ij} = a_{ji}$ of A are replaced by zeros in the transformed matrix. We have only to choose φ so that

$$\tan 2\varphi = \frac{2a_{ij}}{a_{ii} - a_{jj}}$$

to annihilate the elements $a_{ij} = a_{ji}$. Jacobi annihilated the maximum off-diagonal element of $A_0 = A$ using an angle φ_0 and matrix $U_{i_0 j_0}$, obtaining a new matrix

$$A_1 = U_{i_0 j_0}^{-1} A U_{i_0 j_0}.$$

He then annihilated the maximum off-diagonal element of A_1 using an angle φ_1 and matrix $U_{i_1 j_1}$, obtaining the matrix

$$A_2 = U_{i_1 j_1}^{-1} A_1 U_{i_1 j_1}.$$

By continuing this process, sequences of matrices $U_{i_k j_k}$ and A_k are obtained such that

$$A_{k+1} = U_{i_k j_k}^{-1} A_k U_{i_k j_k}.$$

Jacobi showed that by repeating this procedure a sufficiently large number of times, we eventually reach a stage N for which all off-diagonal elements are less than any fixed preassigned value. At this stage the diagonal elements of A_N are close to the characteristic values and the matrix

$$U = U_{i_0 j_0} U_{i_1 j_1} U_{i_2 j_2} \cdots U_{i_N j_N}$$

is approximately the required matrix of characteristic vectors.

Scanning the matrix after each rotation for the largest off-diagonal element is time-consuming, and so a number of variations of the original Jacobi method have been proposed. One method consists in systematically annihilating all the off-diagonal elements in the first row, then in the second, etc. Of course, if any element is already within the required limits of accuracy, it is passed over. It must be remembered that an element once annihilated may be increased again under subsequent rotations. Consequently, after passing through the matrix once, there is no guarantee that all off-diagonal elements are zero. It is necessary to iterate the process until all elements are sufficiently small as in the original Jacobi method.

Another variation of the Jacobi method proceeds systematically in the same serial fashion as the above method, but annihilates only those elements whose values exceed some preassigned threshold value t. The iteration continues until all off-diagonal elements are less than t. Then the threshold is decreased and the process is repeated for the lower value of the threshold.

The procedure is repeated, continually reducing the threshold until the desired accuracy is obtained.

Another method proposed by Givens [9] is also based on the use of plane rotations to eliminate off-diagonal elements of the original matrix. The angle in the rotation matrix U_{ij} is chosen in such a way that the elements $a_{i-1,j} = a_{j,i-1}$ of the matrix to which the rotation is applied are annihilated. The elements are annihilated in the order $a_{13}, a_{14}, \cdots,$ $a_{1n}, a_{24}, \cdots, a_{2n}, a_{35}, \cdots, a_{3n},$ etc. Once an element is annihilated it is never altered in successive rotations; thus in one pass through the matrix all possible elements are annihilated. Instead of a diagonal matrix, however, we obtain a tri-diagonal matrix in which not only the principal diagonal but also the two symmetric parallel diagonals adjacent to it may contain nonzero elements. This simplified matrix is then used to find the characteristic numbers and vectors by methods which we shall not describe here.

Since the methods described in this section are principally of use when the calculations are performed on high-speed electronic computers, no numerical examples of their use have been included.

4.16 REAL NONSYMMETRIC MATRICES

If all the characteristic numbers and vectors of a matrix are required, an automatic method that will work in all cases is desirable. The power method described in Section 4.13 depends too much on the skill of the computer to be useful with high-speed computing machinery. The Jacobi method and its variations described in Section 4.15 provide suitable methods for finding all the characteristic numbers and vectors of a real symmetric matrix. For nonsymmetric matrices, the situation is much less favorable. A number of methods have been proposed, but most of them have not yet been adequately tested.

We describe one such method which has been proposed by Lanczos [17]. This method will reduce any matrix to tri-diagonal form.

First, we must introduce the concept of a bi-orthogonal system of vectors. Two sets of vectors $\mathbf{x}^1, \mathbf{x}^2, \cdots, \mathbf{x}^n$ and $\mathbf{y}^1, \mathbf{y}^2, \cdots, \mathbf{y}^n$ are called a bi-orthogonal system if $(\mathbf{x}^i, \mathbf{y}^j) = 0$ when $i \neq j$. We start with two arbitrary vectors $\mathbf{x}^1$ and $\mathbf{y}^1$ and construct two sets of n vectors which form a bi-orthogonal system in the following manner. Proceeding by induction, if $\mathbf{x}^1, \mathbf{x}^2, \cdots, \mathbf{x}^k$ and $\mathbf{y}^1, \mathbf{y}^2, \cdots, \mathbf{y}^k$ have already been constructed to form a bi-orthogonal system, the next two vectors are defined by the equations

$$\mathbf{x}^{k+1} = A\mathbf{x}^k - a_k\mathbf{x}^k - b_{k-1}\mathbf{x}^{k-1}, \tag{4.16.1}$$

$$(\mathbf{y}^{k+1})^T = (\mathbf{y}^k)^T\bar{A} - \bar{a}_k(\mathbf{y}^k)^T - \bar{b}_{k-1}(\mathbf{y}^{k-1})^T \tag{4.16.2}$$

where

$$a_k = \frac{(\bar{\mathbf{y}}^k)^T A \mathbf{x}^k}{(\mathbf{x}^k, \mathbf{y}^k)}, \qquad b_{k-1} = \frac{(\bar{\mathbf{y}}^{k-1})^T A \mathbf{x}^k}{(\mathbf{x}^{k-1}, \mathbf{y}^{k-1})}, \qquad b_0 = 0. \qquad (4.16.3)$$

It can be shown that the two sets of vectors remain bi-orthogonal.

The recursion formula (4.16.1) for the set of vectors $\mathbf{x}^1, \mathbf{x}^2, \cdots, \mathbf{x}^n$ can be written in the form

$$A\mathbf{x}^1 = \mathbf{x}^2 + a_1\mathbf{x}^1$$
$$A\mathbf{x}^2 = \mathbf{x}^3 + a_2\mathbf{x}^2 + b_1\mathbf{x}^1$$
$$\cdots \cdots \cdots \cdots \cdots$$
$$A\mathbf{x}^k = \mathbf{x}^{k+1} + a_k\mathbf{x}^k + b_{k-1}\mathbf{x}^{k-1}$$
$$\cdots \cdots \cdots \cdots \cdots$$
$$A\mathbf{x}^n = a_n\mathbf{x}^n + b_{n-1}\mathbf{x}^{n-1}$$

because it can be shown that both $\mathbf{x}^{n+1}$ and $\mathbf{y}^{n+1}$ are zero. The alternative matrix form is

$$AS = ST \qquad (4.16.4)$$

where S is an $n \times n$ matrix whose columns are the vectors $\mathbf{x}^1, \mathbf{x}^2, \cdots, \mathbf{x}^n$ and T is the tri-diagonal matrix

$$T = \begin{bmatrix} a_1 & b_1 & 0 & 0 & \cdots & 0 & 0 & 0 \\ 1 & a_2 & b_2 & 0 & \cdots & 0 & 0 & 0 \\ 0 & 1 & a_3 & b_3 & \cdots & 0 & 0 & 0 \\ \cdot & \cdot & \cdot & \cdot & \cdot & \cdot & \cdot & \cdot \\ 0 & 0 & 0 & 0 & \cdots & a_{n-2} & b_{n-2} & 0 \\ 0 & 0 & 0 & 0 & \cdots & 1 & a_{n-1} & b_{n-1} \\ 0 & 0 & 0 & 0 & \cdots & 0 & 1 & a_n \end{bmatrix}.$$

From (4.16.4) we see that $T = S^{-1}AS$ so that T is obtained from A by a similarity transformation. The characteristic numbers of T are therefore the same as those of A, and the characteristic vectors of A are simply related to those of T.

After the tri-diagonal form is reached, it is not too hard to find its characteristic equation and the roots of this equation but we shall omit a discussion of these matters.

Various modifications of this procedure have been proposed.

Givens [10] has proposed a method for finding characteristic values and vectors of a general complex matrix by transforming the matrix to semi-triangular form.

chapter 5 Solution of ordinary differential equations

5.1 INTRODUCTION

A large number of problems of applied mathematics and also many problems of pure mathematics can be conveniently formulated in terms of differential equations. Indeed the differential equation is the primary mathematical instrument for the precise expression of the laws of nature, for these laws are nearly always statements of relationships between variables and their relative rates of change, namely, their derivatives.

A differential equation is an equation involving variables and their derivatives. If there is a single independent variable so that the derivatives are total derivatives, the equation is called an ordinary differential equation. Examples of such equations are

$$y' = 2x^2 + y, \tag{5.1.1}$$

$$y''' - 7y' = 6y, \tag{5.1.2}$$

and

$$y'' + 4y = 6 \sin x \tag{5.1.3}$$

where, as usual, primes denote differentiation with respect to x. If there are two or more independent variables so that the derivatives are partial derivatives, the equation is called a partial differential equation. Examples of such equations are

$$\frac{\partial^2 u}{\partial x^2} + \frac{\partial^2 u}{\partial y^2} = 0 \tag{5.1.4}$$

and

$$\frac{\partial^2 Z}{\partial x^2} + \frac{\partial Z}{\partial t} = Zt. \tag{5.1.5}$$

In this chapter we study only ordinary differential equations.

By the order of a differential equation is meant the order of the highest derivative which appears. Thus (5.1.1) is of first order, (5.1.2) is of third order, and (5.1.3), (5.1.4) and (5.1.5) are all of second order. The most general ordinary differential equation of the nth order can be written in the form

$$f(x, y, y', y'', \cdots, y^{(n)}) = 0 \tag{5.1.6}$$

if only two variables are involved

We may also consider simultaneous differential equations in which there are two or more dependent variables satisfying two or more differential equations. For example, we may consider a system of m first order differential equations involving m dependent variables $y_1, y_2, \cdots, y_m$. Such a system may be written in the form

$$\begin{aligned}
y_1' &= f_1(y_1, y_2, \cdots, y_m, x), \\
y_2' &= f_2(y_1, y_2, \cdots, y_m, x), \\
&\cdot \quad \cdot \quad \cdot \quad \cdot \quad \cdot \quad \cdot \quad \cdot \quad \cdot \quad \cdot \quad \cdot \\
y_m' &= f_m(y_1, y_2, \cdots, y_m, x).
\end{aligned} \tag{5.1.7}$$

It should be observed that the nth order differential equation (5.1.6) can be replaced by an equivalent set of n first-order equations. This is accomplished by making the substitutions

$$y_1 = y, \qquad y_2 = y', \qquad y_3 = y'', \qquad \cdots, \qquad y_n = y^{(n-1)}.$$

Then, if (5.1.6) is solved for $y^{(n)}$, yielding

$$y^{(n)} = F(x, y, y', \cdots, y^{(n-1)}),$$

an equivalent system is

$$\begin{aligned}
y_1' &= y_2 \\
y_2' &= y_3 \\
&\cdots \\
y_{n-1}' &= y_n \\
y_n' &= F(x, y_1, y_2, \cdots, y_n).
\end{aligned}$$

Conversely, from a system of m first-order differential equations such as (5.1.7), it is theoretically possible to obtain a differential equation of order not exceeding m and containing only one dependent variable, although it may be impossible to carry out the actual eliminations in practice.

By a solution or integral of the differential equation (5.1.6) we mean a function $y = g(x)$ such that if $g(x)$ and its derivatives are substituted into (5.1.6), there results an identity in x. For example, $y = e^x - 2x^2 - 4x - 4$ is a solution of (5.1.1), for on making the substitution we have $e^x - 4x - 4 = 2x^2 + e^x - 2x^2 - 4x - 4$ which is an identity in x. Similarly, $y = e^{-x}$ is a solution of (5.1.2), as is easily verified.

The solution of a differential equation is, however, not unique as is easily seen by considering the very simple differential equation

$$y' = f(x)$$

where $f(x)$ is any continuous function. Then clearly

$$y = \int f(x)\, dx + C = F(x) + C$$

where $F(x)$ is any indefinite integral of $f(x)$ and C is an arbitrary constant of integration. Thus the solution $F(x) + C$ of the differential equation $y' = f(x)$ represents a one-parameter family of curves. This family includes every continuous solution of the differential equation. A solution which results from giving a particular value to the arbitrary constant is called a particular solution. By particularizing this constant we are able to make the solution satisfy one additional condition. It is frequently convenient to choose this constant to make a specified value y_0 of y correspond to a certain value x_0 of x. Geometrically this means that the curve passes through the point (x_0, y_0).

The situation just described is typical. The general solution of a first-order differential equation will involve one arbitrary constant and the general solution of an nth order differential equation will involve n arbitrary constants. In certain exceptional cases there will be solutions of the differential equations which are not included in the general solution, but we do not discuss these here.

As an example, we note that the general solution of the differential equation (5.1.2) is

$$y = C_1 e^{-x} + C_2 e^{-2x} + C_3 e^{3x}$$

as is easily verified by direct substitution in the differential equation. The solution $y = e^{-x}$ is obtained by choosing $C_1 = 1$, $C_2 = C_3 = 0$.

5.2 FIRST-ORDER EQUATIONS.   EXISTENCE THEOREM

We begin by considering first-order differential equations which have the general form $F(x, y, y') = 0$. We shall suppose that it is possible to solve for y' and hence we may write a first-order equation in the form

$$y' = f(x, y). \tag{5.2.1}$$

If it is possible to write (5.2.1) in the form

$$M(x)\, dx + N(y)\, dy = 0 \tag{5.2.2}$$

where $M(x)$ is a function of x alone and $N(y)$ is a function of y alone, then we say that the variables are separable. Here it is at once clear that the solution is

$$\int M(x)\, dx + \int N(y)\, dy = C \tag{5.2.3}$$

where C is an arbitrary constant. The problem is then reduced to the problem of evaluating the two integrals in (5.2.3).

Example 1. Find the general solution of the differential equation

$$\frac{dy}{dx} = \frac{x\sqrt{1 + x^2}}{y}.$$

Find also the particular solution for which $y = 3$ when $x = 0$.

Separating the variables, we have

$$y\, dy - x\sqrt{1 + x^2}\, dx = 0.$$

Integrating

$$\tfrac{1}{2}y^2 - \tfrac{1}{3}(1 + x^2)^{3/2} = C$$

or

$$y^2 - (1 + x^2)^{3/2} = C', \qquad C' = 2C.$$

This is the general solution. To find the particular solution we set $x = 0$ and $y = 3$, obtaining $C' = 8$, so that the particular solution is

$$y^2 - (1 + x^2)^{3/2} = 8.$$

In many of the simpler equations encountered in applied mathematics, we find that the variables can be separated so that this method is often useful. But there are, of course, a great many differential equations in which the variables are not separable. There are a number of artifices available for solving certain classes of first-order equations. Since these methods apply to limited classes of equations and since they are adequately described in most elementary books on differential equations, we omit them here. Instead we turn our attention to the problem of getting as much information as possible about the solution of an equation (5.2.1) without actually finding an explicit solution of the equation. To achieve this may involve a determination of the general appearance of the solution curves by graphical means or it may involve an approximation to the solution.

We first consider a graphical procedure. The general solution of (5.2.1) is an equation connecting x and y and an arbitrary constant C. For each value of the arbitrary constant we have a particular solution $y = g(x)$. The graph of such a particular solution is called an integral curve of the differential equation. Corresponding to the infinitely many values which the arbitrary constant may assume, we have infinitely many integral curves. At each point of an integral curve, equation (5.2.1) enables us to calculate the slope of the tangent to the curve. If (x, y) is any point in the domain of definition of $f(x, y)$ then (5.2.1) gives the slope of the tangent to the integral curve which passes through this point. Thus associated with each point in the domain of definition of $f(x, y)$ there is a definite direction, namely the direction of the tangent line whose slope is calculated from (5.2.1). We say that (5.2.1) defines a direction field. The direction field can be represented graphically by drawing at (x, y) a short line segment whose slope is $f(x, y)$. Such a line segment will be called a lineal element.

An integral curve will have at any point the same direction as the direction field. Thus if we draw the direction field for a differential equation, we can easily sketch the integral curves, since any curve which is drawn so that it is tangent at each of its points to the lineal element there is an integral curve.

To draw the direction field of the differential equation (5.2.1) it is convenient to first draw some of the isoclines which are curves in the direction field along which $f(x, y)$ is constant. Note that an isocline is not an integral curve. The family of isoclines is the family of curves $f(x, y) = k$. By giving k a series of values we may sketch a series of isoclines. Then on each isocline we may draw several parallel lineal elements each having slope k, where k is the constant associated with the particular isocline. We thus obtain a sketch of the direction field from which we may sketch the integral curves as indicated previously.

Example 2.   Draw several isoclines and sketch the direction field of the differential equation

$$\frac{dy}{dx} = -\frac{x}{2y}.$$

Draw the integral curve which passes through the point (1,3).

The isoclines are the straight lines $-x/2y = k$ or $y = -x/2k$. They are drawn in Fig. 5.1 with dotted lines for $k = -1, -\frac{1}{2}, -\frac{1}{4}, 0, \frac{1}{4}, \frac{1}{2}, 1,$ ∞. Several lineal elements are indicated on each isocline. The heavy solid curve is approximately the integral curve passing through (1, 3) and was drawn to coincide as well as possible with the direction field.

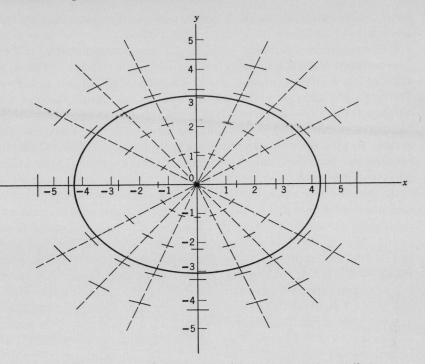

Fig. 5.1. Isoclines and lineal elements for the equation $y' = -x/2y$.

Since the variables are separable in the differential equation of this example we may find the general solution and compare it with the graphical solution obtained here. We have at once

$$x \, dx + 2y \, dy = 0.$$

The general solution is found to be $x^2 + 2y^2 = C$ which is seen to be a family of ellipses. The appearance of the direction field is clearly consistent with this result. The equation of the integral curve which passes through $(1, 3)$ is $x^2 + 2y^2 = 19$.

It may often be desirable to obtain a numerical approximation to a particular solution of the differential equation (5.2.1). In such cases the solution would take the form of a table of values of corresponding values of x and y together with the values of y' associated with them.

Suppose, then, that we wish to find a solution of (5.2.1) such that $y = y_0$ when $x = x_0$; in other words, the integral curve is to pass through the point (x_0, y_0). By substituting in (5.2.1), we find the slope of the tangent at (x_0, y_0) to the integral curve is $f(x_0, y_0)$ which we shall denote by y_0'. To find the value y_1 of y corresponding to $x = x_1 = x_0 + h$ where h is a small quantity, we may use the tangent as an approximation to the actual integral curve and thus obtain as an approximation to y_1 the value $y_0 + hy_0'$. Having thus obtained the point (x_1, y_1) which is very close to the integral curve, we may repeat the process computing the slope y_1' of the curve through (x_1, y_1) by means of (5.2.1). Then, if $x_2 = x_1 + h$, we have approximately $y_2 = y_1 + hy_1'$, and we take (x_2, y_2) as a point on the integral curve. This step-by-step procedure may be repeated as often as desired to obtain further points on the integral curve. We express this step-by-step procedure by means of a general formula. Suppose that the solution of (5.2.1) has been carried from (x_0, y_0) to (x_n, y_n) where $x_n = x_0 + nh$, then for the next point we have $x_{n+1} = x_n + h = x_0 + (n + 1)h$ and

$$y_{n+1} = y_n + hy_n' = y_n + hf(x_n, y_n). \qquad (5.2.4)$$

This method of step-by-step solution, often called Euler's method, is a very crude method. Its accuracy depends on the size of the step h which is used, and h must usually be taken very small in order to obtain desired accuracy. If we are forced to choose h small, a large number of steps will be necessary to continue the solution over any desired domain of x values. This method therefore entails a large amount of calculation, and also the large number of steps may cause the introduction of serious round-off errors. It is therefore desirable to introduce more accurate formulas for the numerical procedure of calculating the solution. This will be done in Sections 5.7–5.11.

Example 3. For the differential equation

$$\frac{dy}{dx} = -\frac{x}{2y}$$

obtain a numerical approximation to the solution between $x = 1$ and $x = 3$ if $y = 3$ when $x = 1$.

To avoid large amounts of calculation we choose $h = 0.4$ so that $x_0 = 1$, $x_1 = 1.4$, $x_2 = 1.8$, $x_3 = 2.2$, $x_4 = 2.6$, and $x_5 = 3.0$. Then from the differential equation we find that $y_0' = -0.167$. Hence $y_1 = 3 + (0.4)(-0.167) = 2.933$. Again from the differential equation $y_1' = -0.239$. The next value of y is $y_2 = 2.933 + (0.4)(-0.239) = 2.837$. Continuing in this manner we obtain the following table of values of x, y, and y' (Table 5.1). We have also included the values obtained from the exact solution $x^2 + 2y^2 = 19$ which was obtained previously.

We see that the calculated solution exhibits rather large errors. The error could be reduced by decreasing the size of h but with a corresponding increase in the labor. The more accurate formulas of Sections 5.9 and

5.10 would enable us to obtain greater accuracy with a very modest increase in the labor of calculation.

The previous discussion has furnished us with geometric evidence that the differential equation (5.2.1) has infinitely many solutions and that these solutions form a one-parameter family. The particular value of the parameter which determines a particular solution may be determined in a variety of ways, for example, by specifying one pair of corresponding values of x and y. We have no right to believe that (5.2.1) always possesses

TABLE 5.1

Numerical Solution of $y' = -\dfrac{x}{2y}$,

$y = 3$ when $x = 1$

x	y	y'	True y
1.0	3.000	−0.167	3.000
1.4	2.933	−0.239	2.919
1.8	2.837	−0.317	2.807
2.2	2.710	−0.406	2.661
2.6	2.548	−0.510	2.474
3.0	2.344	−0.640	2.236

such a family of solutions, but we may expect it under certain circumstances. We now state without proof the fundamental existence theorem for first-order differential equations which tells us under what circumstances (5.2.1) will possess solutions.

EXISTENCE THEOREM. In a closed region R of the xy-plane, let $f(x, y)$ be continuous and satisfy there a Lipschitz condition; that is, suppose that there exists a constant A such that

$$|f(x, y) - f(x, z)| \leq A |y - z|$$

for all (x, y) and (x, z) in R. Let (x_0, y_0) be an interior point of R. Then the differential equation

$$\frac{dy}{dx} = f(x, y)$$

has a unique solution $y = Y(x)$ such that $y = y_0$ when $x = x_0$; in other words, in a suitable interval $x_0 - h_1 < x < x_0 + h_2$ there exists one and only one function $Y(x)$ continuous and having a continuous derivative in the interval, such that $Y'(x) = f[x, Y(x)]$ in the interval and $Y(x_0) = y_0$.

We remark that the Lipschitz condition is satisfied if, in particular, $\partial f/\partial y$ is continuous in R.

A similar existence theorem may be stated for systems of first-order differential equations. We have previously remarked that a differential equation of higher order may be reduced to a system of differential equations of first order, and so we may state existence theorems of similar type for such differential equations as well.

5.3 LINEAR DIFFERENTIAL EQUATIONS WITH CONSTANT COEFFICIENTS

The general linear differential equation of order n is of the form

$$\frac{d^n y}{dx^n} + P_1(x)\frac{d^{n-1}y}{dx^{n-1}} + \cdots + P_{n-1}(x)\frac{dy}{dx} + P_n(x)y = R(x). \quad (5.3.1)$$

Clearly no loss of generality results from taking the coefficient of the derivative of highest order to be 1, since this can always be accomplished by division. We note that the term $R(x)$ is different from the other terms of the equation in that it is free of y and its derivatives. For this reason, if $R(x)$ is not identically zero, the equation (5.3.1) is called nonhomogeneous whereas, if $R(x)$ is identically zero, (5.3.1) is homogeneous. In studying the nonhomogeneous equation (5.3.1), we often study the reduced equation which is the corresponding homogeneous equation obtained by replacing $R(x)$ by zero in (5.3.1). By contrast, the original equation (5.3.1) is called the complete equation.

In this section we shall consider the special case in which all the functions $P_1(x), P_2(x), \cdots, P_n(x)$ are constants. Although such differential equations are treated in great detail in most elementary textbooks on differential equations, we shall study these here because of their great importance in nearly every field of physical science and engineering. They appear very frequently in the study of electrical circuits and vibrating mechanical systems.

To describe the important ideas as clearly as possible and with a minimum of complications, we shall at first consider second-order linear differential equations with constant coefficients. The equations which we shall consider are therefore of the form

$$y'' + Py' + Qy = R(x). \quad (5.3.2)$$

If we replace $R(x)$ by zero, we have the reduced equation

$$y'' + Py' + Qy = 0. \quad (5.3.3)$$

If $y_1(x)$ and $y_2(x)$ are any two solutions of (5.3.3), then $C_1y_1(x) + C_2y_2(x)$, where C_1 and C_2 are arbitrary constants, is also a solution. This may be verified by direct substitution in the equation. As a direct consequence of the general existence theorem, it may be shown that if $y_1(x)$ and $y_2(x)$ are linearly independent solutions of (5.3.3), the general solution of (5.3.3) is of the form $C_1y_1(x) + C_2y_2(x)$, where C_1 and C_2 are arbitrary constants. The definition of linearly independent functions is completely analogous to the definition given in Section 4.1 for linearly independent vectors. Thus the functions $y_1(x)$ and $y_2(x)$ are linearly independent if $Ay_1(x) + By_2(x) = 0$ implies that $A = B = 0$.

Notice that the foregoing properties hold only for homogeneous equations. For the nonhomogeneous equation (5.3.2) it is easily verified by direct substitution that if $y_0(x)$ and $y_1(x)$ are any two solutions of (5.3.2), then $y_0(x) - y_1(x)$ is a solution of (5.3.3). Also if $y_1(x)$ is any solution of (5.3.3) and $u(x)$ is any solution of (5.3.2), then $u(x) + y_1(x)$ is a solution of (5.3.2). From this it follows that the general solution of the complete equation (5.3.2) is obtained by adding to a particular solution of (5.3.2) the general solution of the reduced equation (5.3.3). Thus to find the general solution of the complete equation (5.3.2) we must solve two problems: first, the problem of finding the complementary function which is the general solution of the reduced equation, and second, the problem of finding any particular solution of the complete equation.

We turn now to the problem of finding the solution of the reduced equation (5.3.3). It is natural to try a solution of the form $y = e^{mx}$, where m is a constant to be determined, because all derivatives of this function are alike except for a numerical coefficient. Substituting in equation (5.3.3) and dividing out the common factor e^{mx} which can never be zero, we obtain

$$m^2 + Pm + Q = 0 \qquad (5.3.4)$$

which is called the auxiliary equation. Solving this equation for m we have

$$m = \frac{-P \pm \sqrt{P^2 - 4Q}}{2}.$$

If we denote these roots by m_1 and m_2, we have two solutions e^{m_1x} and e^{m_2x}. If $m_1 \neq m_2$, these solutions are independent and the general solution of (5.3.3) is

$$y = C_1e^{m_1x} + C_2e^{m_2x}.$$

If $m_1 = m_2$, we do not have two independent solutions. But direct substitutions shows that here xe^{m_1x} is also a solution of the equation and hence the general solution is

$$y = (C_1 + C_2x)e^{m_1x}.$$

Example 4. Find the general solution of

$$y'' - 2y' - 8y = 0.$$

The auxiliary equation is $m^2 - 2m - 8 = 0$, so the roots are $m_1 = 4$ and $m_2 = -2$. Hence the general solution is

$$y = C_1 e^{4x} + C_2 e^{-2x}.$$

Example 5. Find the general solution of

$$y'' + 6y' + 9y = 0.$$

The auxiliary equation is $m^2 + 6m + 9 = 0$ which has the equal roots $-3, -3$. Hence the general solution is

$$y = (C_1 + C_2 x)e^{-3x}.$$

If the roots of the auxiliary equation (5.3.4) are complex, the preceding expressions still give the general solution, but the form is inconvenient because complex quantities are involved. Here the roots are conjugate complex and may be written $\alpha \pm i\beta$ where α and β are real. Thus the general solution is

$$y = C_1 e^{(\alpha + i\beta)x} + C_2 e^{(\alpha - i\beta)x}$$
$$= e^{\alpha x}(C_1 e^{i\beta x} + C_2 e^{-i\beta x}).$$

Using the formulas

$$e^{\pm i\beta x} = \cos \beta x \pm i \sin \beta x$$

and setting $A = C_1 + C_2$ and $B = i(C_1 - C_2)$, the general solution may be written in the form

$$y = e^{\alpha x}(A \cos \beta x + B \sin \beta x).$$

Alternative forms, which are often useful, are

$$y = Ce^{\alpha x} \cos (\beta x + \gamma) = Ce^{\alpha x} \sin (\beta x + \delta).$$

These merely involve changes in the definition of the constants. For example, $C = \sqrt{A^2 + B^2}$.

Example 6. Find the general solution of

$$y'' + 4y' + 13y = 0.$$

The auxiliary equation is $m^2 + 4m + 13 = 0$ which has complex roots $-2 \pm 3i$, so that the general solution is

$$y = e^{-2x}(A \cos 3x + B \sin 3x).$$

Next we turn our attention to the problem of finding a particular integral of the complete equation (5.3.2). In many practical problems the function

$R(x)$ is some combination of polynomials, exponentials, sines, and cosines. In many such problems the method of undetermined coefficients is applicable and, when it is, it is probably the most convenient method.

The method consists in assuming a likely expression for the particular integral and then substituting this guess into (5.3.2). The result of this substitution provides us with the necessary equations to determine the values of one or more unknown coefficients which were included in the trial solution. The form of $R(x)$ will indicate what form of trial solution should be used. If $R(x)$ contains e^{rx}, the trial solution should contain Ae^{rx}. If $R(x)$ contains a polynomial of degree n, then the trial solution should also contain such a polynomial whose coefficients are to be found. If $R(x)$ contains $\sin rx$ or $\cos rx$, the trial solution should contain $A \cos rx + B \sin rx$. If $R(x)$ contains products of these basic functions, so should also the trial solution. If any term in the trial solution happens to be a solution of the reduced equation, the portion of the trial solution which contains this term should be multiplied by x to obtain a revised trial solution.

We give several examples which will clarify the application of the method

Example 7. Find a particular solution of

$$y'' + 2y' - 8y = x^2 - x.$$

Since the right-hand member is a polynomial of degree 2, we seek a trial solution of the form

$$y_p = Ax^2 + Bx + C.$$

Substituting this in the differential equation we obtain

$$2A + 2(2Ax + B) - 8(Ax^2 + Bx + C) = x^2 - x.$$

This equation will be an identity in x if the coefficients of like powers of x are equal. Equating corresponding coefficients, we obtain

$$-8A = 1$$
$$4A - 8B = -1$$
$$2A + 2B - 8C = 0.$$

Solving these equations for A, B, and C and substituting the values found into the trial solution we find the particular solution

$$y_p = \frac{-8x^2 + 4x - 1}{64}.$$

Example 8. Find the general solution of

$$y'' - 2y' - 8y = 3 \cos x.$$

In example 4 the complementary function was found to be

$$y_c = C_1 e^{4x} + C_2 e^{-2x}.$$

To find a particular solution of the complete equation we seek a trial solution of the form

$$y_p = A \cos x + B \sin x.$$

Substitution into the differential equation yields

$$(-9A - 2B) \cos x + (-9B + 2A) \sin x = 3 \cos x.$$

Equating coefficients, we have

$$-9A - 2B = 3$$
$$2A - 9B = 0$$

and we find that $A = -\frac{27}{85}$, $B = -\frac{6}{85}$. The general solution is

$$y = C_1 e^{4x} + C_2 e^{-2x} - \frac{27 \cos x + 6 \sin x}{85}.$$

Example 9. Find the general solution of

$$y'' - 2y' - 8y = 12e^{-2x}.$$

The complementary function is as in example 8. To find a particular solution we would expect to try Ae^{-2x}, but we observe that this is a solution of the reduced equation Hence instead we try

$$y_p = Axe^{-2x}.$$

Substitution into the differential equation yields

$$4Axe^{-2x} - 4Ae^{-2x} + 4Axe^{-2x} - 2Ae^{-2x} - 8Axe^{-2x} = 12e^{-2x}.$$

Equating coefficients we find that $-6A = 12$ or $A = -2$. The general solution is therefore

$$y = C_1 e^{4x} + C_2 e^{-2x} - 2xe^{-2x}.$$

Example 10. Find the general solution of

$$y'' + 4y = 4 \sin 2x + 8e^{2x}.$$

The auxiliary equation is $m^2 + 4 = 0$ and hence the complementary function is

$$y_c = C_1 \cos 2x + C_2 \sin 2x.$$

Since $\sin 2x$, which appears on the right side of the equation is a solution of the reduced equation but e^{2x} is not, we take for our trial solution

$$y_p = Ax \cos 2x + Bx \sin 2x + Ce^{2x}.$$

Substitution into the differential equation yields

$$-4A \sin 2x + 4B \cos 2x + 8Ce^{2x} = 4 \sin 2x + 8e^{2x}.$$

Equating coefficients, we have

$$-4A = 4$$
$$4B = 0$$
$$8C = 8$$

and we find that $A = -1$, $B = 0$, $C = 1$. The general solution is

$$y = C_1 \cos 2x + C_2 \sin 2x - x \cos 2x + e^{2x}.$$

The methods of this section are applicable to higher-order linear differential equations with constant coefficients. The auxiliary equation may be formed in exactly the same way, but will, or course, be a polynomial equation of degree greater than 2. Methods for solution of such an equation are discussed in Chapter 3. The method of undetermined coefficients used for finding a particular solution of the complete equation is also available for higher-order differential equations. No changes are necessary except that, of course, the labor is considerably greater. It is still true that the general solution of the complete equation is obtained by adding to the general solution of the reduced equation a particular solution of the complete equation. It does not appear to be necessary to include examples of such differential equations.

5.4   GENERAL LINEAR DIFFERENTIAL EQUATIONS

As in Section 5.3, it will be convenient to confine our discussion to linear equations of second order, that is, we consider the special case, $n = 2$, of the differential equation (5.3.1).

Only in special cases is it possible to obtain solutions of the reduced equation in terms of elementary functions. We, therefore, cannot give specific methods of solution as we did in Section 5.3.

If we are able to find the general solution of the reduced equation, there is a very useful method known as the method of variation of parameters, which may be used to find a particular integral of the complete equation. We proceed to describe this method

We consider the linear differential equation

$$y'' + P(x)y' + Q(x)y = R(x). \tag{5.4.1}$$

Suppose that $u_1(x)$ and $u_2(x)$ are linearly independent solutions of the reduced equation so that the general solution of the reduced equation is

$$y = C_1 u_1(x) + C_2 u_2(x) \tag{5.4.2}$$

where C_1 and C_2 are arbitrary constants. To form a trial solution of the complete equation (5.4.1), we replace the constants or parameters C_1 and C_2 by (variable) functions $C_1(x)$ and $C_2(x)$. It is from this that the method derives its name.

We then seek to determine functions $C_1(x)$ and $C_2(x)$ such that

$$y = C_1(x)u_1(x) + C_2(x)u_2(x) \tag{5.4.3}$$

shall be a solution of (5.4.1). Differentiating (5.4.3) we have

$$y' = C_1u_1' + C_2u_2' + C_1'u_1 + C_2'u_2. \tag{5.4.4}$$

Since we seek a solution of (5.4.1) and have two functions $C_1(x)$ and $C_2(x)$ at our disposal, we may impose one additional restriction on $C_1(x)$ and $C_2(x)$. We choose to set

$$C_1'u_1 + C_2'u_2 = 0. \tag{5.4.5}$$

Note that these are the terms which appear in (5.4.4) because $C_1(x)$ and $C_2(x)$ are not constant. Differentiating (5.4.4) and remembering that (5.4.5) holds, we have

$$y'' = C_1u_1'' + C_2u_2'' + C_1'u_1' + C_2'u_2'. \tag{5.4.6}$$

Substituting (5.4.6) into (5.4.1), we have

$$C_1u_1'' + C_2u_2'' + C_1'u_1' + C_2'u_2'$$
$$+ P(C_1u_1' + C_2u_2') + Q(C_1u_1 + C_2u_2) = R(x)$$

or

$$C_1(u_1'' + Pu_1' + Qu_1) + C_2(u_2'' + Pu_2' + Qu_2) + C_1'u_1' + C_2'u_2' = R(x).$$

Remembering that u_1 and u_2 are solutions of the reduced equation, we see that the coefficients of C_1 and C_2 are zero. Hence this reduces to

$$C_1'u_1' + C_2'u_2' = R(x). \tag{5.4.7}$$

Equations (5.4.5) and (5.4.7) constitute two linear equations which may be solved for C_1' and C_2'. We may then obtain C_1 and C_2 by integration. Substitution of these functions $C_1(x)$ and $C_2(x)$ into (5.4.2) provides a solution of the complete equation (5.4.1).

We emphasize that this method is applicable to general linear equations and not just to equations with constant coefficients. We illustrate the method by applying it to an example with constant coefficients, since it is only here that we can be sure of finding the general solution of the reduced equation.

Example 11.   Find the general solution of

$$y'' + y = \sec x.$$

The general solution of the reduced equation is

$$y = C_1 \cos x + C_2 \sin x.$$

We try the solution

$$y_p = C_1(x) \cos x + C_2(x) \sin x.$$

Then

$$y_p{}' = -C_1 \sin x + C_2 \cos x + C_1{}' \cos x + C_2{}' \sin x,$$

and we set

$$C_1{}' \cos x + C_2{}' \sin x = 0.$$

For the second derivative we find

$$y_p{}'' = -C_1 \cos x - C_2 \sin x - C_1{}' \sin x + C_2{}' \cos x.$$

Substitution into the differential equation yields

$$-C_1{}' \sin x + C_2{}' \cos x = \sec x.$$

Solving the equations for $C_1{}'$ and $C_2{}'$, we obtain

$$C_1{}' = -\tan x,$$

$$C_2{}' = 1,$$

from which

$$C_1 = \ln \cos x,$$

$$C_2 = x.$$

The resulting particular solution is

$$y_p = \cos x \ln \cos x + x \sin x$$

and the general solution is

$$y = C_1 \cos x + C_2 \sin x + \cos x \ln \cos x + x \sin x.$$

We remark that example 11 cannot be solved by the method of undetermined coefficients described in Section 5.3. However examples 7, 8, 9, and 10 which we solved by the method of undetermined coefficients can also be solved by the method of variation of parameters.

The method of variation of parameters may also be applied to linear equations of order higher than two with obvious modifications. The method tends to become rather lengthy and tedious.

5.5 INTEGRATING FACTORS AND THE ADJOINT EQUATION

We begin with a linear differential equation of the first order which may be written in the form

$$P_0(x)y' + P_1(x)y = R_1(x). \tag{5.5.1}$$

This differential equation is said to be exact if its left member is the derivative of some function $F(x, y)$, where it is to be remembered that y is a function of x. Here we see that

$$\frac{d}{dx} F(x, y) = F_x + F_y y' = P_0(x)y' + P_1(x)y$$

where F_x and F_y denote the partial derivatives of F with respect to x and y respectively. Since this is an identity, we have

$$F_x = P_1(x)y \quad \text{and} \quad F_y = P_0(x).$$

From this we see that $F(x, y) = P_0(x)y$ and that we must have $P_0'(x) = P_1(x)$. This condition is necessary for (5.5.1) to be exact; it is also easily seen that it is sufficient. Thus if $P_0'(x) = P_1(x)$, the differential equation (5.5.1) is exact and may be written in the form

$$\frac{d}{dx} [P_0(x)y] = R_1(x)$$

and its solution is

$$P_0(x)y = \int R_1(x) \, dx + C.$$

In general, of course (5.5.1) will not be exact. As we now show, however, it is always possible to multiply (5.5.1) by a suitable function of x so that the resulting equation is exact. Such a function is called an integrating factor. It will first be convenient to divide equation (5.5.1) by $P_0(x)$, thus obtaining

$$y' + P(x)y = R(x) \tag{5.5.2}$$

where $P(x) = P_1(x)/P_0(x)$, $R(x) = R_1(x)/P_0(x)$. We may take (5.5.2) as the usual form of the first-order linear differential equation. Suppose that $\mu(x)$ is an integrating factor for (5.5.2). Then

$$\mu(x)y' + \mu(x)P(x)y = \mu(x)R(x)$$

is exact, and as in the previous discussion we must have

$$\mu'(x) = \mu(x)P(x),$$

from which we find that

$$\mu(x) = e^{\int P(x) \, dx}. \tag{5.5.3}$$

Thus we have found an integrating factor and the differential equation becomes

$$\frac{d}{dx}\left(ye^{\int P(x) \, dx}\right) = R(x)e^{\int P(x) \, dx}.$$

The general solution is

$$ye^{\int P(x)\,dx} = \int R(x)e^{\int P(x)\,dx}\,dx + C.$$

Example 12. Find the general solution of

$$y' + y \tan x = \cos x.$$

The integrating factor is

$$e^{\int \tan x\,dx} = \sec x.$$

The differential equation becomes

$$y' \sec x + y \sec x \tan x = 1$$

or

$$\frac{d}{dx}(y \sec x) = 1$$

whose general solution is

$$y \sec x = x + C.$$

Next we consider a second-order linear differential equation which we write in the form

$$P_0(x)y'' + P_1(x)y' + P_2(x)y = R(x). \tag{5.5.4}$$

This differential equation is said to be exact if its left member is the derivative of an expression linear in y and y'. We now show that the necessary and sufficient condition for (5.5.4) to be exact is that

$$P_0''(x) - P_1'(x) + P_2(x) = 0. \tag{5.5.5}$$

First suppose that (5.5.4) is exact; there then exist functions $A(x)$ and $B(x)$ for which

$$P_0 y'' + P_1 y' + P_2 y = \frac{d}{dx}(Ay' + By)$$

$$= Ay'' + A'y' + By' + B'y.$$

Equating coefficients, we have

$$P_0 = A, \qquad P_1 = A' + B, \qquad P_2 = B'.$$

Substituting these expressions in (5.5.5) we find that (5.5.5) is identically satisfied.

Conversely, suppose that (5.5.5) is satisfied. If we use (5.5.5) to substitute for P_2, we find that

$$P_0 y'' + P_1 y' + P_2 y = P_0 y'' + P_1 y' + (P_1' - P_0'')y$$

$$= \frac{d}{dx}[P_0 y' + (P_1 - P_0')y].$$

Thus the left member of (5.5.4) is the derivative of a linear expression and the differential equation is exact.

In general, of course, (5.5.4) is not exact. The function $\mu(x)$ will be an integrating factor if an exact equation is obtained when (5.5.4) is multiplied by $\mu(x)$. By (5.5.5) this will happen if and only if

$$\frac{d^2}{dx^2}(\mu P_0) - \frac{d}{dx}(\mu P_1) + \mu P_2 = 0. \tag{5.5.6}$$

This differential equation for μ may be written in the form

$$P_0\mu'' + (2P_0' - P_1)\mu' + (P_0'' - P_1' + P_2)\mu = 0. \tag{5.5.7}$$

Equation (5.5.6) or (5.5.7) is called the adjoint equation of the reduced equation

$$P_0y'' + P_1y' + P_2y = 0. \tag{5.5.8}$$

Thus a function $\mu(x)$ is an integrating factor for a given differential equation if and only if it is a solution of the adjoint equation.

We note that the adjoint of equation (5.5.7) is found to be (5.5.8). Thus each is the adjoint of the other.

In most cases, the use of the adjoint equation to find an integrating factor for a given differential equation is impractical because the adjoint equation is likely to be as difficult to solve as the original equation. The adjoint equation, however, is of theoretical interest, particularly in connection with the study of the properties of the solutions of the equation.

If it is possible to find an integrating factor for (5.5.4), the solution of (5.5.4) can be obtained easily, because the first integral of the exact equation is a first-order linear equation whose general solution can always be found by one additional integration as shown earlier in this section.

Sometimes it is possible to find an integrating factor by finding a solution of the adjoint equation by inspection or by a few systematic trials.

Example 13. Find the general solution of

$$x^3y'' + 2xy' - 2y = 0.$$

The equation is not exact, since

$$P_0'' - P_1' + P_2 = 6x - 2 - 2 \neq 0.$$

The adjoint equation is

$$x^3\mu'' + (6x^2 - 2x)\mu' + (6x - 4)\mu = 0.$$

We try a solution of the form $\mu = x^k$. Substituting in the adjoint equation we have

$$k(k - 1)x^{k+1} + (6x^2 - 2x)kx^{k-1} + (6x - 4)x^k = 0.$$

Equating the coefficients of x^{k+1} and x^k to zero we find that $k = -2$. Hence x^{-2} is an integrating factor for the original equation. Thus the multiplied equation

$$xy'' + 2x^{-1}y' - 2x^{-2}y = 0$$

is exact and may be written

$$\frac{d}{dx}[xy' + (2x^{-1} - 1)y] = 0.$$

The first integral then is

$$xy' + (2x^{-1} - 1)y = C_1$$

or

$$y' + (2x^{-2} - x^{-1})y = C_1 x^{-1}.$$

This is a first-order linear equation, and its integrating factor is found to be $x^{-1}e^{-2/x}$. The general solution is

$$y = C_1 x + C_2 x e^{2/x}.$$

The notion of an integrating factor and the adjoint equation can be extended to linear differential equations of any order. We write the homogeneous nth order linear differential equation in the form

$$P_0(x)y^{(n)} + P_1(x)y^{(n-1)} + P_2(x)y^{(n-2)} + \cdots + P_{n-1}(x)y' + P_n(x)y = 0.$$

Then the adjoint equation is

$$\frac{d^n}{dx^n}(P_0\mu) - \frac{d^{n-1}}{dx^{n-1}}(P_1\mu) + \frac{d^{n-2}}{dx^{n-2}}(P_2\mu) - \cdots$$

$$+ (-1)^{n-1}\frac{d}{dx}(P_{n-1}\mu) + (-1)^n P_n\mu = 0.$$

5.6 LINEAR DIFFERENTIAL EQUATIONS.   GREEN'S FUNCTION

In Sections 5.3 an 5.4 we have given methods for finding the general solution of the complete linear differential equation when the general solution of the reduced equation was known. In these methods we assumed that the function $R(x)$ on the right side of the equation was continuous. When the function $R(x)$ is piecewise continuous, however, it is possible to obtain solutions by other means. A function $R(x)$ is called piecewise continuous if it is continuous except at a finite number of points, at each of which it has a jump discontinuity. At a jump discontinuity x_0, $R(x)$ approaches different limits as x approaches x_0 from the left and from the right. If we write $x \to x_0^+$ to indicate that $x \to x_0$ with $x > x_0$ and $x \to x_0^-$

to indicate that $x \to x_0$ with $x < x_0$, then, at a jump discontinuity x_0, we have

$$\lim_{x \to x_0+} R(x) - \lim_{x \to x_0-} R(x) \neq 0.$$

In many problems of electrical or mechanical vibrations linear differential equations arise in which the right member represents an impressed force or voltage which is of an intermittent type. In such cases the function $R(x)$ is discontinuous.

The simplest function possessing a jump discontinuity is the unit step function defined by

$$\varphi(x) = \begin{cases} 0, & x < 0 \\ 1, & x \geq 0. \end{cases} \tag{5.6.1}$$

This function is continuous for $x \neq 0$ and has a jump of 1 at $x = 0$. We note that $h\varphi(x - x_0)$ is similar except that it has a jump of h at $x = x_0$.

The general step function $S(x)$ defined on an interval (a, b) has the property that (a, b) can be divided up into a finite number of intervals in each of which $S(x)$ is constant. Any step function can be expressed as a linear combination of unit step functions. Thus if $x_0 = a$, $x_n = b$, and $x_1 < x_2 < \cdots < x_{n-1}$ are the discontinuities of $S(x)$ in (a, b), and if $S(x) = S_i$ for $x_i \leq x < x_{i+1}(i = 0, 1, 2, \cdots, n - 1)$, then

$$S(x) = S_0\varphi(x - x_0) + (S_1 - S_0)\varphi(x - x_1)$$
$$+ \cdots + (S_{n-1} - S_{n-2})\varphi(x - x_{n-1}). \tag{5.6.2}$$

It is known that every piecewise continuous function can be approximated by such a step function and indeed as closely as desired. In other words, if a function $f(x)$ is to be approximated in a finite interval (a, b), then for any given $\epsilon > 0$, it is possible to find a step function which differs from $f(t)$ by no more than ϵ in the whole interval (a, b).

Suppose now that we wish to find a solution of

$$y'' + P(x)y' + Q(x)y = \begin{cases} 0, & x < x_0 \\ R(x), & x \geq x_0 \end{cases} \tag{5.6.3}$$

where $R(x)$ is a piecewise continuous function. In addition, we wish the solution to satisfy the initial conditions

$$y(x_0) = y'(x_0) = 0. \tag{5.6.4}$$

Since $y(x)$ may be discontinuous at x_0, these equations are to be interpreted in the sense that $y(x)$ and $y'(x)$ both approach zero as $x \to x_0$ from the left, and also from the right. Thus we seek a particular solution of (5.6.3).

Since $R(x)$ can be approximated by a step function, we first solve the problem for the special case in which $R(x) \equiv 1$. In other words, we wish to solve the differential equation

$$y'' + P(x)y' + Q(x)y = \varphi(x - x_0) \tag{5.6.5}$$

subject to the initial conditions (5.6.4). Here φ is the function defined in (5.6.1).

Then for $x < x_0$, we have $\varphi(x - x_0) = 0$ and it is obvious that the solution for $x < x_0$ is $y(x) = 0$. But for $x \geq x_0$ we have from (5.6.5),

$$y'' + P(x)y' + Q(x)y = 1 \tag{5.6.6}$$

and so if we can find the general solution of the reduced equation we can find the desired solution of the complete equation. Although we cannot give specific directions for finding this solution, we can be sure that it does exist on the basis of our remarks in Section 5.2. We denote this solution of (5.6.6) which satisfies (5.6.4) by $y_1(x, x_0)$ where x_0 is included as a parameter to indicate that the solution depends on the choice of x_0.

Thus for all x we have found a solution of (5.6.5) satisfying (5.6.4) which is

$$y = K(x, x_0) = \begin{cases} 0, & x \leq x_0 \\ y_1(x, x_0), & x \geq x_0. \end{cases}$$

We call $K(x, x_0)$ the indicial function belonging to the left member of (5.6.5). Clearly, $K(x, x_0)$ and $K'(x, x_0)$ are continuous for all x. But from (5.6.5) we see that $K''(x, x_0)$ is continuous for $x \neq x_0$ and has a jump of 1 at $x = x_0$.

It is clear that if the right member of (5.6.5) were $h\varphi(x - x_0)$, where h is a constant and nothing else were changed, the solution would be $y = hK(x, x_0)$.

We are now ready to consider the solution of the differential equation (5.6.3) subject to the initial conditions (5.6.4). We observe that for $x < x_0$, the solution is clearly $y(x) = 0$ as before. We then consider an arbitrary value of $\bar{x}$ such that $\bar{x} > x_0$, and seek the solution in the interval $(x_0, \bar{x})$. Now in the interval $(x_0, \bar{x})$ we can approximate $R(x)$ as closely as we please by a step function. To write an expression for this step function, we divide up the interval $(x_0, \bar{x})$ into n parts by points

$$x_0 = \tau_0 < \tau_1 < \tau_2 < \cdots < \tau_{n-1} < \tau_n = \bar{x},$$

and the approximating step function is

$$S(x) = \begin{cases} R(\tau_i), & \tau_i \leq x < \tau_{i+1}, \quad i = 0, 1, \cdots, n-1 \\ R(\tau_n), & x = \bar{x} = \tau_n. \end{cases}$$

According to (5.6.2) this may be written

$$S(x) = R(\tau_0)\varphi(x - \tau_0) + [R(\tau_1) - R(\tau_0)]\varphi(x - \tau_1) + \cdots$$
$$+ [R(\tau_n) - R(\tau_{n-1})]\varphi(x - \tau_n). \quad (5.6.7)$$

We have seen that the solution of (5.6.5) where the right member is

$$[R(\tau_i) - R(\tau_{i-1})]\varphi(x - \tau_i)$$

would be

$$[R(\tau_i) - R(\tau_{i-1})]K(x, \tau_i).$$

Now since (5.6.5) is a linear equation, it is clear that if the right member is a sum of such terms, the solution will also be a sum of corresponding solutions; and so we conclude that if the right member of (5.6.5) is replaced by the sum (5.6.7), the corresponding solution will be

$$R(\tau_0)K(x, \tau_0) + [R(\tau_1) - R(\tau_0)]K(x, \tau_1)$$
$$+ \cdots + [R(\tau_n) - R(\tau_{n-1})]K(x, \tau_n).$$

Now as the number of subdivision points used in the approximation of $R(x)$ increases without limit, and as the distance between successive points approaches zero, we see that this sum approaches the integral

$$y(x) = R(x_0)K(x, x_0) + \int_{x_0}^{\bar{x}} K(x, \tau)R'(\tau)\, d\tau, \quad (5.6.8)$$

provided the function $R(x)$ has a piecewise continuous derivative $R'(x)$.

Observing that $K(x, \tau) = 0$ for $\tau > x$, we may replace the upper limit of integration by x, and hence we find that

$$y(x) = R(x_0)K(x, x_0) + \int_{x_0}^{x} K(x, \tau)R'(\tau)\, d\tau \quad (5.6.9)$$

is the solution of (5.6.3) which satisfies (5.6.4). Since $\bar{x}$ was arbitrary, it is seen that (5.6.9) is valid for all values of x.

Formula (5.6.9) may be written in another form if we perform an integration by parts. We obtain

$$\int_{x_0}^{x} K(x, \tau)R'(\tau)\, d\tau = K(x, x)R(x) - K(x, x_0)R(x_0) - \int_{x_0}^{x} \frac{\partial K}{\partial \tau} R(\tau)\, d\tau$$
$$= -K(x, x_0)R(x_0) - \int_{x_0}^{x} \frac{\partial K}{\partial \tau} R(\tau)\, d\tau$$

since $K(x, x) = 0$ by definition of the indicial function. If we substitute this result in (5.6.9), we obtain

$$y(x) = -\int_{x_0}^{x} \frac{\partial K(x, \tau)}{\partial \tau} R(\tau)\, d\tau. \quad (5.6.10)$$

If we let

$$G(x, \tau) = -\frac{\partial K(x, \tau)}{\partial \tau} \qquad (5.6.11)$$

then (5.6.10) becomes

$$y(x) = \int_{x_0}^{x} G(x, \tau)R(\tau)\,d\tau. \qquad (5.6.12)$$

The function $G(x, \tau)$ that appears in (5.6.12) is called the weighting function or Green's function belonging to the left member of (5.6.3). It is readily verified that $G(x, x_0)$ satisfies the same initial conditions (5.6.4) as does $K(x, x_0)$. We also note that, by the definition of a derivative,

$$G(x, x_0) = -\frac{\partial K(x, \tau)}{\partial \tau}\bigg|_{\tau = x_0}$$

$$= \lim_{h \to 0} \frac{K(x, x_0) - K(x, x_0 + h)}{h}.$$

Thus for sufficiently small values of h, the function

$$\frac{K(x, x_0) - K(x, x_0 + h)}{h} \qquad (5.6.13)$$

may be considered as a good approximation to $G(x, x_0)$. If we remember that $K(x, x_0)$ is a solution of (5.6.3) with $R(x) = \varphi(x - x_0)$, it is clear that (5.6.13) is a solution of the same equation with

$$R(x) = \frac{\varphi(x - x_0) - \varphi(x - x_0 - h)}{h}.$$

The graph of this function is shown in Fig. 5.2. If we consider it as a mechanical or electromotive force, it is an impulse of intensity $1/h$ and duration h, hence of moment $h(1/h) = 1$. We may then give the following interpretation of Green's function:

If equation (5.6.3) represents the behavior of an electrical or mechanical system, the Green's function $G(x, x_0)$ belonging to it represents the effect at time x of an impulse at time x_0 of "infinitesimal" duration, of "infinite" intensity, and of unit moment.

Indicial and weighting functions are useful in solving problems where we require the responses of an oscillating system to a variety of impressed forces. Once the indicial or weighting function has been found, the solution for any impressed force can be found by evaluating the integral in (5.6.9) or (5.6.12). This may often be done by numerical, graphical, or mechanical methods. In many practical problems it is not possible to find the indicial or Green's function directly. It may be possible to find them

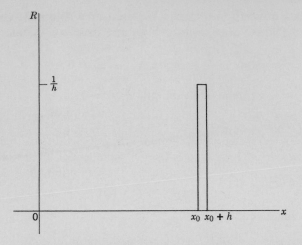

Fig. 5.2. Graph of $R(x) = [\varphi(x - x_0) - \varphi(x - x_0 - h)]/h$.

by experiment, however, by applying to the system a unit-step force to find the indicial function or a unit-impulse force to find the Green's function.

Example 14. Find the indicial and Green's functions belonging to the differential expression

$$y'' + k^2 y, \qquad (5.6.14)$$

and also find the solution of the equation

$$y'' + k^2 y = \begin{cases} 0, & x < x_0 \\ R(x), & x \geq x_0 \end{cases} \qquad (5.6.15)$$

which satisfies the initial conditions

$$y(x_0) = y'(x_0) = 0. \qquad (5.6.16)$$

First we must solve the problem:

$$y'' + k^2 y = 1 \qquad x \geq x_0$$

subject to (5.6.16). We see that a particular solution of this equation is $1/k^2$, and if we add the complementary function we obtain as the general solution

$$y(x) = \frac{1}{k^2} + A \cos k(x - \alpha)$$

where A, α are arbitrary constants. We must now determine these constants so that (5.6.16) are satisfied. Imposing these conditions, we have

$$y(x_0) = \frac{1}{k^2} + A \cos k(x_0 - \alpha) = 0$$

$$y'(x_0) = -Ak \sin k(x_0 - \alpha) = 0.$$

We find at once that $\alpha = x_0$ and $A = -1/k^2$. Substitution yields the desired particular solution and we may at once write the indicial function, which is

$$K(x, x_0) = \begin{cases} 0, & x \leq x_0 \\ \dfrac{1}{k^2} [1 - \cos k(x - x_0)], & x \geq x_0. \end{cases}$$

The Green's function is

$$G(x, x_0) = \begin{cases} 0, & x \leq x_0 \\ \dfrac{1}{k} \sin k(x - x_0), & x \geq x_0. \end{cases}$$

Then the solution of (5.6.15) subject to the conditions (5.6.16) is

$$y(x) = \frac{1}{k} \int_{x_0}^{x_0} R(\tau) \sin k(x - \tau) \, d\tau.$$

5.7 NUMERICAL SOLUTIONS

In previous sections we have described a number of methods for finding explicit solutions of differential equations. In many practical problems, however, it is found that it is not possible to obtain such explicit solutions of the differential equations describing the problem. It may then be desirable to find a numerical approximation to the solution of the differential equation. In Section 5.1 we pointed out that a differential equation of order n can be written as a system of n first-order differential equations. Consequently, in describing numerical methods, it will be convenient to restrict the discussion to first-order equations.

In this and following sections, we shall consider a first-order differential equation $y' = f(x, y)$ and we shall suppose that the value y_0 of y corresponding to $x = x_0$ is prescribed. The extension to systems of equations is simple and will be indicated later.

We seek a table of values of x and y for a sequence of values of x. It will be convenient to take the values of x as equally spaced with h denoting the common spacing. We consider the points $x_1 = x_0 + h$, $x_2 = x_0 + 2h, \cdots, x_n = x_0 + nh, \cdots$, and seek values of y, namely $y_1 = y(x_1)$, $y_2 = y(x_2), \cdots, y_n = y(x_n), \cdots$. The numerical solution of the differential equation is then just this table of values, x_i, y_i. In addition, it is often convenient to include the corresponding values of y' in the table.

In Section 5.2 we explained how the simple formula (5.2.4), namely

$$y_{n+1} = y_n + hy_n' = y_n + hf(x_n, y_n) \tag{5.7.1}$$

could be used to obtain such a numerical solution in a step-by-step manner.

This formula is quite crude and it is desirable to obtain formulas that will give more accurate results. A very simple but more accurate formula is

$$y_{n+1} = y_{n-1} + 2hy_n'. \tag{5.7.2}$$

To see that this formula is more accurate than (5.7.1), we make use of the Taylor's series,

$$y_{n+1} = y_n + hy_n' + \frac{h^2}{2} y_n'' + \frac{h^3}{6} y_n''' + \text{higher powers of } h.$$

If we write a similar expansion for y_{n-1} and subtract from the preceding equation, we obtain

$$y_{n+1} = y_{n-1} + 2hy_n' + \frac{h^3}{3} y_n''' + \text{higher powers of } h. \tag{5.7.3}$$

If h is sufficiently small, the neglected terms in (5.7.2) are smaller than in (5.7.1).

We observe that to get started with formula (5.7.2) it is necessary to know not only y_0 but also y_1'. We therefore need a special method of starting the solution. One possibility is to use several terms of Taylor's series to calculate y_1 and then obtain y_1' from the differential equation. The use of Taylor's series and other methods of starting the solution are described in Section 5.8.

Once the solution has been started, it proceeds step by step by repeated use of (5.7.2). This procedure contains no check on the accuracy of the numerical calculations or of the process. Some improvement in accuracy, as well as a partial check on the arithmetical work can be obtained by recalculating each value of y_{n+1} by means of the formula

$$y_{n+1} = y_n + \frac{h}{2} (y_{n+1}' + y_n'). \tag{5.7.4}$$

This is a closed formula of integration, for it is the trapezoidal rule (2.3.2) applied to the integration of the function $y'(x)$. By contrast, (5.7.2) is an integration formula of open type. The error in (5.7.2) is seen from (5.7.3) to be approximately $(h^3/3)y'''$. On the other hand, the error in (5.7.4) is found from (2.5.3) to be $-(h^3/12)y'''$, which shows that

(5.7.4) is more accurate. We note that to calculate y_{n+1} we need to know y'_{n+1}; thus we need a preliminary estimate of y_{n+1} to use in the calculation of y'_{n+1} from the differential equation. The procedure, then, will be to calculate a "predicted" value of y_{n+1} by means of (5.7.2), to use this value in the differential equation to calculate y'_{n+1}, and then to obtain a "corrected" value of y_{n+1} by means of (5.7.4). This "correction" process may be repeated, if necessary, by applying (5.7.4) repeatedly until no change occurs in the calculated value of y_{n+1}.

We note that the error in (5.7.4) is approximately one-fourth of the error in (5.7.2) and is of the opposite sign. Thus if we take the difference between the predicted and corrected values of y_{n+1}, we should obtain about five times the error in the corrected value. In other words, the error in the corrected value of y_{n+1} is in magnitude approximately one-fifth of the absolute value of the difference between the predicted and corrected values of y_{n+1}. It is often useful to carry along in the solution a column exhibiting this difference. If this column gets too large, it signals a loss of accuracy in the calculations. We can then decrease the step-size h in order to improve the accuracy or make use of more accurate formulas described in subsequent sections.

Following is an example demonstrating the use of these formulas. To get the necessary starting value, we make use of the example used in the next section to show the calculation of starting values.

Example 15. For the differential equation

$$y' = x^2 - y, \qquad y(0) = 1$$

find the values of y corresponding to $x = 0.2, 0.3, \cdots, 0.6$. Use the starting value $y_1 = 0.9052$ for $x = 0.1$, obtained by rounding the result of example 16.

Choosing $h = 0.1$, we first calculate from the differential equation $y_1' = -0.8952$. We then predict the value $\bar{y}_2$ from (5.7.2), obtaining

$$\bar{y}_2 = y_0 + 2hy_1' = 1 + 2(0.1)(-0.8952)$$
$$= 0.8210.$$

Next, from the differential equation we find $\bar{y}_2' = -0.7810$. We then use (5.7.4) to correct the value of y_2, obtaining

$$y_2 = y_1 + 0.5h(\bar{y}_2' + y_1')$$
$$= 0.9052 + 0.05(-0.7810 - 0.8952)$$
$$= 0.8214.$$

The corrected value of y_2' found from the differential equation is -0.7814. If we apply (5.7.4) again we find that no change occurs. We also note that

$y_2 - \bar{y}_2 = 0.0004$; the magnitude of the error is less than one-fifth of this value. We continue this step-by-step pattern, applying (5.7.2) to predict $\bar{y}_{n+1}$ and using (5.7.4) to correct y_{n+1}. We obtain the values in Table 5.2.

TABLE 5.2

Solution of $y' = x^2 - y$, $y(0) = 1$

Simple Predictor-Corrector

x	$\bar{y}$	$\bar{y}'$	y	y'	$y - \bar{y}$
0.0			1.0000	−1.0000	
0.1			0.9052	−0.8952	
0.2	0.8210	−0.7810	0.8214	−0.7814	0.0004
0.3	0.7489	−0.6589	0.7494	−0.6594	0.0005
0.4	0.6895	−0.5295	0.6899	−0.5299	0.0004
0.5	0.6434	−0.3934	0.6437	−0.3937	0.0003
0.6	0.6112	−0.2512	0.6114	−0.2514	0.0002

5.8 STARTING THE SOLUTION

In order to apply formula (5.7.2) to the solution of a differential equation, we saw that it was necessary to obtain by some other means the values of y_1 and y_1'. To use most of the formulas to be obtained in subsequent sections, it will be necessary to know a certain number of the ordinates $y_1, y_2, \cdots, y_r$, in addition to the prescribed ordinate y_0.

One method of starting the solution of the problem

$$y' = f(x, y), \qquad y(x_0) = y_0$$

consists in determining the coefficients of a Taylor's expansion

$$y_s = y(x_0 + hs) = y_0 + \frac{hy_0'}{1!}s + \frac{h^2y_0''}{2!}s^2 + \frac{h^3y_0'''}{3!}s^3 + \cdots$$

$$(5.8.1)$$

where $y_0^{(k)} = (d^k y/dx^k)_{x=x_0}$ by successively differentiating the basic differential equation or otherwise. We assume, of course, that such a convergent expansion exists if s is sufficiently small.

On differentiating the basic differential equation, we obtain

$$y' = f(x, y), y'' = f_x(x, y) + y'f_y(x, y),$$

$$y''' = f_{xx}(x, y) + 2y'f_{xy}(x, y) + y'^2 f_{yy}(x, y) + y''f_y(x, y),$$

and so forth. By substituting in the values of x_0 and y_0 we obtain the desired values of $y_0', y_0'', y_0''', \cdots$.

Fortunately, it is not necessary to compute the general expressions for the higher derivatives which, as can be seen, become quite complicated. In any particular case it is usually possible to compute enough of the derivatives to obtain the desired accuracy without excessive labor. We illustrate the calculation for a simple example.

Example 16. For the differential equation

$$y' = x^2 - y, \qquad y(0) = 1,$$

find the values of y corresponding to $x = 0.1, 0.2,$ and 0.3.

From the given equation, we obtain

$$y' = x^2 - y, y'' = 2x - y', y''' = 2 - y'',$$

$$y^{iv} = -y''', y^v = -y^{iv}, \cdots. \tag{5.8.2}$$

Substituting $x_0 = 0$, we find that

$$y_0 = 1, y_0' = -1, y_0'' = 1, y_0''' = 1, y_0^{iv} = -1, y_0^v = 1, \cdots.$$

We choose $h = 0.1$ and substitute these values in (5.8.1) obtaining

$$y_s = 1 - \frac{s}{10} + \frac{1}{2}\left(\frac{s}{10}\right)^2 + \frac{1}{6}\left(\frac{s}{10}\right)^3 - \frac{1}{24}\left(\frac{s}{10}\right)^4 + \frac{1}{120}\left(\frac{s}{10}\right)^5 - \cdots.$$

Setting $s = 1, 2,$ and 3, we obtain

$$y_1 = 0.90516, \qquad y_2 = 0.82127, \qquad y_3 = 0.74918$$

to five places.

Additional ordinates could be obtained to this accuracy by retaining enough terms in the expression. An alternative method consists in computing the coefficients of a new Taylor's series expansion launched from one of the points just calculated. For example, starting from the point x_3 we have

$$y_{3+s} = y_3 + \frac{hy_3'}{1!} s + \frac{h^2 y_3''}{2!} s^2 + \frac{h^3 y_3'''}{3!} s^3 + \cdots.$$

Here y_3 is known and $y_3', y_3'', \cdots$ are calculated in terms of y_3 from (5.8.2). Thus we must either calculate derivatives of higher order or recalculate all the derivatives to obtain additional ordinates by either of these methods. In the foregoing example, equations (5.8.2) were particularly simple but in more complicated examples, the labor of computing the higher derivatives increases fairly rapidly. Thus it is usually desirable to abandon this procedure in favor of a more convenient one as soon as sufficient starting values have been obtained. The step-by-step procedure of Section 5.7 can be used as soon as y_1 has been calculated by the starting procedure. The more complicated and more accurate procedures of subsequent sections will need more starting values.

Another procedure for finding starting values may be described as a method of successive substitutions. Before we can explain this method we need to obtain some additional closed numerical integration formulas expressing the desired starting ordinates in terms of derivatives.

Suppose we wish to calculate four starting ordinates. To calculate ordinates at points as near as possible to x_0, we shall find it convenient to calculate the ordinates y_{-2}, y_{-1}, y_1, y_2 corresponding to $x_{-2} = x_0 - 2h$, $x_{-1} = x_0 - h$, $x_1 = x_0 + h$, $x_2 = x_0 + 2h$. It is at once clear that

$$y_k - y_0 = \int_{x_0}^{x_k} y'(x)\, dx, \qquad k = -2, -1, 1, 2. \tag{5.8.3}$$

We cannot evaluate this integral because we do not know the function $y'(x)$ until after the differential equation has been solved. However, we may obtain useful formulas for y_k if we approximate y' by means of Stirling's interpolation formula (1.5.10'), obtaining

$$y_k = y_0 + h \int_0^k \left[y_0' + s\mu\delta y_0' + \frac{s^2}{2} \delta^2 y_0' + \frac{s(s^2 - 1)}{6} \mu\delta^3 y_0' \right.$$
$$\left. + \frac{s^2(s^2 - 1)}{24} \delta^4 y_0' + \cdots \right] ds, \qquad k = -2, -1, 1, 2.$$

Carrying out the integration yields the formulas

$$y_{-2} = y_0 + h(-2y_0' + 2\mu\delta y_0' - \tfrac{4}{3}\delta^2 y_0' + \tfrac{1}{3}\mu\delta^3 y_0' - \tfrac{7}{45}\delta^4 y_0' + \cdots),$$
$$y_{-1} = y_0 + h(-y_0' + \tfrac{1}{2}\mu\delta y_0' - \tfrac{1}{6}\delta^2 y_0' - \tfrac{1}{24}\mu\delta^3 y_0' + \tfrac{1}{180}\delta^4 y_0' + \cdots),$$

$$\tag{5.8.4}$$

$$y_1 = y_0 + h(y_0' + \tfrac{1}{2}\mu\delta y_0' + \tfrac{1}{6}\delta^2 y_0' - \tfrac{1}{24}\mu\delta^3 y_0' - \tfrac{1}{180}\delta^4 y_0' + \cdots),$$
$$y_2 = y_0 + h(2y_0' + 2\mu\delta y_0' + \tfrac{4}{3}\delta^2 y_0' + \tfrac{1}{3}\mu\delta^3 y_0' + \tfrac{7}{45}\delta^4 y_0' + \cdots).$$

We may rewrite these formulas in terms of the derivatives themselves instead of their differences. If we neglect differences beyond the fourth and recall the definitions of the differences involved, we obtain, after some calculation, the approximate formulas

$$y_{-2} = y_0 - \frac{h}{90}(29y_{-2}' + 124y_{-1}' + 24y_0' + 4y_1' - y_2'),$$

$$y_{-1} = y_0 - \frac{h}{720}(-19y_{-2}' + 346y_{-1}' + 456y_0' - 74y_1' + 11y_2'),$$

$$\tag{5.8.5}$$

$$y_1 = y_0 + \frac{h}{720}(11y_{-2}' - 74y_{-1}' + 456y_0' + 346y_1' - 19y_2'),$$

$$y_2 = y_0 + \frac{h}{90}(-y_{-2}' + 4y_{-1}' + 24y_0' + 124y_1' + 29y_2').$$

To apply these formulas, we begin with a first approximation by making a rough estimate of the values of y_{-2}, y_{-1}, y_1, y_2. This might be done, for example, by taking one or two terms of the Taylor's series expansion. The corresponding values of $y_{-2}', y_{-1}', y_1', y_2'$ are then calculated from the differential equation. These values are then substituted into (5.8.5), obtaining a second approximation to the values of y_{-2}, y_{-1}, y_1, y_2. The second approximations to the values of y are then substituted in the differential equation to obtain new values for y' which are in turn substituted in (5.8.5), yielding a third approximation. This cycle of operations is repeated until no change occurs in the values of y_{-2}, y_{-1}, y_1, y_2.

For high-speed automatic computers, formulas (5.8.5) are probably the most convenient. If the calculations are performed by hand, it may be more convenient to form the necessary difference table and use formulas (5.8.4).

If it should be undesirable or impossible to calculate values of y for x_{-2} and x_{-1}, we might instead want to calculate the starting values y_1, y_2, y_3, y_4. To obtain such formulas we would again start with (5.8.3) and approximate $y(x)$ by means of Newton's forward formula (1.3.8). We obtain the formulas:

$$y_1 = y_0 + h(y_0' + \tfrac{1}{2}\Delta y_0' - \tfrac{1}{12}\Delta^2 y_0' + \tfrac{1}{24}\Delta^3 y_0' - \tfrac{19}{724}\Delta^4 y_0' + \cdots),$$

$$y_2 = y_0 + h(2y_0' + 2\Delta y_0' + \tfrac{1}{3}\Delta^2 y_0' + 0\,\Delta^3 y_0' - \tfrac{1}{90}\Delta^4 y_0' + \cdots),$$

$$(5.8.6)$$

$$y_3 = y_0 + h(3y_0' + \tfrac{9}{2}\Delta y_0' + \tfrac{9}{4}\Delta^2 y_0' + \tfrac{3}{8}\Delta^3 y_0' + \tfrac{3}{80}\Delta^4 y_0' + \cdots),$$

$$y_4 = y_0 + h(4y_0' + 8\Delta y_0' + \tfrac{20}{3}\Delta^2 y_0' + \tfrac{8}{3}\Delta^3 y_0' + \tfrac{14}{15}\Delta^4 y_0' + \cdots).$$

Neglecting differences beyond the fourth, the corresponding approximate formulas may also be written in the form

$$y_1 = y_0 + \frac{h}{720}\,(251y_0' + 646y_1' - 264y_2' + 106y_3 - 19y_4'),$$

$$y_2 = y_0 + \frac{h}{90}\,(29y_0' + 124y_1' + 24y_2' + 4y_3' - y_4'),$$

$$(5.8.7)$$

$$y_3 = y_0 + \frac{h}{80}\,(27y_0' + 102y_1' + 72y_2' + 42y_3' - 3y_4'),$$

$$y_4 = y_0 + \frac{4h}{90}\,(7y_0' + 32y_1' + 12y_2' + 32y_3' + 7y_4').$$

It should be pointed out that all the formulas (5.8.4)–(5.8.7) involve a truncation error which has been omitted. These truncation errors may be found in Milne [20].

Example 17. For the differential equation

$$y' = x^2 - y, \qquad y(0) = 1,$$

find by the method of successive substitutions values of y corresponding to $x = -0.2, -0.1, 0.1,$ and 0.2.

As a first approximation to the solution, we take

$$y(x) = 1 + xy_0' = 1 - x,$$

and calculate y' for $x = -0.2, -0.1, 0, 0.1,$ and 0.2. These values appear in the first five lines of Table 5.3. Here, $h = 0.1$. These values are then

TABLE 5.3

Solution of $y' = x^2 - y$, $y(0) = 1$

Starting the Solution

x	y	y'	
-0.2	1.2	-1.16	
-0.1	1.1	-1.09	
0.0	1.0	-1.00	1st approximation
0.1	0.9	-0.89	
0.2	0.8	-0.76	
-0.2	1.217	-1.177	
-0.1	1.105	-1.095	
0.0	1.000	-1.000	2nd approximation
0.1	0.905	-0.895	
0.2	0.823	-0.783	
-0.2	1.2186	-1.1786	
-0.1	1.1048	-1.0948	
0.0	1.0000	-1.0000	3rd approximation
0.1	0.9052	-0.8952	
0.2	0.8213	-0.7813	

substituted into (5.8.5) to obtain a second approximation, recorded in the second five lines of the table. Then y' is calculated again from the differential equation and a third approximation obtained by use of (5.8.5). The cycle is repeated until no further change occurs. The fourth approximation agrees with the third approximation to four decimal places.

It would be possible to continue this solution by use of the formulas (5.8.7). We could use the last line of the foregoing computation as the first line of a new computation which would carry us on to $x = 0.6$, and repetitions of this procedure would take us as far as we wished to go.

However, this method of continuing the computation is quite inefficient and is not recommended. The step-by-step method of Section 5.7 or more accurate step-by-step methods are to be preferred.

5.9 MILNE'S METHOD

The method of prediction and correction of the ordinate y_{n+1} described in Section 5.7 can be extended by the use of more elaborate formulas in place of (5.7.2) and (5.7.4). Milne's method consists in using as a predictor a formula obtained from the integration formula (2.4.1) and as a corrector a formula derived from Simpson's formula (2.3.3). The formulas to be obtained will be more accurate than those of Section 5.7.

If the solution of the differential equation $y' = f(x, y)$ with $y(x_0) = y_0$ has been obtained for $x_1, x_2, \cdots, x_n$ as $y_1, y_2, \cdots, y_n$, then we predict the value of y_{n+1} by the formula

$$\bar{y}_{n+1} = y_{n-3} + \frac{4h}{3} (2y'_{n-2} - y'_{n-1} + 2y_n').$$ (5.9.1)

From the differential equation we obtain the value $\bar{y}'_{n+1} = f(x_{n+1}, \bar{y}_{n+1})$ and then obtain a corrected value of y_{n+1} by means of the formula

$$y_{n+1} = y_{n-1} + \frac{h}{3} (y'_{n-1} + 4y_n' + \bar{y}'_{n+1}).$$ (5.9.2)

We may apply the correction formula (5.9.2) repeatedly, each time recalculating y'_{n+1} from the differential equation until no change occurs in the calculated value of y_{n+1}.

If we observe that the truncation errors in formulas (5.9.1) and (5.9.2) are given by (2.5.6) and (2.5.4) respectively, we see that the error in (5.9.1) is approximately 28 times the error in (5.9.2), and of opposite sign. Hence the magnitude of the error in the corrected value y_{n+1} will be approximately the magnitude of

$$\tfrac{1}{29}(y_{n+1} - \bar{y}_{n+1}).$$

Hence it will be useful to tabulate the quantity $y_{n+1} - \bar{y}_{n+1}$ when carrying out a solution by this method. Its values will serve as a control for the truncation error and may also reveal arithmetical mistakes. Whenever its values exhibit abrupt changes, it is wise to check the last line or two of the computation.

Example 18. Use Milne's method to continue the solution of

$$y' = x^2 - y, \qquad y(0) = 1,$$

which was started in example 16.

As before, we choose $h = 0.1$. Table 5.4 shows the values of y_1, y_2, y_3 calculated in example 16, as well as the corresponding values of y_1', y_2', y_3' calculated from the differential equation. These values are used to predict the value of $\bar{y}_4$ by means of (5.9.1). Then $\bar{y}_4'$ is calculated from the differential equation and (5.9.2) is used to correct the value of y_4. The same method is used to carry the calculation on to $x = 0.5$ and $x = 0.6$.

TABLE 5.4

Milne's Method

Solution of $y' = x^2 - y, \qquad y(0) = 1$

x	$\bar{y}$	$\bar{y}'$	y	y'	$y - \bar{y}$
0.0			1.00000	−1.00000	
0.1			0.90516	−0.89516	
0.2			0.82127	−0.78127	
0.3			0.74918	−0.65918	
0.4	0.68968	−0.52968	0.68966	−0.52966	−0.00002
0.5	0.64347	−0.39347	0.64347	−0.39347	0.00000
0.6	0.61118	−0.25118	0.61117	−0.25117	−0.00001

The column exhibiting $y - \bar{y}$ shows that the error in each step is very small indeed. This calculation was carried to five decimal places because it is considerably more accurate than the calculation of example 15 where only four places seemed appropriate.

It has been pointed out by several authors, including Hildebrand [12, pp. 202–214], that Milne's method is unstable. The basic cause of the instability is the use of Simpson's rule in (5.9.2). Simpson's rule integrates over two intervals and under certain conditions can produce an error which alternates in sign from step to step and which increases in magnitude exponentially. Because Simpson's rule integrates over two intervals, we see that in (5.9.2) the calculation of y_{n+1} is based on the value of y_{n-1} and thus the successive values of y are somewhat "loosely" connected with each other. Thus, there are, in a sense, two distinct sequences of y values, corresponding respectively to odd and even subscripts, which may tend to depart from each other, and thus an oscillation of the calculated solution about the true solutions begins to appear. Milne and Reynolds [21] have shown that an occasional application of Newton's "three-eighths" rule (2.3.6) will effectively damp out the unwanted oscillation without harm to the desired solution. Other methods of dealing with the stability problem have been discussed by Milne and Reynolds [22] and Hamming [11].

By contrast the simple predictor-corrector method of Section 5.7 uses (5.7.4) to calculate y_{n+1} from the immediately preceding ordinate y_n. Thus the successive values of y are more tightly connected together and instability does not occur.

In the following section we give a method which makes use of more extended formulas of integration but which bases the calculation of y_{n+1} on y_n and hence does not exhibit the instability of Milne's method.

5.10 ADAMS' METHOD

In deriving formulas for obtaining starting values of the solution of a differential equation, we began with (5.8.3), approximating the derivative by means of Stirling's interpolation formula in one case, and by means of Newton's forward interpolation formula in another case. The formulas obtained gave the ordinates in terms of derivatives which were ahead of the ordinates being calculated and therefore only known approximately. To rectify this situation it seems desirable to approximate the derivative in question by means of Newton's backward formula to obtain a formula for the ordinate in terms of derivatives at previously calculated points.

We begin with the obvious formula analogous to (5.8.3), namely

$$y_{n+1} = y_n + \int_{x_n}^{x_n+h} y'(x)\,dx. \qquad (5.10.1)$$

We use Newton's backward interpolation formula (1.4.6) launched from y_n' to approximate $y'(x)$ by a polynomial which assumes the calculated values at $x_n, x_{n-1}, x_{n-2}, \cdots$. We let $s = (x - x_n)/h$ and substitute the resulting polynomial in (5.10.1), obtaining

$$y_{n+1} = y_n + h\int_0^1\left[y_n' + s\nabla y_n' + \frac{(s+1)s}{2}\nabla^2 y_n' + \frac{(s+2)(s+1)s}{6}\nabla^3 y_n'\right.$$
$$\left. + \frac{(s+3)(s+2)(s+1)s}{24}\nabla^4 y_n' + \cdots\right]ds. \quad (5.10.2)$$

Carrying out the integration yields the formula

$$y_{n+1} = y_n + h(y_n' + \tfrac{1}{2}\nabla y_n' + \tfrac{5}{12}\nabla^2 y_n' + \tfrac{3}{8}\nabla^3 y_n' + \tfrac{251}{720}\nabla^4 y_n' + \cdots).$$
$$(5.10.3)$$

If this formula is truncated to a suitable number of terms, it may be used for carrying on a step-by-step solution of a differential equation after the appropriate number of starting values has been obtained. This method is known as Adams' method.

In particular, if we wish to obtain accuracy at each step comparable to that obtained by use of Milne's predictor formula (5.9.1), whose error is obtained from (2.5.6), it will be necessary to retain third differences in (5.10.3). Here it will be necessary to have the starting values y_0, y_1, y_2, y_3 from which we can obtain the corresponding values of the derivatives from the differential equation. We then form a difference table from the values of the derivatives and calculate y_4 from (5.10.3). The value of y_4' is added to the table and another line of differences formed. The procedure is repeated, advancing the solution a line at a time.

If we do not want to make use of differences, the formula may be written in terms of the ordinates themselves. Thus if third differences are retained, we obtain from (5.10.3) the formula

$$y_{n+1} = y_n + \frac{h}{24}(55y_n' - 59y_{n-1}' + 37y_{n-2}' - 9y_{n-3}'). \qquad (5.10.4)$$

Although the step-by-step solution can be carried forward as described using either (5.10.3) or (5.10.4), it is desirable as in Milne's method to have a formula to use as a corrector for the values of y_{n+1}.

To obtain such a formula we again start with (5.10.1) and again make the substitution $s = (x - x_n)/h$, but in using Newton's backward formula we launch it from y_{n+1}' instead of from y_n'. Substitution in (5.10.1) yields

$$y_{n+1} = y_n + h\int_0^1 \left(y_{n+1}' + (s-1)\nabla y_{n+1}' + \frac{s(s-1)}{2}\nabla^2 y_{n+1}' \right.$$

$$\left. + \frac{(s+1)s(s-1)}{6}\nabla^3 y_{n+1}' + \frac{(s+2)(s+1)s(s-1)}{24}\nabla^4 y_{n+1}' + \cdots \right)ds.$$

$$(5.10.5)$$

Carrying out the integration yields the formula

$$y_{n+1} = y_n + h(y_{n+1}' - \tfrac{1}{2}\nabla y_{n+1}' - \tfrac{1}{12}\nabla^2 y_{n+1}'$$

$$- \tfrac{1}{24}\nabla^3 y_{n+1}' - \tfrac{19}{720}\nabla^4 y_{n+1}' - \cdots). \qquad (5.10.6)$$

This formula suitably truncated may also be written in terms of the ordinates themselves. Thus if third differences are retained, we obtain from (5.10.6) the formula

$$y_{n+1} = y_n + \frac{h}{24}(9y_{n+1}' + 19y_n' - 5y_{n-1}' + y_{n-2}'). \qquad (5.10.7)$$

In the modified Adams' method we may predict a value of y_{n+1} by means of (5.10.4), use the differential equation to calculate the derivative y_{n+1}', and then use (5.10.7) to obtain a corrected value of y_{n+1}. This in turn may be used in the differential equation to obtain an improved value of y_{n+1}'

and (5.10.7) used again. This cycle is repeated until no further change occurs.

If we want to use (5.10.3) suitably truncated, then, after predicting y_{n+1} and calculating y'_{n+1} from the differential equation, we will have to extend the difference table tentatively so that (5.10.6) suitably truncated can be used to correct y_{n+1}. Then y'_{n+1} must be recalculated from the differential equation and the last line of the difference table suitably revised and the cycle repeated until no further change occurs.

In deducing (5.10.4) from (5.10.3), the first neglected term was $(\frac{251}{720})h\nabla^4 y_n'$. Since it is not difficult to show that in general $\nabla^4 f(x) \approx h^4 f^{iv}(x)$, the error in (5.10.4) can be shown to be approximately $(\frac{251}{720})h^5 y^v$. In a similar manner, the error in (5.10.7) can be shown to be approximately $-(\frac{19}{720})h^5 y^v$. Thus the error in (5.10.4) is approximately thirteen times the error in (5.10.7) and of opposite sign. Hence the magnitude of the error in the corrected value y_{n+1} will be approximately the magnitude of

$$\tfrac{1}{14}(y_{n+1} - \bar{y}_{n+1}),$$

where $\bar{y}_{n+1}$ denotes the predicted value calculated by (5.10.4). Thus, as in Milne's method, tabulation of the quantity $y_{n+1} - \bar{y}_{n+1}$ provides a useful indication of the error in each step of the method.

We remark that the error in Milne's corrector formula (5.9.2) is of the same order as that in the modified Adams' corrector formula (5.10.7), but that in Milne's method the coefficient $(\frac{1}{90})$ is only about 40 per cent of that in the modified Adams' method $(\frac{19}{720})$.

If we repeat example 18, using Adams' method in place of Milne's method, the results are practically the same as shown in Table 5.4. No result differs by more than two units in the fifth decimal place, and it is found that the predicted and corrected values in Adams' method are equal so that the column $y - \bar{y}$ is zero here.

5.11 RUNGE-KUTTA METHOD

In the preceding two sections we have discussed step-by-step methods of carrying on the numerical solution of the problem

$$y' = f(x, y), \qquad y(x_0) = y_0 \qquad (5.11.1)$$

after a suitable number of starting values have been obtained. Methods for obtaining such starting values were described in Section 5.8. One of these methods depended on the expansion of the solution in a Taylor's series of the form

$$y_1 = y(x_0 + h) = y_0 + hy_0' + \frac{h^2}{2!}y_0'' + \frac{h^3}{3!}y_0''' + \cdots. \qquad (5.11.2)$$

The coefficients of this Taylor's series were expressed in terms of the function $f(x, y)$ and its partial derivatives. It was observed that the calculation of these partial derivatives may become difficult or tedious. The methods associated with the names of Runge, Kutta, and others effectively replace the result of truncating the Taylor's series by formulas which involve combinations of the values of $f(x, y)$ at certain points near the starting point (x_0, y_0). These formulas are designed in such a way that if they were expanded in powers of h, the coefficients of a certain number of the leading terms would agree with the corresponding coefficients of the Taylor's series (5.11.2).

One of the more useful of these methods, due to Kutta, but usually referred to as a Runge-Kutta method, may be described by means of the following formula:

$$y_1 = y_0 + \tfrac{1}{6}(k_0 + 2k_1 + 2k_2 + k_3), \tag{5.11.3}$$

where

$$
\begin{aligned}
k_0 &= hf(x_0, y_0) \\
k_1 &= hf(x_0 + \tfrac{1}{2}h, y_0 + \tfrac{1}{2}k_0) \\
k_2 &= hf(x_0 + \tfrac{1}{2}h, y_0 + \tfrac{1}{2}k_1) \\
k_3 &= hf(x_0 + h_1, y_0 + k_2).
\end{aligned}
\tag{5.11.4}
$$

This formula is of fourth-order accuracy, for it can be shown that it agrees with the Taylor's series expansion up through the h^4 term. It is of interest to note that this formula would reduce to Simpson's rule if f were independent of y. We omit the proof of this formula as it is straightforward but tedious. It is only necessary to expand k_1, k_2, k_3 in powers of h, substitute in (5.11.3), and compare the coefficients of the powers of h with the corresponding coefficients in (5.11.2).

One of the advantages of the Runge-Kutta method is that it is self-starting and hence may be used at the beginning of the solution. The solution may then be carried on with the Runge-Kutta method, making in the formulas (5.11.3) and (5.11.4) the obvious substitution of (x_n, y_n) for (x_0, y_0) and y_{n+1} for y_1. Alternatively, after a suitable number of starting values have been obtained by this method, the solution may be continued by means of a predictor-corrector method such as that of Adams or Milne. Since the Runge-Kutta method is self-starting, a change in spacing is easily effected at any intermediate stage of the calculation. Other methods require special restarting procedures when the spacing is changed at intermediate stages. Another advantage of the Runge-Kutta method is that the evaluation of derivatives of $f(x, y)$ is not required, and so it may be used when $f(x, y)$ is not given by an analytical expression. A disadvantage of the method is that each step in the calculation requires several evaluations of $f(x, y)$ and this may be excessively laborious. Also, the estimation of errors is more difficult than in the previously described methods.

Example 19. Use the Runge-Kutta method to obtain the solution of

$$y' = x^2 - y, \qquad y(0) = 1$$

for $x = 0.1$ and $x = 0.2$.

Starting from the point $(0, 1)$, we have from (5.11.4) $k_0 = -0.1, k_1 = -0.09475, k_2 = 0.09501, k_3 = -0.08950$. Then

$$y_1 = 1 + \tfrac{1}{6}[-0.1 + 2(-0.09475 - 0.09501) - 0.08950]$$
$$= 0.90516.$$

Next we start from $(0.1, 0.90516)$ and obtain $k_0 = -0.08952, k_1 = -0.08379, k_2 = -0.08408, k_3 = -0.07811$. Then

$$y_2 = 0.90516 + \tfrac{1}{6}[-0.08952 + 2(-0.08379 - 0.08408) - 0.07811]$$
$$= 0.82126.$$

5.12 SYSTEMS OF EQUATIONS; EQUATIONS OF HIGHER ORDER

In the previous sections we have developed and illustrated numerical methods for the solution of a single differential equation of first order. The extension to systems of first-order equations and to equations of higher order involves relatively little that is new. We shall first indicate the procedure for a system of two first-order equations. The extension to more than two such equations will then be obvious.

We consider the system

$$\begin{aligned} y' &= f(x, y, z) \\ z' &= g(x, y, z) \end{aligned} \tag{5.12.1}$$

with $y = y_0$ and $z = z_0$ when $x = x_0$. The solution can be started by the use of Taylor's series (or otherwise) as described in Section 5.8. A Taylor's series can be obtained for each of the functions y and z. Any of the predictor-corrector methods previously described can then be used to continue the solution. For example, if Milne's method is used, we would have the two predictor formulas

$$\bar{y}_{n+1} = y_{n-3} + \frac{4h}{3}(2y'_{n-2} - y'_{n-1} + 2y_n') \tag{5.12.2}$$

and

$$\bar{z}_{n+1} = z_{n-3} + \frac{4h}{3}(2z'_{n-2} - z'_{n-1} + 2z_n'). \tag{5.12.3}$$

From the system of differential equations we obtain the values $\bar{y}'_{n+1} = f(x_{n+1}, \bar{y}_{n+1}, \bar{z}_{n+1})$ and $\bar{z}'_{n+1} = g(x_{n+1}, \bar{y}_{n+1}, \bar{z}_{n+1})$. We then obtain corrected values of y_{n+1} and z_{n+1} by means of the formulas

$$y_{n+1} = y_{n-1} + \frac{h}{3}(y'_{n-1} + 4y_n' + \bar{y}'_{n+1}) \tag{5.12.4}$$

and

$$z_{n+1} = z_{n-1} + \frac{h}{3}(z'_{n-1} + 4z_n' + \bar{z}'_{n+1}). \tag{5.12.5}$$

Again the application of the correction formulas may be repeated if desired.

It was pointed out in Section 5.1 that a single differential equation of order higher than the first can always be replaced by an equivalent system of first-order equations. Thus the numerical solution of higher-order equations is a special case of systems of first-order equations. Since the equivalent system of equations assumes a particularly simple form, there is a slight simplification in the application of the predictor-corrector methods. We illustrate the situation by considering an equation of second order

$$y'' = f(x, y, y') \tag{5.12.6}$$

with $y(x_0) = y_0$ and $y'(x_0) = y_0'$. We make the substitution $y' = z$ so that the equivalent system of equations is seen to be

$$\begin{aligned} y' &= z \\ z' &= f(x, y, z) \end{aligned} \tag{5.12.7}$$

with $y = y_0$ and $z = y_0'$ when $x = x_0$. The solution can again be started by the use of Taylor's series (or otherwise). To continue the solution, a predictor formula can be used to obtain a value of z from the values of z' or y'', but since $y' = z$ it is obviously unnecessary to use the predictor to find a value for y. For example, with Milne's method we would use the predictor formula

$$\bar{z}_{n+1} = z_{n-3} + \frac{4h}{3}(2z'_{n-2} - z'_{n-1} + 2z_n'),$$

that is,

$$\bar{y}'_{n+1} = y'_{n-3} + \frac{4h}{3}(2y''_{n-2} - y''_{n-1} + 2y_n''), \tag{5.12.8}$$

whereas to obtain a value for y we would use

$$\bar{y}_{n+1} = y_{n-1} + \frac{h}{3}(y'_{n-1} + 4y_n' + \bar{y}'_{n+1}). \tag{5.12.9}$$

We would then calculate $\bar{z}'_{n+1} = \bar{y}''_{n+1}$ from the differential equation and then use the formulas

$$z_{n+1} = z_{n-1} + \frac{h}{3}(z'_{n-1} + 4z_n{}' + \bar{z}'_{n+1}),$$

or

$$y'_{n+1} = y'_{n-1} + \frac{h}{3}(y''_{n-1} + 4y_n{}'' + \bar{y}''_{n+1}) \qquad (5.12.10)$$

and

$$y_{n+1} = y_{n-1} + \frac{h}{3}(y'_{n-1} + 4y_n{}' + y'_{n+1}). \qquad (5.12.11)$$

The application of the last pair of formulas may be repeated if desired.

Example 20. For the differential equation

$$y'' = y + 2xy', \qquad y(0) = 1, \qquad y'(0) = 0$$

find the solution up to $x = 0.6$ at intervals of 0.1.

We choose $h = 0.1$. We shall apply Milne's method after we have obtained the solution at $x = 0.1, 0.2, 0.3$ by means of Taylor's series.

From the given equation we obtain

$$y'' = y + 2xy', \quad y''' = 3y' + 2xy'', \quad y^{iv} = 5y'' + 2xy''',$$

$$y^{v} = 7y''' + 2xy^{iv}, \quad y^{vi} = 9y^{iv} + 2xy^{v}, \cdots.$$

Hence with $x_0 = 0$ we have

$$y_0 = 1, \quad y_0{}' = 0, \quad y_0{}'' = 1, \quad y_0{}''' = 0, \quad y_0{}^{iv} = 5, \quad y_0{}^{v} = 0, \quad y_0{}^{vi} = 45, \cdots.$$

Thus, if we remember that $h = 0.1$, we obtain

$$y_s = 1 + \left(\frac{1}{2}\right)\left(\frac{s}{10}\right)^2 + \frac{5}{24}\left(\frac{s}{10}\right)^4 + \left(\frac{1}{16}\right)\left(\frac{s}{10}\right)^6 + \cdots$$

$$y_s{}' = \frac{s}{10} + \frac{5}{6}\left(\frac{s}{10}\right)^3 + \frac{3}{8}\left(\frac{s}{10}\right)^5 + \cdots.$$

Setting $s = 1, 2,$ and 3 we obtain

$$y_1 = 1.0050, \quad y_2 = 1.0203, \quad y_3 = 1.0467,$$

$$y_1{}' = 0.1008, \quad y_2{}' = 0.2068, \quad y_3{}' = 0.3234$$

to four places. From the differential equation we find that

$$y_1{}'' = 1.0252, \quad y_2{}'' = 1.1030, \quad y_3{}'' = 1.2407.$$

All of these values are shown in Table 5.5.

We are now in a position to continue the solution by the use of the Milne predictor and corrector formulas. First a predicted value $\bar{y}_4'$ is calculated from equation (5.12.8) and then a value of $\bar{y}_4$ is obtained from

TABLE 5.5

Milne's Method

Solution of $y'' = y + 2xy'$, $y(0) = 1$, $y'(0) = 0$

x	$\bar{y}$	$\bar{y}'$	$\bar{y}''$	y	y'	y''	$y' - \bar{y}'$
0.0				1.0000	0.0000	1.0000	
0.1				1.0050	0.1008	1.0252	
0.2				1.0203	0.2068	1.1030	
0.3				1.0467	0.3234	1.2407	
0.4	1.0856	0.4572	1.4514	1.0856	0.4574	1.4515	0.0002
0.5	1.1390	0.6166	1.7556	1.1390	0.6168	1.7558	0.0002
0.6	1.2102	0.8123	2.1850	1.2102	0.8127	2.1854	0.0004

equation (5.12.9). Next $\bar{y}_4''$ is calculated from the differential equation and (5.12.10) and (5.12.11) are used to obtain corrected values y_4' and y_4 respectively. The same method is used to carry the calculation on to $x = 0.5$ and $x = 0.6$. The column exhibiting $y' - \bar{y}'$ shows that the error in each step is very small indeed. The solution is tabulated in Table 5.5.

chapter 6 Fourier series

6.1 INTRODUCTION

In many scientific problems, periodic functions are encountered. A function $f(x)$ is said to be periodic with period p if $f(x + p) = f(x)$ for all x. For example, the functions $\sin x$ and $\cos x$ both have period 2π. For periodic functions, it would be inappropriate to use polynomial approximations as in Chapters 1 and 2. It seems preferable to seek to approximate general periodic functions by sums of periodic functions such as sines and cosines. In this connection it will be recalled that in Section 5.3 we solved nonhomogeneous differential equations whose right members involved (among other functions) $\sin mx$ and $\cos mx$. The method was quite easy and we might expect to use the same method for differential equations in which the right member is a general periodic function if this general function could be expressed as a sum of terms each of the form $\sin mx$ or $\cos mx$.

We therefore consider the possibility of expressing a periodic function in the form of a series

$$f(x) = \tfrac{1}{2}a_0 + \sum_{n=1}^{\infty}(a_n \cos nx + b_n \sin nx) \qquad (6.1.1)$$

where the factor $\tfrac{1}{2}$ in the first term is introduced for convenience, as will be seen later. We are here assuming that $f(x)$ has a period 2π. Such series were used in the nineteenth century by Fourier in the study of heat conduction problems and are usually called Fourier series. They were, however, used even earlier, in the eighteenth century, by Daniel Bernoulli who used them to solve certain problems connected with vibrating strings.

6.2 CALCULATION OF THE COEFFICIENTS

To obtain expressions for the coefficients a_n and b_n in the expansion (6.1.1), the following definite integrals will be needed. In these formulas m and n are assumed to be integers.

$$\int_{-\pi}^{\pi} \cos mx \cos nx \, dx = 0, \qquad m \neq n \tag{6.2.1}$$

$$= \pi, \qquad m = n \neq 0 \tag{6.2.2}$$

$$= 2\pi, \qquad m = n = 0 \tag{6.2.3}$$

$$\int_{-\pi}^{\pi} \sin mx \sin nx \, dx = 0, \qquad m \neq n \tag{6.2.4}$$

$$= \pi, \qquad m = n \neq 0 \tag{6.2.5}$$

$$\int_{-\pi}^{\pi} \sin mx \cos nx \, dx = 0. \tag{6.2.6}$$

These formulas may be proved by methods of the elementary calculus. Because of the periodicity of the integrands, it is clear that the interval of integration which is from $-\pi$ to π may be replaced by any interval of length 2π.

If we now assume that the series (6.1.1) can be integrated term by term from $-\pi$ to π, we find at once that

$$\int_{-\pi}^{\pi} f(x) \, dx = \tfrac{1}{2} a_0 (2\pi) + 0$$

on making use of (6.2.3), (6.2.1) with $m = 0$, $n \neq 0$, and (6.2.6) with $m \neq 0$, $n = 0$. Thus

$$a_0 = \frac{1}{\pi} \int_{-\pi}^{\pi} f(x) \, dx. \tag{6.2.7}$$

Next we multiply both sides of equation (6.1.1) by $\cos nx$ and integrate from $-\pi$ to π, again assuming that termwise integration is justified. We obtain

$$\int_{-\pi}^{\pi} f(x) \cos nx \, dx = 0 + a_n(\pi) + 0$$

on making use of (6.2.1), (6.2.2) and (6.2.6). Thus

$$a_n = \frac{1}{\pi} \int_{-\pi}^{\pi} f(x) \cos nx \, dx. \tag{6.2.8}$$

In a similar manner, multiplying both sides of equation (6.1.1) by $\sin nx$ and integrating we obtain

$$b_n = \frac{1}{\pi} \int_{-\pi}^{\pi} f(x) \sin nx \, dx. \tag{6.2.9}$$

We note that (6.2.7) can be obtained by setting $n = 0$ in (6.2.8) and need not be listed separately. For this reason, $\frac{1}{2}a_0$ was introduced in (6.1.1).

If we assume that the function $f(x)$ is integrable over the interval $(-\pi, \pi)$, the coefficients a_n and b_n can always be calculated by formulas (6.2.8) and (6.2.9). We may then associate the series which appears on the right side of (6.1.1) with the function $f(x)$. There is no guarantee, however, that this series is convergent, or even if convergent, that its sum is $f(x)$. Fortunately for most functions $f(x)$ which arise in practical problems, it is true that the Fourier series does represent the function in a suitable sense.

Most functions which arise in practice are either continuous or have only finite discontinuities. As in Section 5.6, we say that a function $f(x)$ has a jump discontinuity or a finite discontinuity at a point x_0 if the right- and left-hand limits

$$\lim_{h \to 0^+} f(x_0 + h) \quad \text{and} \quad \lim_{h \to 0^+} f(x_0 - h)$$

both exist but are not equal. Thus a finite discontinuity is represented by a finite gap or jump in the graph of the function.

We state without proof the following theorem of Dirichlet which is sufficient to cover most situations which arise in practical problems.

THEOREM. If $f(x)$ is a bounded function of period 2π, and if in any one period it has at most a finite number of maxima and minima and a finite number of discontinuities, the Fourier series of $f(x)$ converges to $f(x)$ at all points where $f(x)$ is continuous and converges to the average of the left- and right-hand limits of $f(x)$ at each point where $f(x)$ is discontinuous.

It should be remarked that because of the hypothesis on $f(x)$ in this theorem, all of the discontinuities of $f(x)$ must be finite discontinuities.

6.3 EXAMPLES OF FOURIER SERIES

In this section we construct the Fourier series of various functions and point out certain interesting properties of the expansions.

Example 1. Expand the function

$$f(x) = x, \qquad -\pi < x < \pi$$

in a Fourier series.

We note that this is an odd function, that is, $f(-x) = -f(x)$. Since $\cos n(-x) = \cos nx$, the function $\cos nx$ is an even function. Consequently $x \cos nx$ is an odd function, and since the integral of an odd function over a symmetric interval is obviously zero, we see at once that $a_n = 0$ for all n.

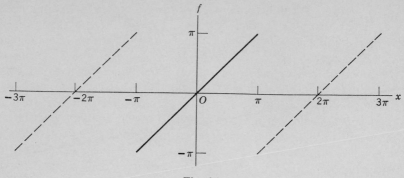

Fig. 6.1.

Also $x \sin nx$ is similarly seen to be an even function, and if we take account of the symmetry of its graph about the y-axis we see that

$$b_n = \frac{1}{\pi} \int_{-\pi}^{\pi} x \sin nx \, dx = \frac{2}{\pi} \int_{0}^{\pi} x \sin nx \, dx$$

$$= \frac{2}{\pi} \left[\frac{-x \cos nx}{n} + \frac{\sin nx}{n^2} \right]_{0}^{\pi} = \frac{-2}{n} \cos n\pi = \frac{2}{n}(-1)^{n+1}.$$

Thus

$$f(x) = 2 \sum_{n=1}^{\infty} (-1)^{n+1} \frac{\sin nx}{n} = 2\left(\frac{\sin x}{1} - \frac{\sin 2x}{2} + \frac{\sin 3x}{3} - \cdots \right).$$

By the theorem of Dirichlet, we know that this series converges to x for $-\pi < x < \pi$. Since the series is periodic with period 2π it must converge to the periodic extension of $f(x)$ for values of x outside of this interval. The graph of this periodic extension is shown in Fig. 6.1. Note that the Fourier series converges to 0 for $x = \cdots, -3\pi, -\pi, \pi, 3\pi, \cdots$, and thus converges to the average of the left- and right-hand limits of the extended function. Specifically we can say that

$$2 \sum_{n=1}^{\infty} (-1)^{n+1} \frac{\sin nx}{n} = x, \qquad -\pi < x < \pi$$

$$= x - 2\pi, \qquad \pi < x < 3\pi$$

$$= x + 2\pi, \qquad -3\pi < x < -\pi$$

$$= 0, \qquad x = (2m+1)\pi, \qquad m = 0, \pm 1, \pm 2, \cdots.$$

Example 2. Expand the function

$$f(x) = 0, \qquad -\pi < x < 0$$

$$= 1, \qquad 0 < x < \pi$$

in a Fourier series.

We have

$$a_n = \frac{1}{\pi} \int_0^\pi 1 \cdot \cos nx \, dx = 1, \qquad n = 0$$

$$= 0, \qquad n \neq 0.$$

$$b_n = \frac{1}{\pi} \int_0^\pi 1 \cdot \sin nx \, dx = -\frac{1}{\pi n} \cos nx \Big|_0^\pi = \frac{2}{\pi n}, \qquad n \text{ odd}$$

$$= 0, \qquad n \text{ even.}$$

Thus

$$f(x) = \frac{1}{2} + \frac{2}{\pi} \left(\frac{\sin x}{1} + \frac{\sin 3x}{3} + \frac{\sin 5x}{5} + \cdots \right)$$

$$= \frac{1}{2} + \frac{2}{\pi} \sum_{n=0}^\infty \frac{\sin (2n + 1)x}{2n + 1}.$$

It is instructive to study the extended function in order to see why so many of the coefficients of the Fourier series are zero. The graph of the extended function is shown in Fig. 6.2.

It is clear from (6.2.7) that the constant term in a Fourier series is always the average value of the function. Here it is $\frac{1}{2}$. The graph is readily seen to be symmetric with respect to the point $(0, \frac{1}{2})$ and consequently the function $f(x) - \frac{1}{2}$ is an odd function. For this reason all a_n for the latter function must be zero as in example 1. It is also interesting to observe that the graph of the extended function is symmetric about the line $x = \pi/2$. Since the graphs of $y = \sin x$, $\sin 3x$, $\cdots$ possess the same symmetry but those of $y = \sin 2x$, $\sin 4x$, $\cdots$ do not, it is not surprising that the latter functions do not appear in the series expansion.

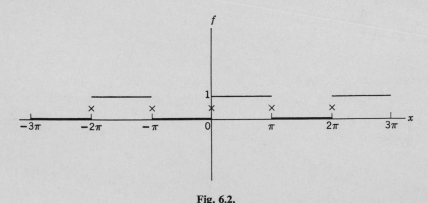

Fig. 6.2.

Example 3. Expand the function

$$f(x) = |x|, \qquad -\pi < x < \pi$$

in a Fourier series.

Since this is an even function, that is, $f(-x) = f(x)$, it follows that $f(x) \sin nx$ is an odd function and hence $b_n = 0$ for all n. Then

$$a_n = \frac{1}{\pi} \int_{-\pi}^{\pi} |x| \cos nx \, dx = \frac{2}{\pi} \int_0^{\pi} x \cos nx \, dx = \pi, \qquad n = 0$$

$$= \frac{2}{\pi} \left[\frac{x \sin nx}{n} + \frac{\cos nx}{n^2} \right]_0^{\pi} = \frac{-4}{\pi n^2}, \qquad n \text{ odd}$$

$$= 0, \qquad n \text{ even} \neq 0.$$

Hence

$$f(x) = \frac{\pi}{2} - \frac{4}{\pi} \sum_{n=0}^{\infty} \frac{\cos (2n + 1)x}{(2n + 1)^2}.$$

Example 4. Expand the function

$$f(x) = -1, \qquad -\pi < x < 0$$

$$= +1, \qquad 0 < x < \pi$$

in a Fourier series.

Since this is an odd function it follows that $f(x) \cos nx$ is an odd function and hence $a_n = 0$ for all n. Then

$$b_n = \frac{1}{\pi} \int_{-\pi}^{0} (-1) \sin nx \, dx + \frac{1}{\pi} \int_0^{\pi} 1 \cdot \sin nx \, dx$$

$$= \frac{2}{\pi} \int_0^{\pi} \sin nx \, dx = \frac{-2}{\pi n} \cos nx \Big|_0^{\pi} = \frac{-2}{\pi n} [(-1)^n - 1] = 0, \qquad n \text{ even}$$

$$= \frac{4}{\pi n}, \qquad n \text{ odd}.$$

Hence

$$f(x) = \frac{4}{\pi} \sum_{n=0}^{\infty} \frac{\sin (2n + 1)x}{2n + 1}.$$

Again note that this series converges to 0 for $x = 0, \pm\pi, \pm 2\pi, \cdots$, this being the average of the left- and right-hand limits at these points of discontinuity.

Example 5. Expand the function

$$f(x) = -\pi, \qquad -\pi < x < 0$$

$$= x, \qquad 0 < x < \pi$$

in a Fourier series.

This function possesses no obvious symmetry. We find at once that

$$a_n = \frac{1}{\pi} \int_{-\pi}^{0} -\pi \cos nx \, dx + \frac{1}{\pi} \int_{0}^{\pi} x \cos nx \, dx$$

$$= -\frac{\pi}{2}, \qquad n = 0$$

$$= -\frac{2}{\pi n^2}, \qquad n \text{ odd}$$

$$= 0, \qquad n \text{ even} \neq 0.$$

$$b_n = \frac{1}{\pi} \int_{-\pi}^{0} -\pi \sin nx \, dx + \frac{1}{\pi} \int_{0}^{\pi} x \sin nx \, dx$$

$$= \frac{1 - 2\cos n\pi}{n} = \frac{1 - 2(-1)^n}{n}.$$

Hence

$$f(x) = -\frac{\pi}{4} - \frac{2}{\pi} \sum_{n=0}^{\infty} \frac{\cos(2n+1)x}{(2n+1)^2} + \sum_{n=1}^{\infty} \frac{1 - 2(-1)^n}{n} \sin nx.$$

6.4 HALF-RANGE SERIES

In examples 1 and 4 we encountered an odd function, and we observed that $a_n = 0$ for all n. This will be true whenever $f(x)$ is an odd function. Here,

$$b_n = \frac{2}{\pi} \int_{0}^{\pi} f(x) \sin nx \, dx \qquad (6.4.1)$$

and

$$f(x) = \sum_{n=1}^{\infty} b_n \sin nx. \qquad (6.4.2)$$

Thus for any $f(x)$ defined only in $(0, \pi)$, the equations (6.4.1) and (6.4.2) may be used to find a Fourier sine series of period 2π, which represents $f(x)$ in $(0, \pi)$. The use of these formulas means that $f(x)$ has been extended to form an odd function of period 2π. If $f(x)$ satisfies the conditions of Dirichlet's theorem, the series (6.4.2) with coefficients calculated by (6.4.1) will represent the extended odd periodic function and hence will represent $f(x)$ in $0 < x < \pi$.

In example 3 we encountered an even function and we observed that $b_n = 0$ for all n. This will be true whenever $f(x)$ is an even function. Here,

$$a_n = \frac{2}{\pi} \int_{0}^{\pi} f(x) \cos nx \, dx \qquad (6.4.3)$$

and

$$f(x) = \frac{a_0}{2} + \sum_{n=1}^{\infty} a_n \cos nx. \qquad (6.4.4)$$

Thus for any $f(x)$ defined only in $(0, \pi)$, the equations (6.4.3) and (6.4.4) may be used to find a Fourier cosine series of period 2π which represents $f(x)$ in $(0, \pi)$. The use of these formulas means that $f(x)$ has been extended to form an even function of period 2π. If $f(x)$ satisfies the conditions of Dirichlet's theorem, the series (6.4.4) with coefficients calculated by (6.4.3) will represent the extended even periodic function and hence will represent $f(x)$ in $0 < x < \pi$.

As an example, suppose it is desired to represent the function $f(x) = x$ in $0 < x < \pi$. The Fourier sine series is just the series of example 1 and the Fourier cosine series is just the series of example 3.

6.5 CHANGE OF INTERVAL

If the function $f(x)$ has period $2L$ instead of 2π, a change of variable $x' = \pi x/L$ may be used to change an interval of length $2L$ into one of length 2π. The formulas (6.1.1), (6.2.8), and (6.2.9) then take the form

$$f(x) = \frac{1}{2} a_0 + \sum_{n=1}^{\infty} \left(a_n \cos \frac{n\pi x}{L} + b_n \sin \frac{n\pi x}{L} \right) \qquad (6.5.1)$$

with

$$a_n = \frac{1}{L} \int_{-L}^{L} f(x) \cos \frac{n\pi x}{L} \, dx, \qquad (6.5.2)$$

$$b_n = \frac{1}{L} \int_{-L}^{L} f(x) \sin \frac{n\pi x}{L} \, dx. \qquad (6.5.3)$$

Since $f(x)$ has period $2L$, the interval of integration in these two formulas may be replaced by any interval of length $2L$.

Similar remarks apply to the half-range series; it seems unnecessary to write down the obvious modifications of formulas (6.4.1)–(6.4.4).

6.6 APPLICATION OF FOURIER SERIES TO SOLUTION OF ORDINARY DIFFERENTIAL EQUATIONS

In Section 5.3 we discussed the solution of nonhomogeneous differential equations in which the right member involved $\sin mx$ and $\cos mx$. We now show how to solve such equations when the right hand member is an arbitrary periodic function.

We consider the second-order differential equation

$$\frac{d^2y}{dx^2} + p\frac{dy}{dx} + qy = f(x) \tag{6.6.1}$$

where p and q are constants and $f(x)$ has period 2π. We assume that $f(x)$ satisfies the conditions of Dirichlet's theorem; therefore, it can be represented by the Fourier series

$$f(x) = \tfrac{1}{2}a_0 + \sum_{n=1}^{\infty}(a_n\cos nx + b_n\sin nx), \tag{6.6.2}$$

where a_n and b_n are given by (6.2.8) and (6.2.9).

Using the method of Section 5.3, we find that particular integrals of the equations

$$\frac{d^2y}{dx^2} + p\frac{dy}{dx} + qy = a_n\cos nx$$

and

$$\frac{d^2y}{dx^2} + p\frac{dy}{dx} + qy = b_n\sin nx$$

are respectively

$$y_p = \frac{q - n^2}{(q - n^2)^2 + n^2p^2}\,a_n\cos nx + \frac{np}{(q - n^2)^2 + n^2p^2}\,a_n\sin nx$$

and

$$y_p = \frac{-np}{(q - n^2)^2 + n^2p^2}\,b_n\cos nx + \frac{q - n^2}{n^2p^2 + (q - n^2)^2}\,b_n\sin nx.$$

Also the particular integral of

$$\frac{d^2y}{dx^2} + p\frac{dy}{dx} + qy = \frac{a_0}{2}$$

is $a_0/2q$. If we apply the principle of superposition we obtain as a particular integral of (6.6.1) the function

$$y_p = \frac{a_0}{2q} + \sum_{n=1}^{\infty}\left(\frac{(q - n^2)a_n - npb_n}{(q - n^2)^2 + n^2p^2}\cos nx + \frac{npa_n + (q - n^2)b_n}{(q - n^2)^2 + n^2p^2}\sin nx\right).$$

To obtain the complete solution we must, of course, add the complementary function.

As a further example of the method we discuss the solution of a differential equation arising in the study of the deflection of a column; (for the derivation of the differential equation see Hoff [13, pp. 230–232]). The differential equation is

$$EIy^{iv} + Py'' = -Py_0'' \tag{6.6.3}$$

where E, I, and P are constants and y_0 is a given function of x. The end conditions are

$$y = y'' = 0 \quad \text{when} \quad x = 0, L. \tag{6.6.4}$$

The complementary function is easily found to be

$$y_c = A \cos kx + B \sin kx + Cx + D \tag{6.6.5}$$

where $k^2 = P/EI$.

We assume the function y_0 can be expanded in a Fourier sine series

$$y_0 = \sum_{n=1}^{\infty} b_n \sin \frac{n\pi x}{L}$$

where

$$b_n = \frac{2}{L} \int_0^L y_0 \sin \frac{n\pi x}{L} \, dx.$$

Then

$$y_0'' = -\sum_{n=1}^{\infty} b_n \left(\frac{n\pi}{L}\right)^2 \sin \frac{n\pi x}{L}.$$

Proceeding as in Section 5.3, we find that a particular integral of the differential equation

$$EIy^{\text{iv}} + Py'' = Pb_n \left(\frac{n\pi}{L}\right)^2 \sin \frac{n\pi x}{L}$$

is

$$y_p = \frac{Pb_n}{EI\left(\frac{n\pi}{L}\right)^2 - P} \sin \frac{n\pi x}{L} = \frac{b_n \sin(n\pi x/L)}{n^2 P_E/P - 1}$$

where

$$P_E = \pi^2 \frac{EI}{L^2}$$

is Euler's buckling load. Then by the principle of superposition the particular integral of (6.6.3) is

$$y_p = \sum_{n=1}^{\infty} \frac{b_n \sin(n\pi x/L)}{n^2 P_E/P - 1}.$$

If we add the complementary function (6.6.5) we obtain as the complete solution of (6.6.3)

$$y = A \cos kx + B \sin kx + Cx + D + \sum_{n=1}^{\infty} \frac{b_n \sin(n\pi x/L)}{n^2 P_E/P - 1}. \tag{6.6.6}$$

The values of the four constants A, B, C, D must next be determined from the boundary conditions (6.6.4).

The second derivative of the solution is

$$y'' = -Ak^2 \cos kx - Bk^2 \sin kx - \sum_{n=1}^{\infty} \frac{b_n(n\pi/L)^2 \sin (n\pi x/L)}{n^2 P_E/P - 1}.$$

$$(6.6.7)$$

When $x = 0$, then $y'' = 0$. Substitution of these values in (6.6.7) yields $A = 0$. Also when $x = 0$, then $y = 0$. Substitution of these values in (6.6.6) yields $D = 0$. Moreover $y'' = 0$ when $x = L$ so that $B = 0$ unless $\sin kL = 0$. For certain particular values of k, the function $\sin kL$ vanishes. These values of k correspond to certain physical conditions which we do not discuss here. (See Hoff [13, p. 228].) For all other values of k we must have $B = 0$. Finally $y = 0$ when $x = L$ so that $C = 0$. We conclude that the desired solution of the differential equation (6.6.3) is

$$y = \sum_{n=1}^{\infty} \frac{b_n \sin (n\pi x/L)}{n^2 P_E/P - 1}.$$

6.7 SOLUTION OF THE HEAT EQUATION BY MEANS OF FOURIER SERIES

In this section we illustrate the use of Fourier series in the solution of partial differential equations, by discussing the solution of the heat equation.

We consider a thin uniform rod of length π having its sides thermally insulated. There is no loss of generality in taking the length of the rod to be π, since any length can be considered to be π if a suitable unit of length is chosen. We assume that its ends are kept at temperature 0 at all time t. We assume that the initial temperature is given by a function $f(x)$ where x is the distance from one end of the rod. If we denote the temperature at point x and time t by $u(x, t)$, then $u(x, t)$ satisfies the differential equation

$$\frac{\partial u}{\partial t} = c^2 \frac{\partial^2 u}{\partial x^2} \qquad (6.7.1)$$

where c^2 is a physical constant known as the thermal diffusivity. Moreover $u(x, t)$ satisfies the initial condition

$$u(x, 0) = f(x), \qquad 0 < x < \pi \qquad (6.7.2)$$

and the boundary conditions

$$u(0, t) = 0, \qquad u(\pi, t) = 0, \qquad t \geq 0. \qquad (6.7.3)$$

We begin by seeking a solution of equation (6.7.1) in the form $u = X(x)T(t)$. Substituting this into equation (6.7.1) we obtain

$$\frac{1}{c^2 T}\frac{dT}{dt} = \frac{1}{X}\frac{d^2 X}{dx^2} = -k^2. \tag{6.7.4}$$

Here k^2 is a constant since x and t are independent variables, and we have written $-k^2$ because the constant is negative in the case useful for our problem. Solving the differential equations which result from (6.7.4) we obtain

$$u(x, t) = (A\cos kx + B\sin kx)e^{-c^2 k^2 t}$$

as a particular solution of (6.7.1).

We must choose $A = 0$ to satisfy the first of the conditions (6.7.3). The second condition (6.7.3) will be satisfied if

$$B\sin k\pi = 0 \quad\text{or}\quad k = n,$$

where n is any positive integer. Hence

$$B_n e^{-c^2 n^2 t}\sin nx, \qquad n = 1, 2, 3, \cdots$$

is a set of terms each of which satisfies (6.7.1) and (6.7.3). By superposition we see that

$$u(x, t) = \sum_{n=1}^{\infty} B_n e^{-c^2 n^2 t}\sin nx \tag{6.7.5}$$

also satisfies (6.7.1) and (6.7.3). To satisfy condition (6.7.2) we must have

$$u(x, 0) = \sum_{n=1}^{\infty} B_n \sin nx = f(x).$$

Thus B_n are the coefficients of the Fourier sine series of $f(x)$ and may be calculated by means of formula (6.4.1). With these values of B_n the solution of our problem is given by equation (6.7.5).

The series solution (6.7.5) is reasonably convenient for numerical calculations utilizing high-speed automatic computers. Because of the exponential factors which decrease rapidly, the number of terms required for accurate results is usually not excessive except for $t = 0$, but, since the initial values are given, there is no need to carry out the calculations for this value of t.

Next we consider a modification of the problem just discussed. We again assume that $u(x, t)$ satisfies (6.7.1) and the initial condition (6.7.2), but we change the boundary conditions to

$$u(0, t) = A, \qquad u(\pi, t) = B, \qquad t \geq 0 \tag{6.7.6}$$

where A and B are constants. We show how to reduce this problem to the previous case. We must make use of the steady-state solution of equation

(6.7.1). Since this is independent of t it will be a solution of

$$\frac{\partial^2 u}{\partial x^2} = 0$$

and consequently will be of the form $u = c_1 x + c_2$. Thus the steady-state solution satisfying (6.7.6) is easily seen to be

$$u_s = \frac{B - A}{\pi} x + A. \tag{6.7.7}$$

If we let $u_T = u - u_s$, it is easily verified that u_T satisfies (6.7.1) and (6.7.3) and that (6.7.2) is replaced by

$$u_T(x, 0) = f(x) - \frac{B - A}{\pi} x - A. \tag{6.7.8}$$

We have calculated the Fourier sine series of x and 1 in examples 1 and 4. Using these results we see that if B_n and C_n denote the coefficients of the Fourier sine series of $f(x)$ and $u_T(x, 0)$ respectively, we have

$$C_n = B_n + \frac{B - A}{\pi} \cdot \frac{2(-1)^n}{n} - \frac{2A}{\pi n}(1 - (-1)^n). \tag{6.7.9}$$

Then the solution of the problem is given by

$$u(x, t) = \frac{B - A}{\pi} x + A + \sum_{n=1}^{\infty} C_n e^{-c^2 n^2 t} \sin nx$$

with C_n given by (6.7.9).

The methods discussed are rather special and would not solve the more general problem in which the boundary conditions (6.7.3) are replaced by

$$u(0, t) = g_1(t), \qquad u(\pi, t) = g_2(t), \qquad t \ge 0. \tag{6.7.10}$$

In Chapter 7 we discuss finite difference methods for solving the heat equation, and these methods are applicable to this more general problem without appreciable change.

As an example of the use of a Fourier cosine series we consider another modification of the heat conduction problem discussed at the beginning of this section. We again seek $u(x, t)$ satisfying the equation (6.7.1) and the initial condition (6.7.2), but for boundary conditions we take

$$\frac{\partial u(0, t)}{\partial x} = 0, \qquad \frac{\partial u(\pi, t)}{\partial x} = 0, \qquad t \ge 0. \tag{6.7.11}$$

As before, a particular solution of (6.7.1) is

$$u(x, t) = (A \cos kx + B \sin kx)e^{-c^2 k^2 t}$$

Hence

$$\frac{\partial u}{\partial x} = (-Ak \sin kx + Bk \cos kx)e^{-c^2 k^2 t}.$$

We must choose $B = 0$ to satisfy the first of conditions (6.7.11). The second condition will be satisfied if $k = n$ where n is any nonnegative integer. Thus

$$u(x, t) = \frac{A_0}{2} + \sum_{n=1}^{\infty} A_n e^{-c^2 n^2 t} \cos nx \qquad (6.7.12)$$

provides a solution of (6.7.1) which satisfies (6.7.11). To satisfy the initial condition (6.7.2), we must have

$$u(x, 0) = \frac{A_0}{2} + \sum_{n=1}^{\infty} A_n \cos nx = f(x).$$

Thus A_n are the coefficients of the Fourier cosine series of $f(x)$ and may be calculated by means of formula (6.4.3). With these values of A_n the solution of our problem is given by equation (6.7.12).

6.8 DOUBLE FOURIER SERIES

We may extend the ideas of Fourier series to obtain an expansion of a function of two variables in a double Fourier series. We consider a function $f(x, y)$ having period 2π in each of its variables x and y. Then $f(x, y)$ may be expanded in a double Fourier series of the form

$$f(x, y) = \frac{a_{00}}{4} + \frac{1}{2} \sum_{m=1}^{\infty} a_{m0} \cos mx + \frac{1}{2} \sum_{n=1}^{\infty} a_{0n} \cos ny$$

$$+ \sum_{m,n=1}^{\infty} (a_{mn} \cos mx \cos ny + b_{mn} \cos mx \sin ny \qquad (6.8.1)$$

$$+ c_{mn} \sin mx \cos ny + d_{mn} \sin mx \sin ny).$$

To obtain formulas for the determination of the coefficients in (6.8.1), we proceed as in Section 6.2, making use of the formulas (6.2.1)–(6.2.6). The formulas for the coefficients are easily found to be

$$a_{mn} = \frac{1}{\pi^2} \int_{-\pi}^{\pi} \int_{-\pi}^{\pi} f(x, y) \cos mx \cos ny \, dx \, dy, \qquad (6.8.2)$$

$$b_{mn} = \frac{1}{\pi^2} \int_{-\pi}^{\pi} \int_{-\pi}^{\pi} f(x, y) \cos mx \sin ny \, dx \, dy, \qquad (6.8.3)$$

$$c_{mn} = \frac{1}{\pi^2} \int_{-\pi}^{\pi} \int_{-\pi}^{\pi} f(x, y) \sin mx \cos ny \, dx \, dy, \qquad (6.8.4)$$

$$d_{mn} = \frac{1}{\pi^2} \int_{-\pi}^{\pi} \int_{-\pi}^{\pi} f(x, y) \sin mx \sin nx \, dx \, dy. \qquad (6.8.5)$$

We do not attempt a discussion of the conditions under which the series (6.8.1) converges to $f(x, y)$. We remark only that conditions similar to those encountered in the single series case but somewhat more restrictive are sufficient to ensure convergence. For most functions which arise in practical problems, the series does represent the function in a suitable sense.

As in the single series we may consider half-range series which represent the given function $f(x, y)$ in the square bounded by the lines $x = 0$, $x = \pi$, $y = 0$, $y = \pi$. There are four possibilities to consider but we confine ourselves to the case in which the function is to be expanded in a pure sine series. This means that we extend the function $f(x, y)$ to be an odd function in both x and y and also make it periodic with period 2π in both variables. We then have

$$f(x, y) = \sum_{m,n=1}^{\infty} d_{mn} \sin mx \sin ny \qquad (6.8.6)$$

with

$$d_{mn} = \frac{4}{\pi^2} \int_0^{\pi} \int_0^{\pi} f(x, y) \sin mx \sin ny \, dx \, dy. \qquad (6.8.7)$$

The remarks in Section 6.5 concerning change of interval are applicable to the double Fourier series case with the obvious modifications.

6.9 APPLICATION OF DOUBLE FOURIER SERIES TO A RECTANGULAR PLATE PROBLEM

We consider a rectangular plate in the xy-plane bounded by the lines $x = 0$, $x = a$, $y = 0$, $y = b$. A load $q = q(x, y)$ is assumed to be distributed over the surface of the plate. Then the differential equation for the deflection $w = w(x, y)$ is found to be

$$\frac{\partial^4 w}{\partial x^4} + 2 \frac{\partial^4 w}{\partial x^2 \, \partial y^2} + \frac{\partial^4 w}{\partial y^4} = \frac{q}{D} \qquad (6.9.1)$$

where D is a physical quantity called the flexural ridigity of the plate. If the edges of the plate are simply supported, the boundary conditions are

$$w = 0, \frac{\partial^2 w}{\partial x^2} = 0 \quad \text{for} \quad x = 0 \quad \text{and} \quad x = a$$

$$w = 0, \frac{\partial^2 w}{\partial y^2} = 0 \quad \text{for} \quad y = 0 \quad \text{and} \quad y = b. \qquad (6.9.2)$$

Before considering the case of a general load we examine the special case in which

$$q = q_0 \sin \frac{\pi x}{a} \sin \frac{\pi y}{b} \qquad (6.9.3)$$

where q_0 denotes the intensity of the load at the center of the plate. It is clear that all boundary conditions (6.9.2) are satisfied if we take for the deflection the expression

$$w = C \sin \frac{\pi x}{a} \sin \frac{\pi y}{b} \qquad (6.9.4)$$

in which C is a constant that must be chosen so that w will satisfy equation (6.9.1) with q given by (6.9.3). If we substitute (6.9.4) into equation (6.9.1) we find that

$$\pi^4 \left(\frac{1}{a^2} + \frac{1}{b^2} \right)^2 C = \frac{q_0}{D}.$$

Solving for C we find that the solution of this special problem is given by

$$w = \frac{q_0}{\pi^4 D \left(\dfrac{1}{a^2} + \dfrac{1}{b^2} \right)^2} \sin \frac{\pi x}{a} \sin \frac{\pi y}{b}. \qquad (6.9.5)$$

If the sinusoidal load distribution is given by

$$q = q_0 \sin \frac{m\pi x}{a} \sin \frac{n\pi y}{b}$$

where m and n are integers then, proceeding as above, the deflection is given by

$$w = \frac{q_0}{\pi^4 D \left(\dfrac{m^2}{a^2} + \dfrac{n^2}{b^2} \right)^2} \sin \frac{m\pi x}{a} \sin \frac{n\pi y}{b}. \qquad (6.9.6)$$

Turning now to the problem with a general load $q(x, y)$, we represent the load function in the form of a double Fourier series

$$q(x, y) = \sum_{m,n=1}^{\infty} d_{mn} \sin \frac{m\pi x}{a} \sin \frac{n\pi y}{b}$$

with

$$d_{mn} = \frac{4}{ab} \int_0^a \int_0^b q(x, y) \sin \frac{m\pi x}{a} \sin \frac{n\pi y}{b} \, dx \, dy.$$

Thus the given load is represented as a sum of partial sinusoidal loadings. The deflection produced by each partial loading was discussed earlier and the total deflection will be obtained by summation of such terms of the form of (6.9.6). Hence we obtain

$$w = \frac{1}{\pi^4 D} \sum_{m,n=1}^{\infty} \frac{d_{mn}}{\left(\dfrac{m^2}{a^2} + \dfrac{n^2}{b^2} \right)^2} \sin \frac{m\pi x}{a} \sin \frac{n\pi y}{b}.$$

6.10 THE TWO-DIMENSIONAL HEAT CONDUCTION PROBLEM

In Section 6.7 we discussed the heat conduction problem in one space dimension. We now consider a similar problem in two space dimensions.

We consider a plate in the xy-plane bounded by the lines $x = 0$, $x = a$, $y = 0$, $y = b$. We assume that its faces are thermally insulated and that its edges are kept at temperature 0 at all times t. We assume that the initial temperature is given by a function $f(x, y)$. Then the temperature $u(x, y, t)$ satisfies the differential equation

$$\frac{\partial u}{\partial t} = c^2 \left(\frac{\partial^2 u}{\partial x^2} + \frac{\partial^2 u}{\partial y^2} \right) \tag{6.10.1}$$

where c^2 is a physical constant. Moreover $u(x, y, t)$ satisfies the initial condition

$$u(x, y, 0) = f(x, y), \qquad 0 < x < a, \qquad 0 < y < b \tag{6.10.2}$$

and the boundary conditions

$$\begin{aligned} u(0, y, t) = 0, \qquad u(a, y, t) = 0, \\ t \geq 0 \\ u(x, 0, t) = 0, \qquad u(x, b, t) = 0. \end{aligned} \tag{6.10.3}$$

As in Section 6.7 we find that a simple solution of equation (6.10.1) which satisfies the boundary conditions (6.10.3) takes the form

$$D_{mn} e^{-c^2 s^2_{mn} t} \sin \frac{m\pi x}{a} \sin \frac{n\pi y}{b}$$

where

$$s^2_{mn} = \pi^2 \left(\frac{m^2}{a^2} + \frac{n^2}{b^2} \right), \qquad m, n, \text{ integers.}$$

By superposition we see that

$$u(x, y, t) = \sum_{m,n=1}^{\infty} D_{mn} e^{-c^2 s^2_{mn} t} \sin \frac{m\pi x}{a} \sin \frac{n\pi y}{b} \tag{6.10.4}$$

also satisfies (6.10.1) and (6.10.3). To satisfy the initial condition (6.10.2) we must have

$$u(x, y, 0) = \sum_{m,n=1}^{\infty} D_{mn} \sin \frac{m\pi x}{a} \sin \frac{n\pi y}{b} = f(x, y).$$

Thus D_{mn} are the coefficients of the double Fourier sine series of $f(x, y)$ and may be calculated by the formula

$$D_{mn} = \frac{4}{ab} \int_0^a \int_0^b f(x, y) \sin \frac{m\pi x}{a} \sin \frac{n\pi y}{b} \, dx \, dy.$$

As a further example of the use of Fourier series we consider the two-dimensional steady-state heat conduction problem. Since the temperature $u(x, y)$ is now independent of time the differential equation (6.10.1) reduces to

$$\frac{\partial^2 u}{\partial x^2} + \frac{\partial^2 u}{\partial y^2} = 0 \qquad (6.10.5)$$

which is the familiar Laplace's equation. We again consider the plate to be in the xy-plane bounded by the lines $x = 0$, $x = a$, $y = 0$, $y = b$. We assume its faces to be thermally insulated, but to consider a nontrivial problem we change the boundary conditions since the boundary conditions (6.10.3) would lead to an identically zero steady-state temperature. This is evident on physical grounds and also follows from equation (6.10.4) by letting t become infinite. For our example we impose the boundary conditions

$$u(0, y) = 0, \qquad u(a, y) = 0,$$

$$\qquad (6.10.6)$$

$$u(x, 0) = 0, \qquad u(x, b) = f(x).$$

There is, of course, no initial condition as the solution is independent of time.

As in Section 6.7, we assume a solution in the form $X(x) Y(y)$ and find that a simple solution of equation (6.10.5) which satisfies the first three of the boundary conditions (6.10.6) takes the form

$$B_n \sin \frac{n\pi x}{a} \sinh \frac{n\pi y}{a}, \qquad n = \text{integer}. \qquad (6.10.7)$$

By superposition we see that

$$u(x, y) = \sum_{n=1}^{\infty} B_n \sin \frac{n\pi x}{a} \sinh \frac{n\pi y}{a} \qquad (6.10.8)$$

also satisfies (6.10.5) and the first three conditions (6.10.6). To satisfy the fourth boundary condition we must have

$$u(x, b) = \sum_{n=1}^{\infty} B_n \sin \frac{n\pi x}{a} \sinh \frac{n\pi b}{a} = f(x).$$

Thus if b_n are the coefficients of the Fourier sine series of $f(x)$, then

$$B_n = \frac{b_n}{\sinh \dfrac{n\pi b}{a}}.$$

Substitution of these coefficients into equation (6.10.8) yields the desired solution of the problem.

chapter 7 Numerical solution of partial differential equations

7.1 INTRODUCTION

In Chapter 6 we made use of Fourier series to obtain the solution of certain problems involving partial differential equations, such as, for example, the problem of heat conduction. It was pointed out that the method described is rather special and would fail in many problems in which the boundary conditions are more general than those used in the examples discussed or in which the differential equations are more general. In this chapter we describe numerical methods of solution which will be suitable for problems of the general type as well as for the more special problems of Chapter 6.

We begin by describing three typical problems which are representative of the three types of differential equations which may be encountered.

Consider a rigid wire whose orthogonal projection on the xy-plane is a simple closed curve C. This frame contains an ideal elastic membrane of uniform density under uniform tension. Let $u(x, y)$ denote the deflection of this membrane measured from the xy-plane. Under suitable physical assumptions it can be shown that $u(x, y)$ satisfies Laplace's differential equation $u_{xx} + u_{yy} = 0$ in the interior R of C. The values of u on the boundary C are the prescribed deflection f of the wire frame. Thus u is a solution of the problem

$$u_{xx} + u_{yy} = 0 \text{ in } R, \qquad u = f \text{ on } C. \tag{7.1.1}$$

This is often called Dirichlet's problem for Laplace's equation.

173

As a second example we consider the longitudinal vibrations of a long, straight rod of small cross section, which coincides with the x-axis. Let $u(x, t)$ denote the displacement at time t from the rest position of the point which, at rest, has the abscissa x. If $u(x, t)$ is small and if the units are suitably chosen, then u is a solution of the wave equation $u_{tt} - u_{xx} = 0$. We may expect the displacement u to be uniquely determined if the initial displacement $u(x, 0)$ and the initial velocity $u_t(x, 0)$ are prescribed. Thus for $t > 0$, u is a solution of the problem

$$u_{tt} - u_{xx} = 0 \text{ for } t > 0, \qquad u(x, 0) = f(x), \qquad u_t(x, 0) = g(x) \quad (7.1.2)$$

where $f(x)$ and $g(x)$ are prescribed functions. This is an example of an initial-value problem or "Cauchy's problem" as it is sometimes called.

As a third example we consider a heat conduction problem. We consider a straight infinite rod of small cross section which coincides with the x-axis. Let $u(x, t)$ denote its temperature at the point x and time t. We assume that the rod is thermally insulated and that the initial temperature $u(x, 0)$ is known. Then the differential equation that ideally governs the flow of heat is $u_t - u_{xx} = 0$, provided the units are defined properly. Thus u is a solution of the problem

$$u_t - u_{xx} = 0 \text{ for } t > 0, \qquad u(x, 0) = f(x). \qquad (7.1.3)$$

Once again we have an initial-value problem.

Both of the problems (7.1.2) and (7.1.3) may be modified by restricting x to lie in a finite interval $a \leq x \leq b$. Here the values of u are prescribed on the boundaries $x = a$ and $x = b$. Thus we add to the conditions stated in (7.1.2) or (7.1.3) the boundary conditions

$$u(a, t) = h_1(t), \qquad u(b, t) = h_2(t) \qquad (7.1.4)$$

where $h_1(t)$ and $h_2(t)$ are prescribed functions of t.

Examination of problems (7.1.1)–(7.1.3) reveals that different subsidiary conditions are associated with each of the three differential equations. It can be shown that no permutation of the subsidiary conditions leads to a well-posed problem. For this reason partial differential equations can be classified according to the type of subsidiary conditions that must be imposed to produce a well-posed problem. This classification can be described in a particularly simple manner for second-order linear differential equations in two independent variables. The most general differential equation of this type is

$$Au_{xx} + 2Bu_{xy} + Cu_{yy} + Du_x + Eu_y + Fu + G = 0$$

with coefficients that are functions of x and y only. This equation is called elliptic, hyperbolic, or parabolic according as the quantity $AC - B^2$

is positive, negative, or zero. It is clear that Laplace's equation $u_{xx} + u_{yy} = 0$ is elliptic, that the wave equation $u_{tt} - u_{xx} = 0$ is hyperbolic, and that the heat conduction equation $u_t - u_{xx} = 0$ is parabolic. In more general equations than these three, it may happen that the type is different in different parts of the xy-plane. For example, the differential equation $u_{xx} + yu_{yy} = 0$ is elliptic for $y > 0$, hyperbolic for $y < 0$, and parabolic for $y = 0$.

It can be shown that the subsidiary conditions imposed in (7.1.1)–(7.1.3) will generate well-posed problems also when combined with more general differential equations of the respective type, but not when combined with differential equations of any other type.

In the sections to follow we describe the numerical solution of each of these types of differential equations. For simplicity we describe the methods in terms of the simple representative of each type, but the methods are applicable to more general equations.

7.2 HYPERBOLIC EQUATIONS

We consider the problem defined by (7.1.2), namely

$$u_{tt} - u_{xx} = 0 \text{ for } t > 0, \qquad u(x, 0) = f(x), \qquad u_t(x, 0) = g(x). \quad (7.2.1)$$

If $F(x)$ and $G(x)$ are arbitrary twice differentiable functions, it is obvious that

$$u(x, t) = F(x + t) + G(x - t) \qquad (7.2.2)$$

is a solution of the differential equation of (7.2.1). The initial conditions require that

$$F(x) + G(x) = u(x, 0) = f(x)$$
$$F'(x) - G'(x) = u_t(x, 0) = g(x).$$

Differentiating the first of these equations, solving for $F'(x)$ and $G'(x)$, and integrating we see that

$$F(x) = \frac{1}{2}\left[f(x) + \int_0^x g(\xi)\, d\xi \right] + C_1$$

$$G(x) = \frac{1}{2}\left[f(x) - \int_0^x g(\xi)\, d\xi \right] + C_2$$

where C_1 and C_2 are constants of integration. If we use (7.2.2) and determine the constant of integration by setting $t = 0$, we obtain as the solution of the problem

$$u(x, t) = \frac{1}{2}\left[f(x + t) + f(x - t) + \int_{x-t}^{x+t} g(\xi)\, d\xi \right]. \qquad (7.2.3)$$

This is almost the only initial-value or boundary-value problem of any interest that can be solved in such an explicit and elementary manner.

From (7.2.3) we observe that the value of $u(x, t)$ at a point (x_0, t_0) depends only on the initial data on a segment of the x-axis cut off by the lines $x + t =$ constant and $x - t =$ constant that pass through (x_0, t_0). This segment is called the interval of dependence of the point (x_0, t_0). Conversely, the set of points (x, t) at which $u(x, t)$ is influenced by the initial data at a point $(x_0, 0)$ is the sector bounded by the lines $x + t = x_0$ and $x - t = x_0$. This sector is called the region of influence of the point $(x_0, 0)$. The lines $x \pm t =$ constant are called the characteristics of the differential equation $u_{tt} - u_{xx} = 0$. The notions of characteristics and domains of dependence arise also in more general hyperbolic problems.

Since equation (7.2.3) provides a complete solution of the problem (7.2.1), we do not really need a numerical solution of it. Because the method is easily described in terms of this problem, however, and because the method is applicable to more general problems, we proceed to describe how the problem (7.2.1) can be solved using a finite-difference approximation.

In Section 2.2 we obtained a number of formulas for finding approximations to the first derivative of a function. To find approximations for the second derivative we may differentiate (2.2.1) with respect to x and then set $s = 0$, obtaining

$$f''(x_0) \approx \frac{1}{h^2} \left(\delta^2 f_0 - \frac{1}{12} \delta^4 f_0 + \cdots \right).$$

If we omit all terms involving differences of fourth and higher order we obtain the approximation

$$f''(x_0) \approx \frac{1}{h^2} \delta^2 f_0 = \frac{f_1 - 2f_0 + f_{-1}}{h^2}.$$

If we proceed in an analogous fashion to obtain approximations to the second partial derivatives, we obtain as an approximation to $u_{tt} = u_{xx}$ the equation

$$\frac{U(x, t + k) - 2U(x, t) + U(x, t - k)}{k^2}$$

$$= \frac{U(x + h, t) - 2U(x, t) + U(x - h, t)}{h^2}. \quad (7.2.4)$$

Here we have taken increments h and k in the x and t directions respectively. We must also replace the initial conditions of (7.2.1) by appropriate finite-difference approximations. It will not be convenient to replace the first derivative by a central difference approximation as was done in Section

2.2. A one-sided difference is indicated because we want the derivatives at $t = 0$ and U is to be defined only for $t > 0$. Such an approximation may be obtained from the definition of the derivative or alternatively by differentiating equation (7.3.8) with respect to x, setting $s = 0$ and omitting terms involving differences of second and higher order. We replace the initial conditions by

$$U(x, 0) = f(x), \qquad \frac{U(x, k) - U(x, 0)}{k} = g(x). \qquad (7.2.5)$$

We now limit the variables x and t to a discrete set $(x_0 + rh, sk)$ where $r = 0, \pm 1, \pm 2, \cdots, s = 0, 1, 2, \cdots$, and x_0 is chosen conveniently. Then only values of U at points of this set occur in the difference equation. To show how the solution can be carried out in a step-by-step fashion, we rewrite our equations in the following form:

$$
\begin{aligned}
U(x, 0) &= f(x) \\
U(x, k) &= kg(x) + f(x) \\
U(x, t + k) &= 2U(x, t) - U(x, t - k) \\
&\quad + \lambda^2[U(x + h, t) - 2U(x, t) + U(x - h, t)]
\end{aligned}
\qquad (7.2.6)
$$

where $\lambda = k/h$. Since both $f(x)$ and $g(x)$ are given, we know U on the initial line and can immediately calculate U at the grid points on the line $t = k$. The third equation of (7.2.6) is then used to calculate the values of U on the line $t = 2k$. This is clearly possible because for $t = k$, the right-hand member involves values of U only on the lines $t = 0$ and k. This same equation can also be used to calculate successively the values of U at the grid points of the lines $t = 3k, 4k, \cdots$. The situation can be indicated graphically by the stencil of grid points that enter into each application of the recursion formula. In Fig. 7.1 a series of such lines are drawn with spacing h in the x-direction and k in the t-direction. The grid points are the intersections of these lines and the stencil is indicated by the heavy dots.

Having explained how the solution of the difference equation problem (7.2.6) can be calculated, it is important to consider whether the solution thus found approximates the solution of the differential equation problem

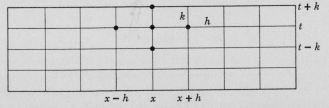

Fig. 7.1. Stencil of grid points for hyperbolic equation.

(7.2.1). For any function $U(x, t)$ with second derivatives, the difference quotients in (7.2.4) and (7.2.5) will tend to the corresponding derivatives which appear in the differential problem (7.2.1) as h and k tend to zero. It does not follow that the solution of the difference problem for U will always tend to the solution u of the differential problem as h and k tend to zero. It can be shown [7, pp. 24–26] that if $\lambda \leq 1$, then indeed $U(x, t)$ tends to $u(x, t)$ as h and k tend to zero. We omit the proof but the following remarks will indicate why $U(x, t)$ may fail to tend to $u(x, t)$ if $\lambda > 1$.

If the initial values are given in an interval $a \leq x \leq b$ (which, for simplicity, we suppose to be bounded by grid points), the formulas (7.2.6) enable us to calculate the values of $U(x, t)$ at the grid points inside a triangle whose base is this interval and whose other two sides have slopes $\pm \lambda$. Then, as for the differential problem, each grid point in the triangle has an interval of dependence on the x-axis which lies in the interval $a \leq x \leq b$, and this interval of dependence depends on λ. Now the corresponding differential problem will have a solution inside a triangle whose base is the interval $a \leq x \leq b$ and whose other sides have slopes ± 1. This triangle lies inside the corresponding triangle for the difference equation if $\lambda > 1$. Moreover, in this case, for each grid point inside the triangle where u is defined, the interval of dependence for the difference equation lies inside the interval of dependence for the differential equation. This situation is illustrated in Fig. 7.2 where PQ is the interval of dependence for the difference equation and RS is the interval of dependence for the differential equation. Thus, if at some point $U(x, t)$ tends to $u(x, t)$

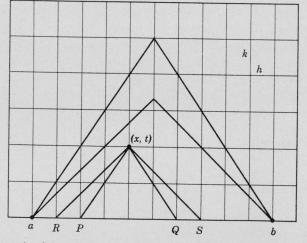

Fig. 7.2. Intervals of dependence for difference and differential equations for the case $\lambda = k/h > 1$.

for some choice of the initial functions, we can alter these functions in a way that changes u at this point (x, t) but leaves the initial values in the interval of dependence of the difference equation the same as before, so that U is unchanged at (x, t). Thus $U(x, t)$ will no longer tend to $u(x, t)$.

If $\lambda > 1$, convergence of U to u is the exception rather than the rule. Hence in using the scheme (7.2.6) it is important to choose $\lambda \leq 1$.

If we wish to solve a hyperbolic differential equation of more general type than the one appearing in (7.2.1), we set up a corresponding difference equation in exactly the same manner as described previously. The calculations will again proceed in a step-by-step fashion, and it will be found necessary to restrict the value of the ratio k/h to guarantee convergence.

We may also consider a problem similar to (7.2.1) but restricting the range of x to be a finite interval, $a \leq x \leq b$. Here we prescribe the values of $u(x, t)$ on the lines $x = a$ and $x = b$. Thus the differential equation problem analogous to (7.2.1) would be

$$u_{tt} - u_{xx} = 0 \quad \text{for} \quad t > 0, \quad a < x < b,$$
$$u(x, 0) = f(x), \quad u_t(x, 0) = g(x) \quad \text{for} \quad a \leq x \leq b,$$
$$u(a, t) = h_1(t), \quad u(b, t) = h_2(t) \quad \text{for} \quad t > 0.$$

By replacing the derivatives by finite-difference approximations, the corresponding difference-equation problem is

$$U(x, 0) = f(x)$$
$$U(x, k) = kg(x) + f(x)$$
$$U(a, t) = h_1(t), \quad U(b, t) = h_2(t)$$
$$U(x, t + k) = 2U(x, t) - U(x, t - k)$$
$$+ \lambda^2[U(x + h, t) - 2U(x, t) + U(x - h, t)]$$

where $\lambda = k/h$.

Example 1. Find a finite difference approximation to the solution of the problem

$$u_{tt} - u_{xx} = 0 \quad \text{for} \quad t > 0, \quad 0 < x < 1,$$
$$u(x, 0) = x(1 - x), \quad u_t(x, 0) = 0 \quad \text{for } 0 \leq x \leq 1,$$
$$u(0, t) = 0, \quad u(1, t) = \sin \pi t \quad \text{for } t > 0.$$

We choose $h = 0.1$, $k = 0.05$ so that $\lambda = 0.5$, and carry out the solution as far as the line $t = 1.0$. Our difference equations become

$$U(x, 0) = x(1 - x)$$
$$U(x, k) = x(1 - x)$$
$$U(0, t) = 0, \quad U(1, t) = \sin \pi t$$
$$U(x, t + k) = 2U(x, t) - U(x, t - k)$$
$$+ 0.25[U(x + h, t) - 2U(x, t) + U(x - h, t)].$$

The calculations were carried out on a high-speed automatic digital computer, retaining eight significant figures throughout. A portion of the solution, rounded to three decimal places, is shown in Table 7.1.

TABLE 7.1

Solution of Hyberbolic Equation

t \ x	0	0.1	0.2	0.3	0.4	0.5	0.6	0.7	0.8	0.9	1.0
0	0.000	0.090	0.160	0.210	0.240	0.250	0.240	0.210	0.160	0.090	0.000
0.05	0.000	0.090	0.160	0.210	0.240	0.250	0.240	0.210	0.160	0.090	0.156
0.10	0.000	0.085	0.155	0.205	0.235	0.245	0.235	0.205	0.155	0.124	0.309
0.15	0.000	0.076	0.145	0.195	0.225	0.235	0.225	0.195	0.155	0.212	0.454
0.20	0.000	0.066	0.130	0.180	0.210	0.220	0.210	0.182	0.179	0.346	0.588
0.25	0.000	0.055	0.112	0.160	0.190	0.200	0.191	0.176	0.246	0.499	0.707
—	—	—	—	—	—	—	—	—	—	—	—
0.80	0.000	−0.040	−0.035	0.090	0.363	0.632	0.756	0.837	0.850	0.751	0.588
0.85	0.000	−0.029	0.016	0.207	0.497	0.691	0.760	0.815	0.766	0.642	0.454
0.90	0.000	0.000	0.104	0.349	0.607	0.718	0.761	0.767	0.664	0.517	0.309
0.95	0.000	0.056	0.227	0.494	0.680	0.729	0.752	0.692	0.550	0.377	0.156
1.00	0.000	0.140	0.374	0.619	0.719	0.733	0.723	0.597	0.429	0.225	0.000

Although the labor of calculating this solution by hand would be considerable, the reader may easily check the calculation of any entry in the table. For example, if $x = 0.3$ and $t + k = 0.20$ we have

$$U(0.3, 0.20) = 2U(0.3, 0.15) - U(0.3, 0.10) + 0.25[U(0.4, 0.15)$$

$$- 2U(0.3, 0.15) + U(0.2, 0.15)]$$

$$= 2(0.195) - 0.205 + 0.25[0.225 - 2(0.195) + 0.145]$$

$$= 0.180.$$

To obtain some indication of the accuracy of this solution, the calculations were repeated with a finer subdivision of the region. It appears that the solution at most of the points is fairly accurate, although at a few of the points near the line $x = 1.0$ and for the smaller values of t the error is as large as 2 units in the second decimal place. For the larger values of t the error is sometimes as large as 7 units in the second decimal place for the large values of the solution.

7.3 PARABOLIC EQUATIONS

We consider the problem defined by (7.1.3) namely

$$u_t - u_{xx} = 0 \quad \text{for} \quad t > 0, \qquad u(x, 0) = f(x). \tag{7.3.1}$$

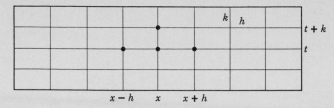

Fig. 7.3. Stencil of grid points for parabolic equation (explicit method).

If we proceed as for the hyperbolic equation, replacing the derivatives by finite-difference approximations, one possible difference equation is

$$\frac{U(x, t + k) - U(x, t)}{k} = \frac{U(x + h, t) - 2U(x, t) + U(x - h, t)}{h^2}.$$

$$(7.3.2)$$

Of course the initial condition becomes $U(x, 0) = f(x)$. Again we limit the variables x and t to a discrete set $(x_0 + rh, sk)$ where $r = 0, \pm 1, \pm 2, \cdots, s = 0, 1, 2, \cdots$. To show how the solution can be carried out in a step-by-step fashion we rewrite our equations in the form

$$U(x, 0) = f(x)$$

$$(7.3.3)$$

$$U(x, t + k) = \lambda U(x + h, t) + (1 - 2\lambda)U(x, t) + \lambda U(x - h, t)$$

where $\lambda = k/h^2$. Starting with the initial values $U(x, 0) = f(x)$, the values of U at the grid points on the lines $t = k, 2k, \cdots$ can be successively calculated from the second equation of (7.3.3). The situation can be indicated graphically by the stencil of grid points that enter into each application of the recursion formula. In Fig. 7.3 the stencil is indicated by the heavy dots on the mesh lines. Application of formula (7.3.3) in this manner may be called an explicit difference method.

It is again important to consider whether the solution thus found approximates the solution of the differential equation problem (7.3.1). An examination of the second formula of (7.3.3) shows that if $\lambda \leq \frac{1}{2}$, $U(x, t + k)$ is a weighted average of the values of $U(x, t)$ with non-negative weight factors. It follows that if $m \leq f(x) \leq M$, then at all grid points we have

$$m \leq U(x, t) \leq M \quad \text{if} \quad \lambda \leq \frac{1}{2}.$$

From the inequalities it is possible to conclude that the difference equation is stable if $\lambda \leq \frac{1}{2}$. But if $\lambda > \frac{1}{2}$, examples can be constructed to exhibit instability [7, pp. 93–94]. Moreover, under suitable conditions on the higher derivatives of u, it can be shown that $U(x, t)$ tends to $u(x, t)$ as h and k tend to zero if $\lambda \leq \frac{1}{2}$ [7, pp. 95–98].

More realistic in a physical sense than the problem (7.3.1) are parabolic problems in which the differential equation is to be satisfied in a finite interval only—for example, heat flow in a rod of finite length as discussed in Section 6.7. A typical problem of this kind can be written in the form

$$u_t - u_{xx} = 0 \quad \text{for} \quad a < x < b, \qquad t > 0$$

$$u(x, 0) = f(x), \qquad u(a, t) = h_1(t), \qquad u(b, t) = h_2(t).$$

(7.3.4)

The method of this section is still applicable. We should choose h so that $b - a$ is an integral multiple of h and make a and b be grid points. We then add to the equations (7.3.3) the two equations

$$U(a, t) = h_1(t), \qquad U(b, t) = h_2(t).$$

(7.3.5)

Again we must have $\lambda \leq \frac{1}{2}$ for stability.

The stability restriction $\lambda \leq \frac{1}{2}$ is much more irksome than the corresponding inequality in hyperbolic problems because it forces us to use very small steps in the t-direction. This difficulty can be circumvented by the use of so-called implicit difference methods which are stable for all $\lambda > 0$ but which are more complicated for calculation.

To obtain an implicit method we again replace the derivatives by finite difference approximations. If in $u_t - u_{xx} = 0$, u_{xx} is replaced by a second difference quotient, not at the level of t as in (7.3.2), but at $t + k$, the difference equation

$$\frac{U(x, t + k) - U(x, t)}{k}$$

$$= \frac{U(x + h, t + k) - 2U(x, t + k) + U(x - h, t + k)}{h^2} \quad (7.3.6)$$

is obtained. The situation can be indicated graphically by the stencil of grid points shown in Fig. 7.4.

This equation cannot be solved explicitly for $U(x, t + k)$ in terms of known values of $U(x, t)$. It is unsuitable for problems in infinite x-regions.

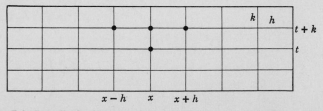

Fig. 7.4. Stencil of grid points for parabolic equation (implicit method).

But for problems in a finite x-interval like that in (7.3.4), it can be used as we shall now explain. If we rewrite (7.3.6) in a slightly different form and adjoin the boundary and initial conditions corresponding to (7.3.4) we see that the system to be solved can be described by the following equations

$$U(x, 0) = f(x)$$

$$
\left.
\begin{aligned}
U(a, t + k) &= h_1(t + k), \\
U(b, t + k) &= h_2(t + k) \\
\lambda U(x - h, t + k) &- (1 + 2\lambda)U(x, t + k) \\
&+ \lambda U(x + h, t + k) = -U(x, t)
\end{aligned}
\right\}
\begin{aligned}
& t = 0, k, 2k, \cdots \\
\\
& x = a + h, a + 2h, \cdots, b - h.
\end{aligned}
\qquad (7.3.7)
$$

Then the last equation of (7.3.7) provides at the level $t + k$ a system of $(b - a)/h - 1$ simultaneous linear algebraic equations for the same number of unknown values of U at the grid points $x = a + h, a + 2h, \cdots$, $b - h$. If the values of U at the grid points of level t are already known, the values for the level $t + k$ can be found by solving this algebraic system, since its determinant can be shown to be different from zero. Thus, since the values of U on the level $t = 0$ are given, solution of an algebraic system provides the values at level k. Solution of the next algebraic system gives the values for level $2k$ and so on for levels $3k, 4k, \cdots$.

The solution of the algebraic system can be carried out by Gaussian elimination as explained in Section 4.5. We note that the matrix of coefficients is tri-diagonal, that is, it has zeros everywhere except on the main diagonal and on the two diagonals parallel to it on either side. Because of this there is a considerable simplication in the calculations. To explain the method we introduce a new notation in order to rewrite the system (7.3.7) for fixed $t + k$ in a more convenient form. We let

$$n = \frac{b - a}{h}$$

$$
\begin{aligned}
u_i &= U(a + ih, t + k) & i &= 1, 2, \cdots, n - 1 \\
a_i &= \lambda & i &= 2, 3, \cdots, n - 1 \\
b_i &= -(1 + 2\lambda) & i &= 1, 2, \cdots, n - 1 \\
c_i &= \lambda & i &= 1, 2, \cdots, n - 2 \\
d_1 &= -U(a + h, t) - \lambda U(a, t + k) \\
&= -U(a + h, t) - \lambda h_1(t + k) \\
d_i &= -U(a + ih, t) & i &= 2, 3, \cdots, n - 2 \\
d_{n-1} &= -U(b - h, t) - \lambda U(b, t + k) \\
&= -U(b - h, t) - \lambda h_2(t + k).
\end{aligned}
$$

Then the system of equations which has to be solved may be written in the form

$$
\begin{aligned}
b_1 u_1 + c_1 u_2 &\qquad\qquad\qquad\qquad\qquad= d_1 \\
a_2 u_1 + b_2 u_2 + c_2 u_3 &\qquad\qquad\qquad\qquad= d_2 \\
a_3 u_2 + b_3 u_3 + c_3 u_4 &\qquad\qquad\qquad= d_3 \\
&\ \cdot\quad\cdot\quad\cdot\quad\cdot\quad\cdot\quad\cdot\quad\cdot\quad\cdot \\
a_{n-2} u_{n-3} + b_{n-2} u_{n-2} + c_{n-2} u_{n-1} &= d_{n-2} \\
a_{n-1} u_{n-2} + b_{n-1} u_{n-1} &= d_{n-1}.
\end{aligned}
$$

By successive subtraction of a suitable multiple of each equation from the succeeding one, this system can be changed into a simpler one of the form

$$
\begin{aligned}
u_1 + c_1{}^* u_2 &\qquad\qquad\qquad\qquad= d_1{}^* \\
u_2 + c_2{}^* u_3 &\qquad\qquad\qquad= d_2{}^* \\
u_3 + c_3{}^* u_4 &\qquad\qquad= d_3{}^* \\
&\ \cdot\quad\cdot\quad\cdot\quad\cdot\quad\cdot\quad\cdot \\
u_{n-2} + c^*_{n-2} u_{n-1} &= d^*_{n-2} \\
u_{n-1} &= d^*_{n-1}
\end{aligned}
$$

where the coefficients are calculated by the recursion formulas

$$
c_1{}^* = \frac{c_1}{b_1}, \qquad d_1{}^* = \frac{d_1}{b_1}
$$

$$
\left.
\begin{aligned}
b_r{}^* &= b_r - a_r c^*_{r-1} \\[4pt]
c_r{}^* &= \frac{c_r}{b_r{}^*} \\[4pt]
d_r{}^* &= \frac{d_r - a_r d^*_{r-1}}{b_r{}^*}
\end{aligned}
\right\} \; r = 2, 3, \cdots, n - 1
$$

(We set $c_{n-1} = 0$, by definition.)

The solution of the tranformed system is now immediate: the desired values of u_r are given successively by

$$
\begin{aligned}
u_{n-1} &= d^*_{n-1} \\
u_r &= d_r{}^* - c_r{}^* u_{r+1}, \qquad r = n - 2, n - 3, \cdots, 2, 1.
\end{aligned}
$$

The comparison of the computational effort required by the explicit and implicit methods of solving the same problem depends to a large extent on the type of computing machine used. On most machines it is believed that calculation of the values of U for $a \leq x \leq b$ for fixed t should not take more than four times as long by the implicit method as by the explicit method. Under this hypothesis the implicit method with $\lambda > 2$ would be preferable to the explicit method with $\lambda = \frac{1}{2}$. This estimate assumes that the errors in the approximations computed by the two methods are not very different and do not depend too strongly on λ.

Example 2. Find a finite-difference approximation to the solution of the problem

$$u_t - u_{xx} = 0 \quad \text{for} \quad 0 < x < 1, \qquad t > 0$$

$$u(x, 0) = 4x(1 - x), \qquad u(0, t) = 0, \qquad u(1, t) = 0.$$

We choose $h = 0.05, k = 0.01$ so that $\lambda = 4.0$ and use the implicit difference method to carry out the solution as far as the line $t = 0.4$. Our difference equations become

$$U(x, 0) = 4x(1 - x), \qquad x = 0, h, 2h, \cdots, 20h$$

$$U(0, t + k) = 0, \qquad U(1, t + k) = 0, \qquad t = 0, k, 2k, \cdots, 39k$$

$$\lambda U(x - h, t + k) - (1 + 2\lambda)U(x, t + k) \quad \begin{cases} x = h, 2h, \cdots, 19h \\ + \lambda U(x + h, t + k) = -U(x, t), & t = 0, k, \cdots, 39k. \end{cases}$$

The calculations were carried out on a high-speed automatic digital computer, retaining eight significant figures throughout. A portion of

TABLE 7.2
Solution of Parabolic Equation

x	0.00	0.05	0.10	0.15	0.20	0.25	0.30	0.35	0.40	0.45	0.50
t											
0.00	0.000	0.190	0.360	0.510	0.640	0.750	0.840	0.910	0.960	0.990	1.000
0.01	0.000	0.159	0.310	0.448	0.571	0.677	0.764	0.833	0.882	0.911	0.921
0.02	0.000	0.139	0.274	0.400	0.513	0.612	0.695	0.760	0.807	0.836	0.845
0.03	0.000	0.125	0.246	0.359	0.463	0.554	0.631	0.693	0.737	0.764	0.773
0.04	0.000	0.112	0.222	0.325	0.420	0.503	0.574	0.631	0.672	0.697	0.706
0.05	0.000	0.102	0.201	0.295	0.381	0.457	0.522	0.575	0.613	0.636	0.644
—	—	—	—	—	—	—	—	—	—	—	—
0.36	0.000	0.005	0.011	0.016	0.021	0.025	0.028	0.031	0.033	0.035	0.035
0.37	0.000	0.005	0.010	0.014	0.019	0.023	0.026	0.028	0.030	0.032	0.032
0.38	0.000	0.005	0.009	0.013	0.017	0.021	0.024	0.026	0.028	0.029	0.029
0.39	0.000	0.004	0.008	0.012	0.016	0.019	0.021	0.024	0.025	0.026	0.026
0.40	0.000	0.004	0.007	0.011	0.014	0.017	0.019	0.021	0.023	0.024	0.024

the solution, rounded to three decimal places, is shown in Table 7.2. Because of symmetry, it suffices to tabulate the solution for $0 \le x \le 0.50$.

The labor of solving the systems of equations required in the implicit method is too great for hand calculation; however, the reader may easily check that the values given satisfy the required difference equation. For example, if $x = 0.20$ and $t + k = 0.03$ we have

$$4U(0.15, 0.03) - (1 + 2 \times 4)U(0.20, 0.03) + 4U(0.25, 0.03)$$
$$= 4(0.359) - 9(0.463) + 4(0.554)$$
$$= -0.515 = -U(0.20, 0.02)$$

approximately.

To obtain some indication of the accuracy of the solution, the calculations were repeated with a finer subdivision of the region. It appears that the maximum error in the solution is about 7 units in the third decimal place, and these larger errors generally occur where the values of the solution are largest.

7.4 ELLIPTIC EQUATIONS

We consider the problem defined by (7.1.1) namely

$$u_{xx} + u_{yy} = 0 \text{ in } R, \qquad u = f \text{ on } C$$

where C is the boundary of the region R in the xy-plane. To set up the finite-difference approximation to this differential equation we subdivide the xy-plane by two families of parallel lines into a square net. Let the lines of the net be $x = \mu h$, $y = \nu h$ ($\mu, \nu = 0, \pm 1, \pm 2, \cdots$). The points $(\mu h, \nu h)$ are called the lattice points of the net. The lattice points in R or on C are called nodes of the net. The smallest squares bounded by four lines of the net are called meshes or cells of the net. Each mesh is bounded by four line segments called links.

If we approximate the derivatives u_{xx} and u_{yy} by centered second differences as in the case of the hyperbolic and parabolic equations, we obtain as an approximation to the left-hand member of the differential equation

$$u_{xx} + u_{yy} \approx h^{-2}[U(x + h, y) + U(x, y + h)$$
$$+ U(x - h, y) + U(x, y - h) - 4U(x, y)]. \quad (7.4.2)$$

For convenience we suppose that the boundary C is composed of horizontal and vertical links of the net so that R is actually a union of meshes of the net. We then apply (7.4.2) at each node in R (not on C) and require that

$$U(x + h, y) + U(x, y + h) + U(x - h, y)$$
$$+ U(x, y - h) - 4U(x, y) = 0 \quad (7.4.3)$$

for each (x, y) which is a node in R. The situation can be indicated graphically by the stencil of grid points that enter into equation (7.4.3). In Fig. 7.5 the stencil is indicated by the heavy dots on the mesh lines.

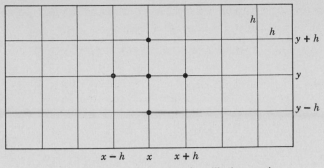

Fig. 7.5. Stencil of grid points for elliptic equation.

U will be given its prescribed boundary value at each node on C. This means that for some nodes in R, some of the neighboring nodes are on C and the corresponding values of U are prescribed constants. The values of U at the nodes in R are to be determined from the equations (7.4.3). We note that equations (7.4.3) are a system of linear equations, and that there are as many equations as there are unknown values of U to be found. Moreover, no equation involves more than five unknown values of U. Thus the matrix of the coefficients of the equations is a rather sparse one, containing many zero elements. In most problems this matrix will be of large order, ranging from perhaps fifty to several thousands in current machine work. This is so because, to get reasonable accuracy, we will need to use a fairly small mesh size, and hence will have many nodes at which U must be calculated. Although it would be possible to solve the resulting equations by any standard method, such as Gaussian elimination, this is likely to be inefficient because it does not take advantage of the special properties of the matrix.

On the other hand, an iterative method of solution is likely to be more efficient for the solution of such a system of equations. If we solve equation (7.4.3) for $U(x, y)$ we see that $U(x, y)$ is the average of the values of U at four neighboring points. We may begin by guessing approximate values for the solution $U(x, y)$ at each node in R. Improved values at each point are obtained by averaging the old values at the four neighboring points. This process may be repeated until there is no change in the values of the solution. The first approximation to the solution does not matter, although a good guess will speed up the convergence to the correct solution.

If we let $U^{(k)}(x, y)$ denote the kth approximation to the solution, the foregoing method is described by the equation

$$U^{(k+1)}(x, y) = (\tfrac{1}{4})[U^{(k)}(x + h, y) + U^{(k)}(x, y + h)$$
$$+ U^{(k)}(x - h, y) + U^{(k)}(x, y - h)]. \quad (7.4.4)$$

A more instructive way of writing this equation is

$$U^{(k+1)}(x, y) = U^{(k)}(x, y) + (\tfrac{1}{4})[U^{(k)}(x + h, y) + U^{(k)}(x, y + h)$$
$$+ U^{(k)}(x - h, y) + U^{(k)}(x, y - h) - 4U^{(k)}(x, y)]. \quad (7.4.5)$$

The quantity in brackets is called the residual at (x, y). Clearly the aim of the method is to reduce all of the residuals to zero.

In the solution of such a problem without the aid of a high-speed automatic computer, so-called relaxation methods are often used. We start with an approximation to the solution and compute the residual at each point. We then reduce the largest residual to zero by the use of equation (7.4.5). In general, this will change the residuals at neighboring points. At each step one of the residuals is reduced to zero, and the process is continued until all of the residuals are sufficiently small. An experienced computer can often guess at a good approximation to the solution. He then uses his experience and intuition and reduces the residuals until he obtains a satisfactory solution.

In using a high-speed automatic computer it is impossible to incorporate intuition in the machine program, so that more systematic techniques must be used. In one method, called the method of simultaneous displacements, each node is taken in turn and the new value of $U(x, y)$ is computed by means of equation (7.4.5). When each of the points of R has been treated once in this fashion, we say that we have made one sweep of R. At the end of each sweep we compute the sum of the squares of the residuals at the nodes and we continue to make sweeps of R until the sum of the squares of the residuals becomes sufficiently small.

Another method, called the method of successive displacements, is a variant of the method of simultaneous displacements. The variation consists of using a new value of $U(x, y)$ in (7.4.5) as soon as it has been computed. Thus if we sweep out R by proceeding from left to right in each row of nodes and taking the rows from bottom to top, we could write instead of (7.4.5) the equation

$$U^{(k+1)}(x, y) = U^{(k)}(x, y) + (\tfrac{1}{4})[U^{(k)}(x + h, y) + U^{(k)}(x, y + h)$$
$$+ U^{(k+1)}(x - h, y) + U^{(k+1)}(x, y - h) - 4U^{(k)}(x, y)]. \quad (7.4.6)$$

Instead of attempting a discussion of the conditions under which the solutions obtained by these methods converge to the solution of the corresponding differential equation we refer the interested reader to Forsythe and Wasow [7].

It has been found that the convergence of the foregoing methods can often be speeded up by using the method of successive overrelaxation. This means that instead of correcting each value $U(x, y)$ by adding one quarter of the residual, we overcorrect by adding a quantity obtained by multiplying this by a suitable factor. Thus we use the formula

$$U^{(k+1)}(x, y) = U^{(k)}(x, y) + \frac{\omega}{4}[U^{(k)}(x + h, y) + U^{(k)}(x, y + h)$$

$$+ U^{(k+1)}(x - h, y) + U^{(k+1)}(x, y - h) - 4U^{(k)}(x, y)] \qquad (7.4.7)$$

where $0 < \omega < 2$. It has been shown that the most rapid convergence occurs for a value called ω_{opt}, with $0 < \omega_{opt} < 2$. For methods of determining ω_{opt} and further details about this method, we again refer to Forsythe and Wasow [7].

In the preceding discussion we have assumed that the region R is a union of meshes of the net and that the boundary C is composed of horizontal and vertical links of the net. If the boundary C is curved so that the preceding conditions are not satisfied, the problem becomes much more difficult. We omit a discussion of this case and refer the reader to Lance [16] and Forsythe and Wasow [7].

We conclude with a simple example illustrating the solution of Laplace's equation for a square region.

Example 3. Find a finite-difference approximation U to the solution of the problem

$$u_{xx} + u_{yy} = 0 \quad \text{for} \quad 0 < x < 1, \qquad 0 < y < 1$$

$$u(x, 0) = 0, \qquad u(1, y) = 0, \qquad u(x, 1) = x(1 - x), \qquad u(0, y) = 0.$$

We choose $h = 0.1$ and use the method of successive displacements, as given by equation (7.4.6), starting with the initial approximation $U = 1$ at all nodes inside the region. The calculations were carried out on a high-speed automatic digital computer, retaining eight significant figures throughout. After one sweep, the values of U rounded to three places of decimals are as shown in Table 7.3. The sum of the squares of the residuals is 73.8.

As an illustration of the calculation of the values in this table we take the case of $x = 0.5$, $y = 0.2$. We obtain from equation (7.4.6)

$$U^{(1)}(0.5, 0.2) = U^{(0)}(0.5, 0.2) + 0.25[U^{(0)}(0.6, 0.2) + U^{(0)}(0.5, 0.3)$$

$$+ U^{(1)}(0.4, 0.2) + U^{(1)}(0.5, 0.1) - 4U^{(0)}(0.5, 0.2)]$$

$$= 1.0 + 0.25[1.0 + 1.0 + 0.883 + 0.666 - 4(1.0)]$$

$$= 0.887.$$

After 81 sweeps, the sum of the squares of the residuals was reduced to 0.992×10^{-6} and the values in Table 7.4 were obtained for the solution U.

TABLE 7.3
Values of U After One Sweep

y \ x	0.0	0.1	0.2	0.3	0.4	0.5	0.6	0.7	0.8	0.9	1.0
1.0	0.000	0.090	0.160	0.210	0.240	0.250	0.240	0.210	0.160	0.090	0.000
0.9	0.000	0.439	0.622	0.699	0.732	0.744	0.746	0.739	0.725	0.370	0.000
0.8	0.000	0.667	0.889	0.963	0.988	0.996	0.998	0.999	1.000	0.666	0.000
0.7	0.000	0.667	0.889	0.963	0.987	0.996	0.998	0.999	0.999	0.666	0.000
0.6	0.000	0.667	0.888	0.962	0.987	0.995	0.997	0.998	0.998	0.665	0.000
0.5	0.000	0.666	0.887	0.960	0.984	0.992	0.995	0.996	0.996	0.663	0.000
0.4	0.000	0.664	0.883	0.954	0.977	0.984	0.987	0.987	0.988	0.656	0.000
0.3	0.000	0.656	0.867	0.934	0.954	0.960	0.962	0.963	0.963	0.635	0.000
0.2	0.000	0.625	0.813	0.867	0.883	0.887	0.888	0.889	0.889	0.576	0.000
0.1	0.000	0.500	0.625	0.656	0.664	0.666	0.667	0.667	0.667	0.417	0.000
0.0	0.000	0.000	0.000	0.000	0.000	0.000	0.000	0.000	0.000	0.000	0.000

To obtain some indication of the accuracy of the solution, the problem was also solved using Fourier series. It appears that the maximum error in the solution does not exceed one unit in the third decimal place.

The same problem was also solved using the method of successive over-relaxation; that is, using equation (7.4.7). With $\omega = 1.8$, the sum of the

TABLE 7.4
Values of U After 81 Sweeps

y \ x	0.0	0.1	0.2	0.3	0.4	0.5	0.6	0.7	0.8	0.9	1.0
1.0	0.000	0.090	0.160	0.210	0.240	0.250	0.240	0.210	0.160	0.090	0.000
0.9	0.000	0.062	0.115	0.153	0.177	0.185	0.177	0.153	0.115	0.062	0.000
0.8	0.000	0.044	0.083	0.112	0.130	0.136	0.130	0.112	0.083	0.044	0.000
0.7	0.000	0.032	0.060	0.082	0.095	0.100	0.095	0.081	0.060	0.032	0.000
0.6	0.000	0.023	0.043	0.059	0.069	0.073	0.069	0.059	0.043	0.023	0.000
0.5	0.000	0.016	0.031	0.043	0.050	0.052	0.050	0.042	0.031	0.016	0.000
0.4	0.000	0.012	0.022	0.030	0.035	0.037	0.035	0.030	0.022	0.011	0.000
0.3	0.000	0.008	0.015	0.020	0.024	0.025	0.024	0.020	0.015	0.008	0.000
0.2	0.000	0.005	0.009	0.013	0.015	0.016	0.015	0.013	0.009	0.005	0.000
0.1	0.000	0.002	0.004	0.006	0.007	0.007	0.007	0.006	0.004	0.002	0.000
0.0	0.000	0.000	0.000	0.000	0.000	0.000	0.000	0.000	0.000	0.000	0.000

squares of the residuals was reduced to 0.713×10^{-6} after 43 sweeps; with $\omega = 1.7$ the sum of the squares of the residuals was reduced to 0.793×10^{-6} after 29 sweeps; and with $\omega = 1.6$ the sum of the squares of the residuals was reduced to 0.179×10^{-9} after 30 sweeps. The values of U so obtained differ from those in Table 7.4 by no more than one unit in the third decimal place. These results demonstrate the marked effect which a suitable choice of ω can have on the rapidity of convergence.

References

1. Aitken, A. C. Studies in practical mathematics II. The evaluation of the latent roots and latent vectors of a matrix. *Proc. Roy. Soc. Edinburgh*, vol. 57 (1937), pp. 269–304.
2. Bodewig, E. *Matrix Calculus*. Interscience Publishers, New York, 1956.
3. Crout, P. D. A short method for evaluating determinants and solving systems of linear equations with real or complex coefficients. *Trans. Amer. Inst. Elec. Engrs.*, vol. 60 (1941), pp. 1235–1240.
4. Davis, H. T. *Tables of the Higher Mathematical Functions, I.* Principia Press, Bloomington, Indiana, 1933.
5. Faddeeva, V. N. *Computational Methods of Linear Algebra*. Translated from the Russian by C. D. Benster, Dover Publications, New York, 1959.
6. Fletcher, A., Miller, J. C. P., Rosenhead, I., and Comrie, L. J. *Index of Mathematical Tables*. 2nd edition, Addison-Wesley Publishing Co., Reading, Massachusetts, 1962.
7. Forsythe, G. E., and Wasow, W. R. *Finite-Difference Methods for Partial Differential Equations*. John Wiley and Sons, New York, 1960.
8. Frazer, R. A., Duncan W. J., and Collar, A. R. *Elementary Matrices and Some Applications to Dynamics and Differential Equations*. Cambridge University Press, New York, 1947.
9. Givens, W. Numerical computation of the characteristic values of a real symmetric matrix. *Oak Ridge National Laboratory*, Report ORNL 1574, February 1954.
10. Givens, W. Computation of plane unitary rotations transforming a general matrix to triangular form. *J. Soc. Indust. Appl. Math.*, vol. 6 (1958), pp. 26–50.
11. Hamming, R. W. Stable predictor-corrector methods for ordinary differential equations. *J. Assoc. Comput. Mach.*, vol. 6 (1959), pp. 37–47.
12. Hildebrand, F. B. *Introduction to Numerical Analysis*. McGraw-Hill Book Company, New York, 1956.
13. Hoff, N. J. *The Analysis of Structures*. John Wiley and Sons, New York, 1956.
14. Householder, A. S. *Principles of Numerical Analysis*. McGraw-Hill Book Company, New York, 1953.
15. Jacobi, C. G. J. Uber ein leichtes Verfahren, die in der theorie der Säkularstörungen vorkommenden Gleichungen numerisch aufzulösen. *J. Reine Angew. Math.*, vol. 30 (1846), pp. 51–95.
16. Lance, G. N. *Numerical Methods for High-Speed Computers*. Iliff and Sons, London, 1960.
17. Lanczos, C. An iteration method for the solution of the eigenvalue problem of linear differential and integral operators. *J. Res. Nat. Bur. Standards*, vol. 45 (1950), pp. 255–282.

18. Lebedev, A. V., and Fedorova, R. M. *Reference Book on Mathematical Tables.* Izdatelestvo akademii nauk USSR Moscow, 1956. Supplement by N. M. Burunova, 1959.

19. Milne, W. E. *Numerical Calculus.* Princeton University Press, Princeton, New Jersey, 1949.

20. Milne, W. E. *Numerical Solution of Differential Equations.* John Wiley and Sons, New York, 1953.

21. Milne, W. E., and Reynolds, R. R. Stability of a numerical solution of differential equations. *J. Assoc. Comput. Mach.*, vol. 6 (1959), pp. 196–203.

22. Milne, W. E., and Reynolds, R. R. Fifth-order methods for the numerical solution of ordinary differential equations. *J. Assoc. Comput. Mach.*, vol. 9 (1962), pp. 64–70.

23. National Bureau of Standards. *Tables of Langrangian Interpolation Coefficients.* Columbia Press Series, vol. 4, Columbia University Press, New York, 1944.

24. Uspensky, J. V. *Theory of Equations.* McGraw-Hill Book Company, New York, 1948.

25. Wilkinson, J. H. The calculation of the latent roots and vectors of matrices on the pilot model of the A.C.E. *Proc. Cambridge Philos. Soc.*, vol. 50 (1954), pp. 536–566.

26. Wilkinson, J. H. The use of iterative methods for finding the latent roots and vectors of matrices. *Math. Tables Aids Comput.*, vol. 9 (1955), pp. 182–191.

Index